BASIC FEEDBACK CONTROL SYSTEM DESIGN

McGraw-Hill Series in Control Systems Engineering

JOHN R. RAGAZZINI AND WILLIAM E. VANNAH, *Consulting Editors*

BASIC FEEDBACK CONTROL
SYSTEM DESIGN

C. J. Savant, Jr., Ph.D.

Director of Engineering, American Electronics, Inc.
Los Angeles, California
and
Visiting Associate Professor of Electrical Engineering
University of Southern California

McGRAW-HILL BOOK COMPANY, INC.

New York   Toronto   London

1958

II

THE MAPLE PRESS COMPANY, YORK, PA.

PREFACE

Once I watched an office manager attempt to teach a secretary to use a ditto machine. He told her the characteristics of the fluid and how the fluid chemically activates the material deposited on the ditto master. Explaining the operation, he said: "The drum is rotated at constant speed by the motor. The master copy is first brought into contact with the fluid, then in contact with the blank paper. . . ." "But how do I do it?" was the doubtful secretary's interruption. About this time another secretary came over and said: "Put the stack of paper here, slip in the purple things with the dirty side up, like this. . . ." In a few minutes the secretary was making copies and getting her job done.

I believe that servo design can best be taught to engineers through the technique of "learning by doing" just as the new secretary learned to use the ditto machine by watching the other girl, then running the machine. This book attempts to teach the fundamentals of servo design by means of practical examples and from the student's own point of view. The book was written by and for students taking the servo courses at the University of Southern California. Prepared notes were distributed to the students and were freely criticized by them. Their criticisms were integrated and used in revising the manuscript. Thus, this resulting book, which presents servo design from a fundamental point of view, is written for undergraduate engineering students and for graduate practicing engineers—by fellow students.

Contact with practicing engineers through courses taught at locations close to industrial plants and on the company's premises, when security permitted, has led me to deviate somewhat from convention in the method of presentation.

The first difference is in the use of the root-locus method as a basic tool for servo design. From my own experience the following philosophy is presented as being basic in feedback-control-system design: Feedback control systems are designed by trial and error. Each trial is analyzed, and the results of the analysis are then examined to determine the next. The first "guess" might possibly be the type of equalizer (series, parallel, etc.) necessary to improve system performance. The next may be the component values of a resistance-capacitance network or the amplifier gain. The engineer continues varying system quantities until satisfactory performance is obtained. This design technique, which I call "synthesis by analysis," requires that the engineer be able to analyze rapidly each subsequent trial. For this reason, the root-locus technique, based strongly upon sketching methods, is recommended for servo synthesis.

Frequency-analysis techniques, especially the Bode construction, that is, a plot of gain in decibels and of phase versus logarithmic frequency, are a necessary part of the complete design for two reasons:

1. The governing equations of certain components, such as pneumatic valves, hydraulic actuators, and jet engines, are found experimentally from frequency-analysis methods. The servo engineer converts the experimental data into an approximate analytic form. The root-locus synthesis procedure is then used to design the servo.

2. For physically constructed equipment, frequency analysis provides a useful experimental method of checking the design.

Since, historically, the frequency-analysis technique (as evidenced, for example, in the Nyquist criterion) preceded the root-locus technique, some engineers seem to feel that the earlier work is simpler. In consequence, frequency methods have been thoroughly treated in many current servo texts and in many college servo courses, whereas the root-locus design is often relegated to the more advanced courses in feedback theory. In the undergraduate servo courses taught at the University of Southern California, both procedures are taught in the undergraduate course. The thought has been expressed by many of the students that design based upon the root locus is basically easier than design based on the frequency technique, for as the science of feedback control develops, the common stabilizing networks such as lag, lead, and lead-lag become less valuable in meeting more stringent specifications. The root-locus technique provides a simple method of analyzing the variations of system performance as any network parameter of a more complicated network is varied.

The second difference is to present servo theory and practical servo design without the requirement of an elaborate mathematical background. The design approach presented in this text, although rigorous, does not require a previous knowledge of Laplace transforms and requires only junior-level alternating-current circuit theory. Two methods of solution of differential equations, which are the basis of servo design, are presented: the classical method and the Laplace-transform method. Emphasis is placed upon this latter operational technique because of its increasing importance in more advanced system thinking and because it places the entire subject of servo design on a firm mathematical foundation. Similarities between the two methods are indicated in the text, and the first two appendixes treat the mechanics of both methods of solution.

Problems are included at the end of each chapter. Detailed derivations are presented in the Appendix. Like the secretary mentioned in the example at the start of this preface, the student can read directly through the text without studying derivations in detail until he knows how to use the material for the design of servo systems.

I would like to express my appreciation to the students of EE482, Introductory Servomechanisms, for suggesting the writing of lecture notes which were the forerunner of this present text. Sincere thanks are due to the following associates at the University of Southern California and at Servomechanisms, Inc.: Dr. Joseph Kukel, Dr. Carleton Solloway, Dr. Louis Weinberg, Mr. Charles Savant, Dr. Robert Howard, and Dr. G. L. Davenport. Particular thanks are due Dr. Charles H. Wilts under whom I studied at the California Institute of Technology. Many of the examples and problems in this book were taken from his excellent class notes. I would like to express my gratitude to Servomechanisms, Inc., for providing the typing and reproduction facilities necessary for such a project. I wish to express sincere thanks to the following:

American Electronics, Inc., Los Angeles, California
American Gyro Division, Daystrom Pacific, Santa Monica, California
Bowmar Instrument Company, Fort Wayne, Indiana
Bristol Company, Waterbury, Connecticut
DeJur-Ansco Corporation, Long Island City, New York
Diehl Manufacturing Company, Somerville, New Jersey
Doelcam Division, Minneapolis-Honeywell, Boston, Massachusetts
Electro-Mec Laboratory, Inc., New York, New York
Fairchild Controls Corporation, Hicksville, New York
Ford Instrument Company, Long Island City, New York
G. M. Giannini and Company, Inc., Pasadena, California
Genisco, Inc., Los Angeles, California
Helipot Corporation, South Pasadena, California
Kearfott Company, Inc., Clifton, New Jersey
Minneapolis-Honeywell, Minneapolis, Minnesota
Reeves Instrument Corporation, New York, New York
Servomechanisms, Inc., Hawthorne, California
Servo-Tek Products, Hawthorne, New Jersey
Statham Laboratories, Los Angeles, California
Summers Gyroscope Company, Santa Monica, California
Westinghouse Electric Corporation, Pittsburgh, Pennsylvania
Wiancko Engineering Company, Pasadena, California

They kindly supplied glossy prints and technical data for many of their products. I would like to express my appreciation to Dr. John Aseltine, Dr. John Truxal, and the other reviewers of the manuscript. Particular thanks is due Mrs. W. T. Shearer who typed the manuscript.

Finally, I wish to express appreciation to my wife, who exhibited much patience during the many hours of manuscript writing.

C. J. Savant, Jr.

CONTENTS

LIST OF SYMBOLS

A	Amplifier gain or amplitude of a complex quantity	L	Torque, Laplace-transformed
a	Resistance ratio of a constant	$\mathcal{L}$	Symbolic representation of the Laplace-transform process
B	Damping coefficient	$\mathcal{L}^{-1}$	Symbolic representation of the inverse Laplace-transform process
$B(p)$	Feedback signal, Laplace-transformed		
b	A constant	l	Fixed linear length or an integer
$b(t)$	Feedback signal, function of time	M	Mass, magnitude of $C(j\omega)/R(j\omega)$, mutual inductance, or momentum
C	Capacitance		
$C(p)$	Output signal, Laplace-transformed		
$c(t)$	Output signal, function of time	M_p	Peak magnitude of $C(j\omega)/R(j\omega)$
D	Gyro damping coefficient	m	Slope of the torque-speed curve
d	Resistance value used in synthesis	N	Ratio of Im $C(j\omega)/R(j\omega)$ to Re $C(j\omega)/R(j\omega)$, number of turns, or gear ratio
$E(p)$	Voltage, function of p or $j\omega$	n	Notch width in network design
e	Base of the Napierian logarithm	$P(p)$	Polynomial in p
$e(t)$	Voltage, function of t	$\#P$	Number of poles
$F(p)$	Force, Laplace-transformed	p	Laplace-transform operator
$f(t)$	Force, function of time	Q	Applied torque used in connection with gyro equations
G_n	Describing function		
$G(p)$	Forward transfer function	$Q(p)$	Polynomial in p
g	Translational mechanical-admittance function or acceleration of gravity $= 32.2$ ft/sec^2	$q(t)$	Charge, function of time
		R	Resistance
		$R(p)$	Input signal, Laplace-transformed
$H(p)$	Feedback transfer function		
h	Rotational mechanical admittance function	r	Notch ratio (depth) in network design or an integer
I	Current, Laplace-transformed, or moment of inertia	r_p	Plate resistance
		$r(t)$	Input signal, function of time
$i(t)$	Current, function of time	s	Length of arc along a curve
J	Moment of inertia	t	Time variable
j	Imaginary operator, $\sqrt{-1}$	U	Undesirable torque used in connection with gyro equations
K	Loop gain or spring constant		
K_a	Acceleration-error coefficient	u	Frequency ratio ω/ω_n
K_0	Position-error coefficient	V	Velocity
K_v	Velocity-error coefficient	$V(p)$	Voltage, Laplace-transformed
k	Integer values used in a summation	$v(t)$	Voltage, function of time
		W	Weight or energy
$\bar{L}$	Inductance or torque, function of time	w	Weighting function

$X(p)$	Linear-motion position variable, Laplace-transformed		p plane, or gyroscope gimbal angle
$x(t)$	Linear-motion position variable, function of time	$\mathcal{K}$	A constant representing a product of other constants
x,y,z	Linear coordinates	λ	Slope on the phase trajectory
$Y(p)$	Admittance function	μ	Vacuum-tube amplification factor
$y(t)$	Dependent variable, function of time	π	3.1416
$Z(p)$	Impedance function	ρ	Ratio of load resistance to potentiometer resistance
$\#Z$	Number of zeros	Σ	Symbolic representation of summation
α	Damping factor or ratio of rate to position feedback signal	σ	Dummy variable of integration
β	Real frequency component of the root or ratio of load resistance to potentiometer resistance	τ	Time constant
		ϕ	Phase angle
γ	Fraction of total potentiometer rotation	ϕ_m	Phase margin
		ψ	Flux variable
Δ	Determinant	ω	Frequency variable used with sinusoidal driving functions or angular velocity in mechanical systems
δ	Unit impulse function		
$E(p)$	Error signal, Laplace-transformed		
$\epsilon(t)$	Error signal, function of time		
ζ	Damping ratio	ω_n	Undamped resonant frequency
θ	Argument of complex quantity, angle of a vector on the	ω_0	Network resonant frequency
		ω_r	Frequency of transient oscillation

CHAPTER 1

INTRODUCTION TO FEEDBACK CONTROL SYSTEMS

1-1. The Control System. Suppose it is desired to drive a load, say a large pump, with a gasoline engine. Even if the engine delivers several hundred horsepower, a small pressure on the engine throttle will cause a large change in the output power. The speed of the engine shaft for a constant load is a function of the position of the throttle. The throttle, carburetor, and engine comprise a type of control system wherein a large power output is controlled with a small power input. Figure 1-1 shows a sketch of a typical control system. A small input signal is amplified electrically, pneumatically, mechanically, or by some other means. This signal controls the magnitude of power delivered from the power source through the power actuator to the output. The input signal to the gasoline engine-pump system is the throttle setting, which may be an angular position. The amount of gasoline, which is the external source of power, delivered to the engine is controlled by the carburetor and the engine valves. A typical plot of engine speed versus throttle position is as sketched in Fig. 1-2.

Many examples of this type of nonfeedback control systems can be cited: galvanometers, electronic amplifiers, magnetic amplifiers, pneumatic valves and actuators, human muscles, etc. In general this type of control system, which is pictured in Fig. 1-1, is called an "open-loop," or nonfeedback system. The input drives the output directly through the intermediate components.

One of the consequences of an open-loop system is the dependence of the output upon the components. For example, if the carburetor on the gasoline engine of Fig. 1-2 should become dirty and the fuel-air ratio change, the curve of output rpm versus throttle position would change. Since the control system depends directly on the intermediate components, variations of temperature, humidity, time, vibration, etc., tend to change the carburetor action and hence the output-input relation. Thus, some of the disadvantages of open-loop systems are

1. The controlled output varies as the intermediate components change.
2. The controlled output varies as the load changes.

With open-loop control, the output varies because of changes other than the input or command signal. In many applications (for example, an automobile engine) maintaining an accurate input-output curve is unimportant. In other applications it suffices to calibrate the system periodically. To calibrate means to establish or reestablish the input-output relation often enough to obtain the desired accuracy. For exam-

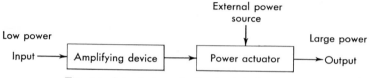

Fig. 1-1. A typical nonfeedback control system.

ple, a d-c galvanometer is "zeroed" (balanced, calibrated) before it is used. Many types of laboratory instrumentation systems are calibrated and balanced before a run. The operator depends upon the balance remaining constant during the period of usage. In many systems (for

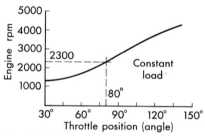

Fig. 1-2. A typical engine rpm versus throttle position curve.

example, driving an automobile) a human operator is capable of making the necessary corrections. When one first drives another's automobile, a new sense of "feel" must be established, since, for example, the accelerator setting on no two automobiles produces exactly the same engine performance.

Thus, open-ended systems have several advantages which should be considered in the planning stages of a control system. Some of these are

1. Simplicity of operation
2. Fewer components
3. Stable operation

If the system requirements cannot be satisfied with an open-loop control system, as is often the case with accurate control devices, a closed-loop system may be required. In order to obtain the desired accuracy of control, the system output is measured to determine the output condition. This actual output is "fed back" and compared with the input. Since the input represents the "desired" output, the difference is the error which actuates the system:

$$\text{Error} = \text{desired output} - \text{actual output} \qquad (1\text{-}1)$$

For the open-loop system, the throttle of the engine is positioned directly. If a certain rpm is desired, the operator refers to the calibration chart of Fig. 1-2 and sets the throttle at the correct angle. For example, if it is desired to operate at 2,300 rpm, a throttle setting of 80° is required.

Suppose that the system comprising a gasoline engine driving a pump is used in a closed-loop manner. In such a system, the quantity that is to be controlled, in this case the engine rpm, is measured. The *desired* rpm, which is the input signal, is compared with the *actual* rpm, and the difference is used to position the throttle. One possible closed-loop engine control system is shown in Fig. 1-3. A tachometer, which produces a voltage proportional to shaft speed, is used to measure output rpm. If the desired speed, which is the input, is converted to a voltage, by means of a potentiometer, the two voltages can be subtracted electrically. The difference, or error voltage, is used to position the throttle

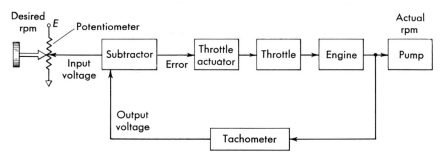

Fig. 1-3. One possible engine controller.

through an appropriate amplifier. The important difference between the closed-loop method (Fig. 1-3) and the open-loop method (Fig. 1-1) lies in the feedback loop. The signal that changes the throttle setting is the difference between the desired rpm and the actual rpm. When the output-shaft speed is equal to the desired speed, that is, the difference or *error* is zero, the throttle actuator (which could be a reversible electric motor whose output is geared to the throttle arm) remains fixed. If any change, such as a change in load, a change in the engine components, or the like, should occur in the system so that the actual rpm is no longer equal to the desired rpm, an error will result. This error causes the motor to change the throttle setting until the actual rpm corresponds to the desired rpm.

A typical "feedback control system," which is shown in Fig. 1-4, comprises one or more feedback loops which combine functions of the controlled signals with functions of the commands to tend to maintain prescribed relationships between the commands and the controlled signals.[28] The same amplifying device and power actuator are used as in the system of Fig. 1-1. It is necessary to add a device to measure the output and a device to subtract actual output from the desired output. The advantages of closed-loop control may be summarized as follows:

1. Variations in load and in major components have little effect upon system accuracy.

2. It is unnecessary to calibrate the system periodically except for the tachometer.

Although closed-loop systems offer many advantages over open-loop controllers, one difficulty may arise—instability. In the case of the gasoline engine, if the speed should decrease because of a change of load, the feedback signal should be such that the throttle is advanced, and the

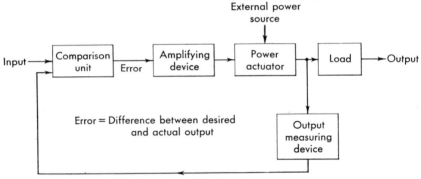

FIG. 1-4. A typical closed-loop system.

speed then is increased to the desired rpm. Suppose that because of delays or reversals in the system the signal fed back is such that the throttle is further retarded. In this case the engine would further decrease in speed, retarding the throttle even more. This process could continue until the engine stalls.

As another example, consider the problem, which is shown schematically in Fig. 1-5, of setting the speed of an electric motor which is driving a very large inertia. As the operator turns the input knob, the motor starts to rotate. Because of the large inertia on the motor, some time is consumed before the flywheel comes up to speed. In the interest of hurrying the process the operator sets the input voltage beyond the value necessary to obtain the correct output. As the motor comes up to speed, the energy in the flywheel carries the tachometer beyond the desired speed. The operator now reduces the voltage to bring down the speed. By the time the motor speed begins to reduce, the input voltage is set too low and the speed drops below that which is desired. This process could continue—the speed increasing while the operator is decreasing the voltage and vice versa. A good operator would begin to anticipate the performance and soon bring the machine to the proper speed. If he did not introduce some anticipation control (phase lead), the system might become unstable. It is usually the phase lags (produced by moments of inertia, inductances, human lags, etc.) in systems that give rise to system instability.

An oscillator is an intentional instability. A portion of the output of a high-gain amplifier is fed back to the input. If just the right amount of energy is fed back, the input can be removed and the system will continue to have an output with no input.

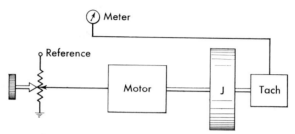

FIG. 1-5. A manual speed regulator system.

Owing to many causes, to be considered later in this book, a feedback control system may be rendered useless because of instability. A formal definition that is applicable for servo stability is: A system is stable if the transients that result when a change due to an impulse applied to the system die out with increasing time. Because of the importance of stability in the operation of feedback control systems or servomechanisms, this book places particular emphasis on the stability problem, to wit:

1. How stable is a system?
2. How can the system be rendered more stable?

The basic approach to the design of servo systems is through analysis which is based on the system differential equations. For physical systems the behavior is determined from the differential equation. A servo engineer must be able to obtain readily an approximation for these equations of the elements in the system. Since these equations contain the essential information about the system, considerable effort is devoted in this text to writing and solving differential equations.

1-2. A Mechanical Suspension. As a first example of finding a differential equation, consider the mechanical suspension shown in Fig.

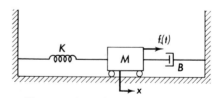

FIG. 1-6. A mechanical suspension.

1-6. A mass M is caused to roll (without bearing friction) on a level track. A spring restrains the motion on the left, and a damper on the right. Small motion is assumed, so that the spring force is linear, as shown in Fig. 1-7a. As the spring is extended $+x$, a force $-f_s$ is produced by the spring, and this force opposes the displacement. The equation for this motion is

$$f_s = -Kx \tag{1-2}$$

where K is the spring constant in units of force per unit length, e.g., pounds per inch. As the spring is compressed $-x$, the spring force f_s still opposes this displacement. The origin, or point at which $x = 0$, is taken as the rest position of the spring.

The mass is restrained on the right with a dashpot (which resembles an automobile shock absorber). This element is termed a "viscous

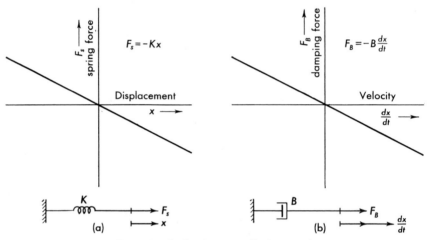

FIG. 1-7a. Spring force vs. displacement.
FIG. 1-7b. Damping force vs. velocity.

damper," since it applies a restoring force proportional to velocity dx/dt. The linear curve is shown in Fig. 1-7b. As the dashpot is stretched or compressed, the unit opposes this motion according to the approximate relationship

$$f_B = -B\frac{dx}{dt} \tag{1-3}$$

where B is the damper constant in units of force per unit length per unit time, e.g., pounds per inch per second.

Application of Newton's second law of motion (i.e., the product of mass and acceleration is equal to the sum of the forces acting on the mass) will yield the desired differential equation. Motions to the right of the equilibrium position are taken as positive $(+x)$, and motions to the left as negative $(-x)$. Reference to Fig. 1-6 yields

$$M\frac{d^2x}{dt^2} = f(t) - B\frac{dx}{dt} - Kx \tag{1-4}$$

or rearranged

$$\frac{d^2x}{dt^2} + \frac{B}{M}\frac{dx}{dt} + \frac{K}{M}x = \frac{f(t)}{M} \quad (1\text{-}5)$$

This last equation represents the differential equation of motion of the system.

Equation (1-5) is representative of the type of equations encountered in linear servo design. It is a "linear differential equation with constant coefficients." The equation and also the system are "linear" because the dependent variable x and the derivatives of x, namely dx/dt and d^2x/dt^2, appear in the equation raised only to the first power. No products of terms, such as $x(dx/dt)$, $x(d^2x/dt^2)$; or terms raised to higher powers, such as $(dx/dt)^2$, x^2, and $(d^2x/dt^2)^3$; or functions of x, such as $\sin x$, $\log x$, and $\cos dx/dt$, are included. The term "constant coefficients" implies that the quantities multiplying the dependent variable or derivatives of the variable are constants independent of time t, displacement x, or velocity dx/dt. That is, M, B, and K are constants. Before Eq. (1-5) is solved, a position servo, with the same differential equation, is considered.

1-3. Equations for a Position Servo. The closed-loop system of Fig. 1-8 is used to position an inertia disk. An output potentiometer meas-

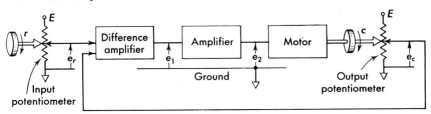

FIG. 1-8. A position servo.

ures the output-shaft position and converts this into a voltage, according to the equation

$$e_c = K_b c \quad (1\text{-}6)$$

where c is the output shaft angle in radians. K_b, which has the units volts per radian, is the "voltage gradient" or "transfer function" of the potentiometer and is found by dividing the total voltage E by the maximum rotation of the potentiometer:

$$K_b = \frac{E}{c_{\max}} \quad \text{volts/radian} \quad (1\text{-}7)$$

The input knob position r is converted to a voltage with an identical potentiometer. A difference amplifier, which is discussed further in Chap. 9, amplifies the difference between the two input signals:

$$e_1 = A_1(e_r - e_c) = A_1 K_b (r - c) \quad (1\text{-}8)$$

This voltage is amplified with A_2 and appears at the motor terminals as

$$e_2 = A_2 e_1 = A_1 A_2 K_b (r - c) \qquad (1\text{-}9)$$

Approximate equations for the motor must be determined. Experimental torque-speed curves for small servomotors are linearized as shown in Fig. 1-9. (Chapter 9 presents more detailed information on servomotors.) The equations for the family of straight lines of Fig. 1-9 are written

$$\omega_c = aL + b \qquad (1\text{-}10)$$

where L is the torque delivered by the motor, ω_c is the angular velocity of the motor shaft, and a and b are constants. Equation (1-10) is the

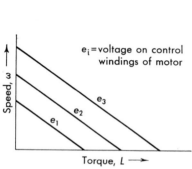

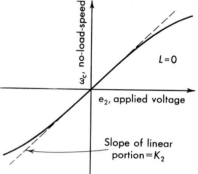

Fig. 1-9. Linear torque-speed curves for a servomotor.

Fig. 1-10. No-load-speed vs. voltage for a typical servomotor.

general equation of a straight line. Depending upon the type of control motor (d-c or a-c), different constants a and b are obtained. The basic equations have the same form.

The slope of all lines is negative and is represented by the same constant

$$a = -k_1 \qquad (1\text{-}11)$$

The quantity b depends upon the control voltage. For $L = 0$, the intersections of the straight lines with the vertical axis yield the no-load-speed versus voltage curve shown in Fig. 1-10. The slope of the linear portion of the curve (near the origin) is k_2. The equation of this curve is

$$\omega_c = k_2 e_2 \qquad (1\text{-}12)$$

where e_2 is the voltage applied to the motor. Rearranging and substituting for ω_c from Eq. (1-12),

$$\omega_c = b = k_2 e_2 \qquad \text{for } L = 0 \qquad (1\text{-}13)$$

The equation for a motor is rearranged and written

$$L + K_2\omega_c = K_1 e_2 \tag{1-14}$$

where $\qquad L =$ torque delivered by motor
$e_2 =$ applied voltage
$\omega_c =$ motor velocity $= dc/dt$
K_1 and $K_2 =$ constants taken from torque-speed curve, $K_1 = k_2/k_1$
and $K_2 = 1/k_1$

In this present example the motor drives an inertia load $L = J(d^2c/dt^2)$ and the differential equation is written

$$J\frac{d^2c}{dt^2} + K_2 \frac{dc}{dt} = K_1 e_2 \tag{1-15}$$

where e_2 is the voltage applied at the motor terminals. When e_2 is substituted from Eq. (1-9), the complete system equation results

$$\frac{d^2c}{dt^2} + \frac{K_2}{J}\frac{dc}{dt} = \frac{K_1}{J}[A_1 A_2 K_b(r - c)] \tag{1-16}$$

which is simplified to

$$\frac{d^2c}{dt^2} + \frac{K_2}{J}\frac{dc}{dt} + \mathcal{K}c = \mathcal{K}r \tag{1-17}$$

where $\qquad\qquad \mathcal{K} = \dfrac{K_1 A_1 A_2 K_b}{J} \tag{1-18}$

The form of Eq. (1-17) is identical with that of Eq. (1-5)—a linear differential equation with constant coefficients. The order of this system, equal to that of the highest derivative in the equation, is two. Such an equation is usually referred to as being of second order.

1-4. Damping Ratio and Undamped Natural Frequency. Before the solution of the differential equations [Eqs. (1-5) and (1-17) of the previous sections] is considered, two important definitions are given. Two quantities that are used throughout the field of control systems are

$\zeta =$ damping ratio
$\omega_n =$ undamped natural frequency

Any linear second-order differential equation can be written in terms of these two quantities. Such a second-order system is written in the form

$$\frac{d^2y}{dt^2} + 2\zeta\omega_n \frac{dy}{dt} + \omega_n^2 y = f(t) \tag{1-19}$$

When Eq. (1-19) is compared with Eq. (1-17), the following relations hold:

$$2\zeta\omega_n = \frac{K_2}{J} \qquad \text{and} \qquad \omega_n^2 = \mathcal{K} \tag{1-20}$$

These relations are solved as follows:

$$\omega_n = \sqrt{\mathcal{K}} = \sqrt{\frac{K_1 A_1 A_2 K_b}{J}} \tag{1-21}$$

$$\zeta = \frac{K_2}{2J\sqrt{\mathcal{K}}} = \frac{K_2}{2}\frac{1}{\sqrt{K_1 A_1 A_2 K_b J}} \tag{1-22}$$

When Eq. (1-19) is compared with the mechanical system of Eq. (1-5), the following relations hold:

$$2\zeta\omega_n = \frac{B}{M} \quad \text{and} \quad \omega_n{}^2 = \frac{K}{M} \tag{1-23}$$

These relations are solved with the result

$$\omega_n = \sqrt{\frac{K}{M}} \tag{1-24}$$

$$\zeta = \frac{B}{2\sqrt{KM}} \tag{1-25}$$

Even with higher-order systems, where there are more than two roots, the system response is often dominated by two "least damped roots" and the results of the second-order system can be extended to approximate the higher-order systems. The two parameters ζ and ω_n are sufficient to describe the second-order equation. These quantities will be discussed in further detail throughout the text.

Equation (1-17) represents the dynamic equation of motion of the position servo of Fig. 1-8. This equation is expressed in terms of ω_n and ζ as follows:

$$\frac{d^2c}{dt^2} + 2\zeta\omega_n\frac{dc}{dt} + \omega_n{}^2c = \omega_n{}^2r \tag{1-26}$$

where ω_n and ζ are given by Eqs. (1-21) and (1-22). The quantity c is the dependent variable or response, and $r(t)$ is the independent variable or driving function.

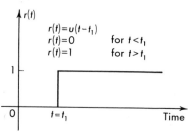

FIG. 1-11. Unit step function in position.

1-5. Laplace-transform Solution of Differential Equations.[9,18] The solution of Eq. (1-26), that is, c as a function of time, can be found with Laplace transforms. The driving function is a step function $u(t)$ which is shown in Fig. 1-11. The system is at rest, that is, $c(0) = 0 = \left.\dfrac{dc}{dt}\right|_{t=0}$, before the application of the step function.

The Laplace-transform solution, which is discussed in Appendix I, starts by transforming both sides of Eq. (1-26) as follows:

$$p^2C + 2\zeta\omega_n pC + \omega_n{}^2 C = \omega_n{}^2 \frac{1}{p} \qquad (1\text{-}27)$$

where p is the Laplace-transform operator, $1/p$ is the Laplace transform of a step function (cf. Table I-1). Since the initial conditions are zero, $p^2C = \mathcal{L}(d^2c/dt^2)$ and $pC = \mathcal{L}(dc/dt)$. The output variable c is capitalized C to indicate that the function of time $c(t)$ and the function of p, $C(p)$, which result after transforming the equation, are different functions.

Equation (1-27) is solved algebraically for C:

$$C = \frac{\omega_n{}^2}{p(p^2 + 2\zeta\omega_n p + \omega_n{}^2)} \qquad (1\text{-}28)$$

This is separated with partial fractions* into

$$C = \frac{1}{p} - \frac{p + 2\zeta\omega_n}{(p + \zeta\omega_n)^2 + \omega_n{}^2(1 - \zeta^2)} \qquad (1\text{-}29)$$

This expression, Eq. (1-29), is inverse Laplace-transformed, using Table I-1, with the result, for $t > 10$,

$$c(t) = u(t) - \frac{e^{-\zeta\omega_n t}}{\sqrt{1 - \zeta^2}} (\sin \omega_n \sqrt{1 - \zeta^2}\, t + \phi) \qquad (1\text{-}30)$$

where $\phi = \tan^{-1}(\sqrt{1 - \zeta^2}/\zeta)$ and $u(t)$ is a unit step function. An alternate form for this expression is written

$$c(t) = 1 - e^{-\zeta\omega_n t}\left(\cos \omega_n \sqrt{1 - \zeta^2}\, t + \frac{\zeta}{\sqrt{1 - \zeta^2}} \sin \omega_n \sqrt{1 - \zeta^2}\, t\right) \qquad (1\text{-}31)$$

This latter form is found from Eq. (1-30) with the identity

$$\sin (a + b) = \sin a \cos b + \cos a \sin b \qquad (1\text{-}32)$$

The curves of Fig. 1-12 show the response [either Eq. (1-30) or (1-31)] of the output shaft $c(t)$ plotted versus dimensionless time $\omega_n t$ after the input knob is subjected to a unit step in rotation, $r(t) = u(t)$. All the curves except $\zeta = 0$ damp down to a steady-state value of 1. The curves for small ζ damp more slowly than for larger ζ. As might be expected, the more damping (ζ large), the less oscillatory is the character of the response. From Eq. (1-22)

$$\zeta = \frac{K_2}{2\sqrt{K_1 A_1 A_2 K_b J}} \qquad (1\text{-}33)$$

The damping ratio depends upon several variables of the system. Adjustment of ζ is possible by variation of any of the quantities in

* See Appendix I for an explanation of partial fractions.

Eq. (1-33). Amplifier gain is commonly decreased to increase the damping.

As the system becomes more oscillatory, small ζ, the response $c(t)$ overshoots the steady-state value (in this case 1) by a greater amount. The per cent overshoot, which is the value to which the output rises

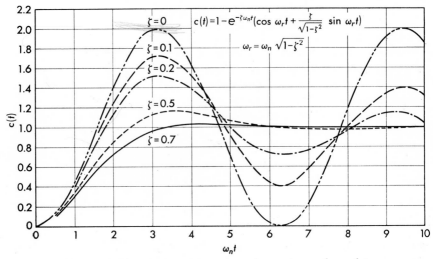

$$c(t) = 1 - e^{-\zeta \omega_n t}\left(\cos \omega_r t + \frac{\zeta}{\sqrt{1-\zeta^2}} \sin \omega_r t\right)$$

$$\omega_r = \omega_n \sqrt{1-\zeta^2}$$

Fig. 1-12. Transient response curves for various values of ζ.

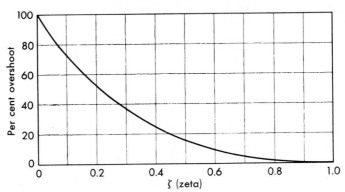

Fig. 1-13. The per cent overshoot versus ζ for a second-order system.

above the steady-state value, is defined

% overshoot

$$= 100 \frac{\text{max value reached in first overshoot} - \text{steady-state value}}{\text{steady-state value}} \quad (1\text{-}34)$$

For the second-order system of Eq. (1-26) the per cent overshoot is plotted in Fig. 1-13.

The speed of response of a system is related to ω_n and ζ.   Since Fig. 1-12 is plotted against $\omega_n t$, the actual time t that is necessary for the curves to reach steady state depends upon ω_n.   For ω_n large the system will reach steady state in less time.   For a simple second-order system of this type, the undamped natural frequency is given by [refer to Eq. (1-21)]

$$\omega_n = \sqrt{\frac{K_1 A_1 A_2 K_b}{J}} \tag{1-35}$$

Variation of ω_n is possible by changing the servo components.   Notice, however, that increasing the $A_1 A_2$ product causes ω_n to increase and ζ to decrease.   Because of this relation between ζ and ω_n, other methods of design must be studied even for this simple system.

1-6. Classical Solution of Differential Equations.[40,56]   The differential equations of dynamic systems can be solved with the classical method, which is presented in Appendix II.   This method is discussed as an aid in understanding servo systems.   The solution is divided into two parts: transient and steady state.   The position servo equation

$$\frac{d^2c}{dt^2} + 2\zeta\omega_n \frac{dc}{dt} + \omega_n{}^2 c = \omega_n{}^2 u(t) \tag{1-36}$$

is solved, as in the previous section, for a step position input and zero initial conditions.

The transient solution is found by setting the driving function [right side of Eq. (1-36)] to zero:

$$\frac{d^2c_t}{dt^2} + 2\zeta\omega_n \frac{dc_t}{dt} + \omega_n{}^2 c_t = 0 \tag{1-37}$$

A solution is assumed for c_t of the form

$$c_t = Ae^{pt} \tag{1-38}$$

and this is substituted into Eq. (1-37):

$$\cancel{A}p^2\cancel{e^{pt}} + \cancel{A}p2\zeta\omega_n\cancel{e^{pt}} + \omega_n{}^2 \cancel{A}\cancel{e^{pt}} = 0 \tag{1-39}$$

The common term Ae^{pt} is canceled in Eq. (1-39), resulting in the characteristic equation

$$p^2 + 2\zeta\omega_n p + \omega_n{}^2 = 0 \tag{1-40}$$

The cancellation of Ae^{pt} is always possible for linear differential equations with constant coefficients.   The Laplace-transform solution, however, is limited to the same type of equation.

Equation (1-40) is factored, in this case using the binomial expression, into two roots

$$p_i = -\zeta\omega_n \pm j\omega_n \sqrt{1 - \zeta^2} \tag{1-41}$$

for the case $\zeta < 1$.   The transient component is written

$$c_t = A_1 e^{-(\zeta\omega_n + j\omega_n\sqrt{1-\zeta^2})t} + A_2 e^{-(\zeta\omega_n - j\omega_n\sqrt{1-\zeta^2})t} \qquad (1\text{-}42)$$

or, as indicated in Appendix II,

$$c_t = e^{-\zeta\omega_n t}(B_1 \sin \omega_r t + B_2 \cos \omega_r t) \qquad (1\text{-}43)$$

where
$$\omega_r = \omega_n \sqrt{1 - \zeta^2} \qquad (1\text{-}44)$$

Before completing the solution, it is now possible to indicate another definition for ζ and ω_n.   This presentation will serve to explain the name given these two quantities.   The quantity ζ is the ratio of the damping that exists in a second-order system to the critical damping.   Higher-order system response is often dominated by two "least damped roots." For this reason, results obtained for the second-order system are often approximately true for higher-order systems.

Critical damping in a second-order system is defined as the value of damping which produces two equal real roots in the characteristic equation.   This corresponds to $\zeta = 1$, since, in Eq. (1-41), substitution of $\zeta = 1$ results in two identical roots

$$p_i = -\zeta\omega_n \qquad (1\text{-}45)$$

For the mechanical system of Fig. 1-6, the characteristic equation is

$$p^2 + \frac{B}{M} p + \frac{K}{M} = 0 \qquad (1\text{-}46)$$

and the roots are

$$p_i = - \frac{B}{2M} \pm \sqrt{\frac{B^2}{4M^2} - \frac{K}{M}} \qquad (1\text{-}47)$$

The critical value of damping, B_c, is the damping constant which makes the term under the radical [of Eq. (1-47)] equal to zero.   For Eq. (1-47), B_c is found from the expression

$$\frac{B_c^2}{4M^2} - \frac{K}{M} = 0 \qquad (1\text{-}48)$$

or solving

$$B_c = 2 \sqrt{KM} \qquad (1\text{-}49)$$

For this value of B, there exists a double real root $-B/2M$.   The damping ratio is

$$\zeta = \frac{B}{B_c} = \frac{B}{2 \sqrt{KM}} \qquad (1\text{-}50)$$

The undamped natural frequency is the frequency of oscillation that occurs for zero damping.   The roots of Eq. (1-46), for $B = 0$, are

$$p_i = \pm \sqrt{\frac{-K}{M}} = \pm j \sqrt{\frac{K}{M}} \qquad (1\text{-}51)$$

where $j = \sqrt{-1}$.   Imaginary roots result in the transient component

$$x = A_1 e^{+j\sqrt{(K/M)}t} + A_2 e^{-j\sqrt{(K/M)}t} \tag{1-52}$$

Equation (1-52) can be written as follows:

$$x = B_1 \cos \sqrt{\frac{K}{M}} t + B_2 \sin \sqrt{\frac{K}{M}} t \tag{1-53}$$

where $\qquad B_1 = (A_1 + A_2) \qquad$ and $\qquad B_2 = j(A_1 - A_2) \tag{1-54}$

The undamped natural frequency is

$$\omega_n = \sqrt{\frac{K}{M}} \tag{1-55}$$

If Eqs. (1-50) and (1-55) are substituted into Eq. (1-46), the following results:

$$p^2 + 2\left(\frac{1}{2}\frac{B}{M}\sqrt{\frac{M}{K}}\right)\sqrt{\frac{K}{M}}\, p + \frac{K}{M} = 0$$
$$\downarrow \quad \downarrow \qquad \downarrow \qquad \downarrow \qquad\quad \downarrow \tag{1-56}$$
$$p^2 + 2 \qquad \zeta \qquad \omega_n \quad p + \omega_n{}^2 = 0$$

This last equation, of course, is identical with the original definition of Sec. 1-4.

The steady-state solution for a step position input is found by assuming a solution of the form

$$c_{ss} = A \tag{1-57}$$

The procedure of Appendix II is followed.   The steady-state solution is substituted into Eq. (1-36):

$$\frac{d^2 c_{ss}}{dt^2} + 2\zeta\omega_n \frac{dc_{ss}}{dt} + \omega_n{}^2 c_{ss} = \omega_n{}^2 \tag{1-58}$$

Since c_{ss} is a constant, the derivatives are zero

$$\omega_n{}^2 c_{ss} = \omega_n{}^2 A = \omega_n{}^2 \tag{1-59}$$

and $A = 1$.   A similar procedure is used for other types of inputs (cf. Appendix II).

The complete solution for this equation is found by adding the transient and steady-state parts as follows:

$$c = c_t + c_{ss} \tag{1-60}$$

These are found from Eqs. (1-43) and (1-59):

$$c(t) = e^{-\zeta\omega_n t}(B_1 \sin \omega_r t + B_2 \cos \omega_r t) + 1 \tag{1-61}$$

Since the system is at rest before the application of the step function, two initial conditions must be imposed:

$$c(0) = 0 = \frac{dc}{dt}\bigg|_{t=0} \tag{1-62}$$

Imposing these initial conditions and solving for the constants,

$$B_1 = \frac{-\zeta}{\sqrt{1 - \zeta^2}} \quad \text{and} \quad B_2 = -1 \tag{1-63}$$

The complete solution is

$$c(t) = 1 - e^{-\zeta\omega_n t}\left(\cos \omega_r t + \frac{\zeta}{\sqrt{1 - \zeta^2}} \sin \omega_r t\right) \tag{1-64}$$

where $\omega_r = \omega_n \sqrt{1 - \zeta^2}$. This equation agrees, of course, with the Laplace-transform solution of Eq. (1-31).

1-7. Transfer Functions and Block Diagrams. The simplification resulting from the use of operational calculus is further increased when transfer functions and block diagrams are introduced. Consider a general differential equation that relates the output of a system to its input:

$$a_n \frac{d^n c}{dt^n} + a_{n-1}\frac{d^{n-1}c}{dt^{n-1}} + \cdots + a_1 \frac{dc}{dt} + a_0 c = b_m \frac{d^m r}{dt} + \cdots + b_1 \frac{dr}{dt} + b_0 r \tag{1-65}$$

where the a_i and b_i are constants, $c(t)$ is the output or response, and $r(t)$ is the input or driving function. Any element which is governed by such an equation is said to be linear. One important property of such elements is that if r_1 produces an output c_1 and r_2 causes an output c_2, then an input

$$\alpha_1 r_1 + \alpha_2 r_2 \tag{1-66}$$

will produce an output

$$\alpha_1 c_1 + \alpha_2 c_2 \tag{1-67}$$

Transforming Eq. (1-65), with zero initial conditions,

$$(a_n p^n + a_{n-1}p^{n-1} + \cdots + a_1 p + a_0)C = (b_m p^m + \cdots + b_1 p + b_0)R \tag{1-68}$$

The ratio of the Laplace-transformed output C to the Laplace-transformed input R is the "transfer function"

$$G(p) = \frac{C}{R} = \frac{b_m p^m + b_{m-1}p^{m-1} + \cdots + b_1 p + b_0}{a_n p^n + a_{n-1}p^{n-1} + \cdots + a_1 p + a_0} \tag{1-69}$$

The transfer function $G(p)$ is a property of the element only. For linear systems it is independent of the driving function and the initial conditions. $G(p)$ is a rational function of p, and the constants a_i and b_i depend only upon the element or the system.

When the transfer function of an element or a system is known, the transformed response can be found from the equation

$$C(p) = G(p)R(p) \tag{1-70}$$

This equation can be represented by a "block diagram," as shown in Fig. 1-14. The block has the signifi-
cance that the output is equal to the input times the function within the box. Hence the block diagram of Fig. 1-14 represents Eq. (1-70).

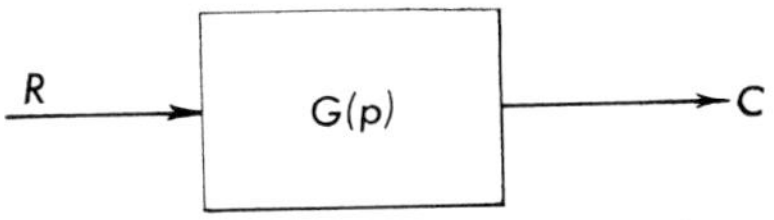

FIG. 1-14. Block diagram of a linear system.

If two such elements are in series, as in Fig. 1-15a, the output of the first is the input to the second, and the following equations must hold:

$$R_1 = G_1(p)R$$
$$C = G_2(p)R_1 \tag{1-71}$$

These equations can be combined algebraically:

$$C = G_1(p)G_2(p)R = G_1G_2R \tag{1-72}$$

This equation shows that the two boxes in series can be transposed as in Fig. 1-15b and also can be replaced by a single box whose transfer function is the product G_1G_2 as shown in Fig. 1-15c. This method can be extended to any number of series elements.

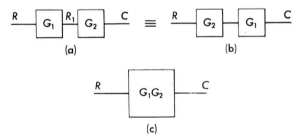

(a)   (b)

(c)

FIG. 1-15. Block-diagram algebra—two blocks in series.

As an example of transfer functions and block diagrams, consider the transfer function for the mechanical suspension of Fig. 1-6. The ratio of the transformed position output X to the transformed force input is found from Eq. (1-5):

$$\left(p^2 + \frac{B}{M}p + \frac{K}{M}\right)X = \frac{F}{M} \tag{1-73}$$

and the transfer function is

$$G_1(p) = \frac{X}{F} = \frac{1/M}{p^2 + (B/M)p + (K/M)} = \frac{\mathcal{K}}{p^2 + K^2p + \mathcal{K}} \tag{1-74}$$

The block diagram is included in Fig. 1-16.

In a similar manner the transformed equation for the position servo is, from Eq. 1-26,

$$(p^2 + 2\zeta\omega_n p + \omega_n{}^2)C = \omega_n{}^2 R \qquad (1\text{-}75)$$

and the over-all transfer function is

$$G_2(p) = \frac{C}{R} = \frac{\omega_n{}^2}{p^2 + 2\zeta\omega_n p + \omega_n{}^2} = \frac{\mathcal{K}}{p^2 + \dfrac{K^2}{J}\,p + \mathcal{K}} \qquad (1\text{-}76)$$

The block diagram is shown in Fig. 1-17.

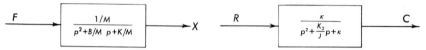

FIG. 1-16. Block diagram of a mechanical suspension.   FIG. 1-17. Block diagram of a position servo.

1-8. Block-diagram Algebra. The combination of several blocks in series (cf. Fig. 1-15) into one box can be extended. The rearranging of block diagrams to effect simplification is termed "block-diagram algebra." The identities presented in this section are used throughout the field of servomechanisms.

As long as it is realized that transformed quantities are used, the $R(p)$ can be discarded and simply R used.

Basic to the subject of feedback control systems is the subtractor,

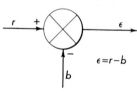

$\epsilon = r - b$

FIG. 1-18. Subtractor symbol.

whose symbol is shown in Fig. 1-18. The input signal (voltage, torque, position, etc.), labeled r, minus the feedback signal (same form as r so a subtraction is effected) equals the error signal ϵ. Practical forms of subtractors are included in Chap. 9.

In Fig. 1-19 are summarized the most important block-diagram identities. Since each of these pairs can be interchanged in a complex system, they aid in reducing a system. All these identities can be verified by finding the output from the two equivalent diagrams. For example, compare the output from both block diagrams of Fig. 1-19b. The diagram on the left yields

$$\varepsilon = K_1 R - K_2 C \qquad (1\text{-}77)$$

The diagram on the right yields

$$\varepsilon = \left(\frac{K_1}{K_2} R - C\right) K_2 = K_1 R - K_2 C \qquad (1\text{-}78)$$

which is identical with Eq. (1-77).

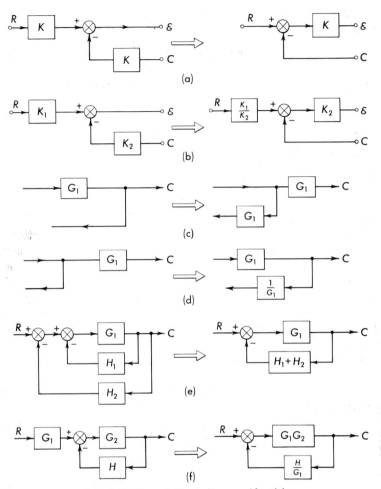

FIG. 1-19. Several block-diagram identities.

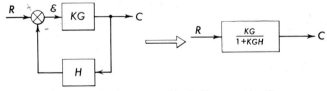

FIG. 1-20. An important block-diagram identity.

The identity shown in Fig. 1-20 is one of the most important. The error ε is written

$$\varepsilon = R - HC = \frac{C}{KG} \tag{1-79}$$

The input-output or closed-loop transfer function is found from Eq. (1-79)

$$\frac{C}{R} = \frac{KG}{1 + KGH} \tag{1-80}$$

and the error to input relation is

$$\frac{\varepsilon}{R} = \frac{1}{1 + KGH} \tag{1-81}$$

It must be remembered that G and H are both functions of p. The variables C, R, and ε are Laplace-transformed and are also functions of p.

Equation (1-80) is the "closed-loop" transfer function of a servo in terms of the open-loop quantities. In words, this equation states that the closed-loop transfer function C/R is the product of forward-loop transfer function KG divided by 1 plus the open-loop transfer functions KGH. Since this expression is frequently needed in feedback-control-system design, it should be memorized.

1-9. Transfer Functions and Convolution. Suppose the differential equation (1-65) is driven by an impulse

$$r(t) = \delta(t) \tag{1-82}$$

$\delta(t)$ is the symbol for a unit impulse function. This function has zero value everywhere except at $t = 0$, where the magnitude is infinite. The impulse is defined so that

$$\int_{-\varepsilon}^{+\varepsilon} \delta(t) \, dt = 1 \tag{1-83}$$

where ϵ is a small positive quantity. The function can be constructed from a pulse, as shown in Fig. 1-21. The pulse has height $1/a$ and width a. The area is $(1/a)(a) = 1$; the impulse is formed by taking the limit as a approaches 0 $(a \to 0)$.

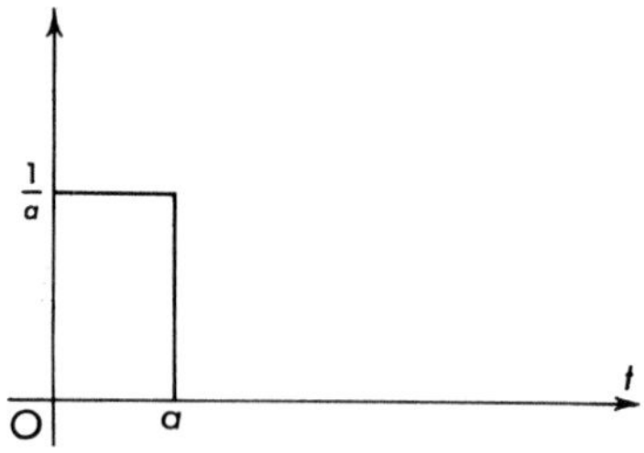

FIG. 1-21. An impulse formed by taking the limit as a approaches zero.

The Laplace transform of an impulse is

$$\mathcal{L}[\delta(t)] = \int_0^\infty e^{-pt}\delta(t) \, dt = e^0 \int_0^\infty \delta(t) \, dt = 1 \tag{1-84}$$

This transform pair is included in Table I-1.

The transformed response $C(p)$ of the system of Eq. (1-65) is given by the transfer function, since $R(p) = 1$.   Hence

$$G(p) = C(p) = \frac{b_m p^m + b_{m-1} p^{m-1} + \cdots + b_1 p + b_0}{a_n p^n + a_{n-1} p^{n-1} + \cdots + a_1 p + a_0} \text{ (1)} \quad \text{(1-85)}$$

is the Laplace transform of the impulse response of the element.

The inverse transform of the transfer function is known as the "weighting function."   If an impulse is applied to an element, as shown in Fig. 1-22, the output is the weighting function $w(t)$.   Any function $r(t)$ can be represented by a series of pulses (impulses in the limit), as shown in Fig. 1-23.   If $w(t)$ is the response of an element when $\delta(t)$ is applied, then

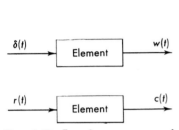

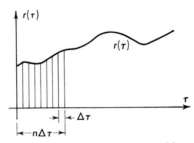

FIG. 1-22. Impulse response and weighting function.

FIG. 1-23. A function represented by a sum of impulses.

$\alpha w(t - n \, \Delta\tau)$ is the response of an element when $\alpha \delta(t - n \, \Delta\tau)$ is applied, where α is a constant.   The response of the element to a pulse which is located at $n \, \Delta\tau$ and is of height $r(n \, \Delta\tau)$ and width $\Delta\tau$ is

$$r(n \, \Delta\tau) w(t - n \, \Delta\tau) \, \Delta\tau \qquad (1\text{-}86)$$

The total solution at time t is the sum of the responses due to each impulse:

$$c(t) = \sum_{n=0}^{N} r(n \, \Delta\tau) w(t - n \, \Delta\tau) \, \Delta\tau \qquad (1\text{-}87)$$

Passing to the limit as $\Delta\tau \to d\tau$, $n \to \infty$, and $\Delta\tau \to 0$ (such that the product $n \, \Delta\tau \to \tau$) Eq. (1-87) reduces to the integral

$$c(t) = \int_0^t r(\tau) w(t - \tau) \, d\tau \qquad (1\text{-}88)$$

Hence the output of a linear system is found by "convolving"* the input with the weighting function.   The weighting function is the inverse Laplace transform of the transfer function

$$\mathcal{L}^{-1} G(p) = w(t) \qquad (1\text{-}89)$$

* This is the process of carrying out the convolution integral of Eq. (1-88).

When the Laplace transform of both sides of Eq. (1-88) is formed,

$$C(p) = R(p)G(p) \tag{1-90}$$

This equation has the same form as Eq. (1-70).   Reference to Appendix I yields further information on the convolution integral.

In Chap. 2 the transfer functions and block diagrams of numerous elements are computed.   Chapters 8 and 9 treat the transfer functions of practical servo components.

1-10. Servo Conventions.   The symbols used in the field of feedback controls have been standardized.   Figure 1-24 shows the block diagram

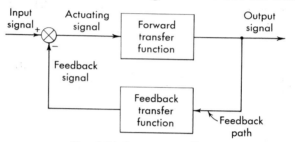

FIG. 1-24. Servo conventions.

with the defined terminology that will be used in this book.   The symbols that represent these are summarized below:

$$\begin{aligned}
\text{Input signal} &= r(t) \text{ or } R(p) &&\text{reference} \\
\text{Output signal} &= c(t) \text{ or } C(p) &&\text{controlled variable} \\
\text{Actuating signal} &= \epsilon(t) \text{ or } \varepsilon(p) &&\text{error} \\
\text{Feedback signal} &= b(t) \text{ or } B(p) &&\text{(if different from } c) \\
\text{Forward transfer functions } & G_1, G_2, \ldots \\
\text{Feedback transfer functions } & H_1, H_2, \ldots
\end{aligned}$$

This notation is used throughout the book.

1-11. Stability and the Location of the Roots of the Characteristic Equation.   The stability of a linear control system is defined in Sec. 1-1. This definition can be reduced to a mathematical criterion for practical servo design.   The stability of a system depends only upon the system and not upon the driving function.   Hence, if a system is unstable, any excitation (driving function) will cause the system to oscillate.   If the system is stable, any bounded excitation will cause a bounded response.

The weighting function, which is the inverse transform of the transfer function, depends only upon the system.   (The Laplace transform of a unit impulse is unity.)   If the weighting function is stable, that is, if it dies out as time increases, all the time constants of the exponentials will be negative:

$$c(t) = A_1 e^{-\alpha_1 t} + e^{-\alpha_2 t}(B \cos \omega_r t + C \sin \omega_r t) + D e^{-\alpha_3 t} \tag{1-91}$$

For large time, $t \to \infty$, this equation reduces to zero.

The Laplace-transformed form of Eq. (1-91) yields the same information.   If

$$C(p) = \frac{A}{p + a} \qquad (1\text{-}92)$$

then
$$c(t) = Ae^{-at} \qquad (1\text{-}93)$$

and if
$$C(p) = \frac{A}{p - b} \qquad (1\text{-}94)$$

then the time response is
$$c(t) = Ae^{bt} \qquad (1\text{-}95)$$

When the root of the transfer function lies in the left half plane, the exponents are negative.   In Eq. (1-92) the root lies at $p_i = -a$ and the weighting function is stable.   In Eq. (1-94) the root lies at $p_i = b$ and the function is unstable, since Eq. (1-95) increases as t becomes large.

The classical solution yields the same information.   The transient component of the solution, which depends only upon the system, is found by setting the driving function to zero and assuming a solution of the form

$$Ae^{pt} \qquad (1\text{-}96)$$

This is substituted into the homogeneous* equation, as in Sec. 1-6, yielding the following characteristic equation:

$$a_n p^n + a_{n-1}p^{n-1} + \cdots + a_1 p + a_0 = 0 \qquad (1\text{-}97)$$

The location of the roots of this equation determines the stability of the system.

The location of the roots on the p plane and the form of the weighting function or the transient component are shown in Fig. 1-25.   Single roots along the negative real axis yield a solution $Ae^{-\alpha_1 t} + Be^{-\alpha_2 t}$.   A complex conjugate pair of roots along the imaginary or j axis yields a transient component $A \cos \omega t + B \sin \omega t$.   Single roots along the positive real axis yield $Ae^{+\alpha_1 t} + Be^{\alpha_2 t}$.   One pair of complex roots in the left half plane gives rise to a transient component of the form

$$e^{-at}(A \cos \omega_r t + B \sin \omega_r t) \qquad (1\text{-}98)$$

A pair of complex roots in the right half plane yields

$$e^{+at}(A \cos \omega_r t + B \sin \omega_r t) \qquad (1\text{-}99)$$

Double roots of the characteristic equation occurring at one point in the left half of the p plane result in a transient component $(A + Bt)e^{-at}$. A single root at the origin gives rise to the solution

$$y_t = \text{constant} = A \qquad (1\text{-}100)$$

* Homogeneous equation is the name given the differential equation when the driving function is set equal to zero.

A double root at the origin yields

$$y_t = A + Bt \tag{1-101}$$

Double complex roots which lie along the j axis give rise to the solution

$$y_{\text{transient}} = (A + Bt) \cos \omega t + (C + Dt) \sin \omega t \tag{1-102}$$

The nature of the stability can now be stated in terms of the location of the roots of the transfer function denominator or the characteristic

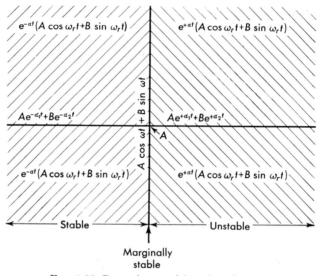

FIG. 1-25. Root plane and location of roots.

equation

A *system is stable*................ If *all* roots lie in the left half plane

A *system is unstable*.............. If *any* of the roots lie in the right half plane or if *any* multiple (double, triple, etc.) complex pairs of roots lie along the j axis or multiple roots at the origin

A *system is marginally stable*...... If any single pair of conjugate roots lies along the j axis and all other roots lie in the left half plane

A *system is conditionally stable*.... If all roots lie in the left half plane only for some particular condition. Often the system is stable in only a range depending upon the loop gain

Roots which lie in the right half plane result in a transient response that builds up with time and is usually unsuitable for a control system. Single roots which lie on the imaginary axis other than at the origin result in an undamped sinusoid, or an oscillatory response. The system is termed an oscillator and is the limiting case between stable and unstable systems.

1-12. Conclusions. The essentials of closed-loop system design are exemplified in the solution of the second-order system. In the design of a servo system no direct-synthesis procedure is available. The servo designer uses a combination of synthesis and analysis. Typically, the designer is faced with several components which must be used (amplifier, motor, etc.). These have differential equations about which the system is constructed. When the loop is closed, theoretically the system may be unstable, may have too large a steady-state error, may have too small a damping ζ or too small a natural frequency ω_n. The engineer must make a change which will bring the system into specification.

Depending upon the experience of the servo engineer, this change will be more or less optimum. In any case it becomes necessary to analyze the system with the "engineering change" to determine the improvement. Having analyzed the first alteration, the servo engineer makes another change and analyzes the resulting system. This process is continued until the system meets the performance specifications.

To be a competent servo designer requires capacity to analyze systems well. Fortunately, a formalized procedure is available for analysis of linear systems. This procedure can be outlined as follows:

1. Obtain the system differential equations.
2. Find the steady-state solution to the differential equations for certain types of inputs (steady-state errors).
3. Determine the degree of stability from the transfer function or characteristic equation.

Each of these steps must be formalized so that the engineer can quickly and accurately complete the analysis. For example, a servo engineer must be capable of obtaining the differential equations for mechanical and electrical systems in a formalized fashion.

PROBLEMS

1-1. List five examples of open-loop control systems, and draw block diagrams for each.

1-2. List five examples of closed-loop control systems, and draw block diagrams for each.

1-3. Use the Laplace integral to find the transform of the following functions of time:

(a) ωt

(b) $\sin \omega t$

(c) e^{-at}

(d) $\frac{1}{2}at^2$

(e) $u(t)$ (unit step function)

(f) $\delta(t)$ (unit impulse)

1-4. Indicate which of the following equations are linear differential equations with constant coefficients:

(a) $\dfrac{d^3y}{dt^3} + 3\left(\dfrac{dy}{dt}\right)^2 + 4y = f(t)$

(b) $\dfrac{d^2y}{dt^2} + 2y\dfrac{dy}{dt} + 3y = \sin \omega t$

(c) $\dfrac{d^3y}{dt^3} + 3t\dfrac{d^2y}{dt^2} + 4\dfrac{dy}{dt} + 1 = e^{j\omega t}$

(d) $\dfrac{d^3y}{dt^3} + 3\dfrac{d^2y}{dt^2} + 2\dfrac{dy}{dt} + 4 = t^2 \sin \omega t$

1-5. Find the solution for the following differential equations. Assume that at $t = 0$, $y = y_0$, dy/dt and all higher derivatives are zero. Since Prob. 1-5f is in transformed form, initial conditions are included.

(a) $\dfrac{d^3y}{dt^3} + 3\dfrac{d^2y}{dt^2} + 10\dfrac{dy}{dt} = 0$ (b) $\dfrac{d^2y}{dt^2} + 10 = 0$

(c) $\dfrac{d^2y}{dt^2} + 7\dfrac{dy}{dt} + 15y = 0$ (d) $\dfrac{d^3y}{dt^3} + 2\dfrac{d^2y}{dt^2} + 11\dfrac{dy}{dt} = 0$

(e) $\dfrac{d^3y}{dt^3} - 3\dfrac{d^2y}{dt^2} + y = 0$ (f) $(p + 1)(p^3 + 8)y = 8y_0$

(Roots $p_i = -0.53,\ +0.65,\ +2.87$)

1-6. Plot on the p plane the roots of the characteristic equations of Prob. 1-5.

1-7. Find the solution to the following differential equations subject to zero initial conditions:

(a) $\dfrac{d^2y}{dt^2} - 2\dfrac{dy}{dt} + 4y = \sin \omega t$

(b) $\dfrac{d^2y}{dt^2} - 2\dfrac{dy}{dt} + 4y = e^{-2t}$

(c) $\dfrac{d^3y}{dt^3} + \dfrac{d^2y}{dt^2} + 4\dfrac{dy}{dt} + 4y = e^{-t}$

1-8. Compare the Laplace-transform and classical methods of solution by solving the following differential equation when subjected to zero initial conditions:

$$\dfrac{d^2c}{dt^2} + 2\zeta\omega_n\dfrac{dc}{dt} + \omega_n{}^2c = \dfrac{1}{2}\alpha t^2$$

Take $\zeta = 0.10$, $\omega_n = 10$ radians/sec, and $\alpha = 1$.

1-9. Plot the frequency of oscillation of the transient component of Eq. (1-43) versus ζ when $\omega_n = 1$.

1-10. Derive an analytic expression which relates per cent overshoot to damping ratio ζ. Plot the corresponding curve to verify Fig. 1-13.

✓**1-11.** (a) Find the complete solution $c(t)$ when the input to the position servo of Fig. 1-8 is a ramp function which is shown in Fig. 1P-11 and is represented mathematically as follows:

$$r(t) = \omega t$$

Assume zero initial conditions at $t = 0$, $c = 0$, and $dc/dt = 0$.

(b) For values of $\zeta = 0.01,\ 0.03,\ 0.06$, and 2.0, plot the solution in the following forms:

    (1) $c(t)$ versus $\omega_n t$

    (2) $\dfrac{dc}{dt}$ versus $\omega_n t$

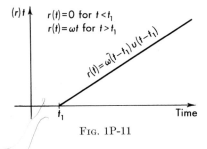

FIG. 1P-11

1-12. After completing the design of a simple position servo of the form shown on Fig. 1-8, the designer finds that the system had 79 per cent overshoot in response to a unit step input. The open-loop transfer function is

$$\frac{C}{R - C} = \frac{C}{\varepsilon} = \frac{A K_m}{p(\tau_m p + 1)}$$

By what factor should he multiply the amplifier gain A so that the overshoot is reduced to 50 per cent? K_m and τ_m are motor constants.

1-13. The open-loop transfer function for a position servo is given by

$$\frac{C}{R - C} = \frac{K}{p(1 + 0.5p)(1 + 0.2p)}$$

$K = 1.6$, and $H(p) = 1$.   Find the response of this system $c(t)$ for a unit step input $r(t) = u(t)$.   The initial conditions are zero.

1-14. Determine the damping ratio, per cent overshoot, and frequency of oscillatory roots for the system of Prob. 1-13.

1-15. Reduce the block diagrams of Fig. 1P-15, and derive expressions for the closed-loop transfer functions.

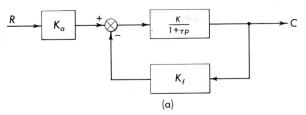

(a)

FIG. 1P-15a

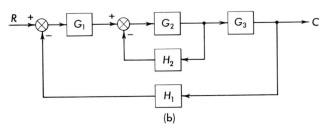

(b)

FIG. 1P-15b

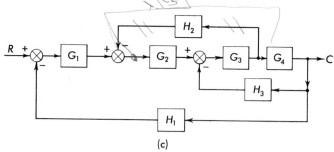

(c)

FIG. 1P-15c

1-16. The transfer function of a system is

$$G(p) = \frac{10}{p + 3}$$

Use the convolution integral of Eq. (1-88) to find the response (output) for zero initial conditions when the input is

    (a) A unit step function $u(t)$
    (b) A unit ramp function $tu(t)$
    (c) A unit-amplitude sinusoid $u(t) \sin t$

1-17. Verify the results of Prob. 1-16 by finding the inverse Laplace transform of the product of the transfer function $G(p)$ and the Laplace transform of the input.

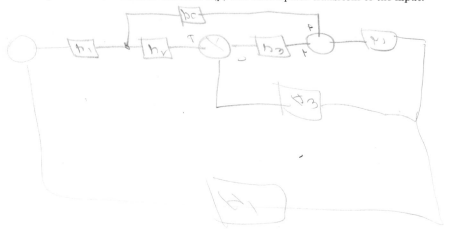

CHAPTER 2

OBTAINING THE SYSTEM DIFFERENTIAL EQUATION

2-1. Introduction. The first step in the synthesis of a feedback control system is to obtain the differential equations of the fixed elements (those elements which must be "lived with"), such as mechanical components, networks, error-sensing devices, and amplifiers. This chapter deals with the writing of linear differential equations for electrical, mechanical, or electromechanical systems. The approach to the problem of finding the differential equation is identical for any of these systems. The method which is outlined in this chapter reduces the analysis of linear systems to a step-by-step procedure.

2-2. Loop Analysis of Electrical Networks.[23,55] The foundation of electrical network analysis rests upon two basic laws, namely, Kirchhoff's laws:

1. The algebraic sum of the voltage drops around a closed loop equals zero. Alternately the sum of the voltage drops equals the sum of voltage rises around a closed loop.

2. The algebraic sum of the currents flowing out of a circuit node equals zero.

A common method of analysis based on the first law is called the "Maxwell mesh" or "loop" method. This method consists of summing the voltage drops around each loop of a multiloop network and setting each equation equal to

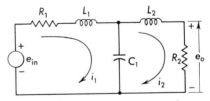

FIG. 2-1. Electric circuit example.

zero. As an example of the loop analysis of an electric circuit, consider the problem of finding the output voltage e_o for the circuit of Fig. 2-1. The steps in the solution of this problem are summarized as follows:

1. Assume loop currents in a clockwise direction (i_1 and i_2 in Fig. 2-1). Although the correct solution will be obtained if some other direction is assumed, certain checks are available if the currents are taken in the same direction. Be certain that a current flows through every element and that the number of currents assumed is sufficient.

One method to assure that a sufficient number of currents is assumed in a network is indicated in Fig. 2-2. This method is applicable to networks that can be drawn with no wires crossing. (These networks are called "planar networks.") The currents are assumed so that (a) through every element a current flows and (b) no element crosses a loop. Condition a is satisfied in Fig. 2-2, since currents flow through all ele-

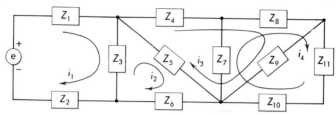

FIG. 2-2. Insufficient number of loop currents.

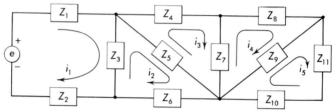

FIG. 2-3. Sufficient number of loop currents.

ments. Condition b is violated, however, in the case of both currents i_3 and i_4. A correct assumption of the currents is shown in Fig. 2-3.

2. Around each loop write Kirchhoff's first law (the sum of voltage drops around the loop equals the sum of voltage rises around the loop). This will result in the same number n of differential equations as there are assumed currents.

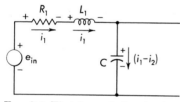

FIG. 2-4. First loop of electric circuit example.

3. Laplace-transform the differential equations.

4. Solve the n algebraic equations for the desired current or currents. In solving these equations treat p as an algebraic quantity. The differential equations are manipulated as algebraic equations.

The equations for the circuit of Fig. 2-1 are found by following the above procedure.

1. The currents i_1 and i_2 are assumed in a clockwise direction.

2. The sum of the voltage drops around each loop is set equal to the voltage rises. In the first loop the input voltage e_{in} is a rise, as indicated by the polarity markings on Fig. 2-4. The voltage drops in the first loop occur across the passive elements R, L, and C in the loop. The sum of the voltage rises equated to the sum of the voltage drops yields

$$e_{in} = R_1 i_1 + L_1 \frac{di_1}{dt} + \frac{1}{C} \int_0^t (i_1 - i_2)\, dt \tag{2-1}$$

When this equation is Laplace-transformed with zero initial conditions,

$$E_{in} = \left(R_1 + L_1 p + \frac{1}{pC} \right) I_1 + \left(\frac{-1}{pC} \right) I_2 \tag{2-2}$$

The variables are capitalized to indicate that they are functions of p.

An equation for each loop must be written. In the second loop, shown in Fig. 2-5, the voltage rises (driving functions) are zero. Equating this to the sum of the voltage drops

$$0 = L_2 \frac{di_2}{dt} + R_2 i_2 + \frac{1}{C} \int_0^t (i_2 - i_1)\, dt \tag{2-3}$$

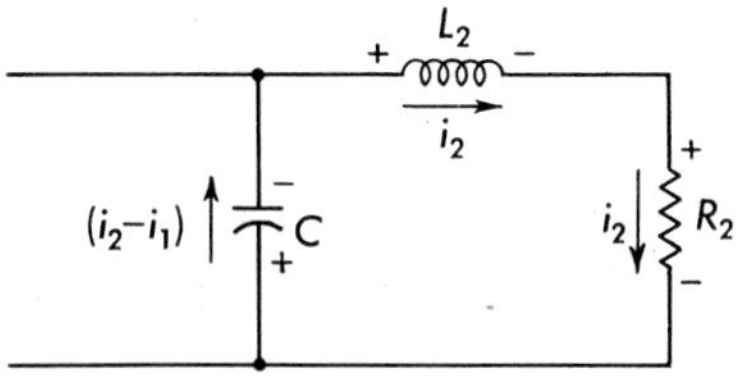

FIG. 2-5. Second loop of electric circuit example.

or in terms of the Laplace-transform operator p

$$0 = \left(-\frac{1}{pC} \right) I_1 + \left(L_2 p + R_2 + \frac{1}{pC} \right) I_2 \tag{2-4}$$

In a shorthand notation Eqs. (2-2) and (2-4) are written in convenient form for solution:

$$E_{in} = Z_{11} I_1 + Z_{12} I_2 \qquad 0 = Z_{21} I_1 + Z_{22} I_2 \tag{2-5}$$

where Z_{11} is the sum of all impedances around the first loop and in this example is

$$Z_{11} = \left(L_1 p + R_1 + \frac{1}{pC} \right) \tag{2-6}$$

Z_{12} is the sum of all impedances common to loops 1 and 2 and in this example is

$$Z_{12} = -\frac{1}{pC} \tag{2-7}$$

For electrical networks that contain only resistors R, capacitors C, inductors L, and transformers M, the network is assumed to be linear and bilateral. Linearity is defined in Chap. 1 and means that the voltage drops across these elements are of the form

$$E_R = RI \qquad E_C = \mathcal{L} \frac{1}{C} \int_0^t i\, dt = \frac{1}{pC} I$$
$$E_L = \mathcal{L} L \frac{di}{dt} = Lp I \qquad E_M = \pm \mathcal{L} M \frac{di}{dt} = \pm M p I \tag{2-8}$$

The dependent variable i and its derivatives and integrals appear only to the first power. Bilateral elements are those whose voltage drop is the same in magnitude for a current flowing in either direction through the element. All the common elements R, L, C, and M are bilateral. A diode, shown in the schematic of Fig. 2-6a, is an example of a non-bilateral element. When a positive polarity voltage is applied, the current flows to the right as shown by the curve of Fig. 2-6b and the diode acts like a low-value resistor. When the same voltage is applied in the opposite direction, only a small current flows. The diode now behaves like a resistor of large value.

Returning to Eq. (2-5), Z_{22} is the sum of all impedances around loop 2 and is given by

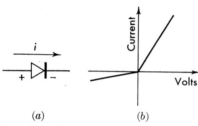

(a)   (b)

Fig. 2-6. Schematic of a diode—non-bilateral element.

$$Z_{22} = L_2 p + R_2 + \frac{1}{pC} \quad (2\text{-}9)$$

Z_{21} is the sum of all impedances common to loops 1 and 2. Since the elements are bilateral, the voltage drop across the common element is independent of the direction of current flow through the element and

$$Z_{21} = Z_{12} = -\frac{1}{pC} \quad (2\text{-}10)$$

This property of linear-bilateral networks will prove useful in checking the accuracy of the result.

Simple equations like Eq. (2-5) are easily solved by substitution:

$$E_{in} = Z_{11}\left(-\frac{Z_{22}}{Z_{12}}\right) I_2 + Z_{12} I_2$$

and
$$E_2 = I_2 R_2 = R_2 \frac{E_{in}}{(Z_{11} Z_{22}/Z_2) - Z_{12}} \quad (2\text{-}11)$$

The solution of more complicated algebraic equations can be accomplished by use of Cramer's rule; the solution appears as the ratio of two determinants. In the simple example of Eq. (2-5) it is desired to find the solution for I_2:

$$I_2 = \frac{\begin{vmatrix} Z_{11} & E_{in} \\ Z_{21} & 0 \end{vmatrix}}{\begin{vmatrix} Z_{11} & Z_{12} \\ Z_{21} & Z_{22} \end{vmatrix}} \quad (2\text{-}12)$$

The determinant in the denominator is formed from the coefficients of the dependent variables. The equations are written in a symmetric fashion, as in Eq. (2-5). The denominator determinant is easily written directly from the network

$$\Delta = \begin{vmatrix} Z_{11} & Z_{12} \\ Z_{21} & Z_{22} \end{vmatrix} \tag{2-13}$$

where the symbol Δ is used to denote the determinant. The numerator determinant is formed by replacing the column in Δ, corresponding to the quantity to be found, by the column of driving functions.

In this example, I_2 is to be found. Replace the I_2 column which contains Z_{12} and Z_{22} with the driving function column, which contains E_{in} and 0. The ratio of

FIG. 2-7. Block diagram of electric circuit example.

these two determinants, shown in Eq. (2-12), yields the solution. A review of the theory of determinants is included in Appendix IV.

For the example of Eq. (2-12), the determinants are expanded:

$$I_2 = \frac{-Z_{21}E_{in}}{Z_{11}Z_{22} - Z_{21}Z_{12}} \tag{2-14}$$

The transfer function E_o/E_{in} is found from Eq. (2-14):

$$E_o = R_2 I_2 = \frac{-R_2 Z_{21} E_{in}}{Z_{11}Z_{22} - Z_{12}Z_{21}} \tag{2-15}$$

Replacing Z_{12}, Z_{21}, Z_{11}, Z_{22} by the values given in Eqs. (2-6), (2-7), (2-9), and (2-10),

$$\frac{E_o}{E_{in}} = \frac{-R_2(-1/pC)}{[L_1 p + R_1 + (1/pC)][L_2 p + R_2 + (1/pC)] - (1/pC)^2} \tag{2-16}$$

This transfer function reduces, after some algebraic manipulations, to

$$G_1(p) = \frac{E_o}{E_{in}}$$

$$= \frac{R_2}{(L_1 L_2 C)p^3 + (R_1 L_2 C + R_2 L_1 C)p^2 + (L_1 + L_2 + R_1 R_2 C)p + (R_1 + R_2)} \tag{2-17}$$

The block diagram for this network is shown in Fig. 2-7 where $G_1(p)$, which is given by Eq. (2-17), is the transfer function.

The n-loop network is treated in the same manner as the example just considered. If there are n independent loops, there will be n loop currents. Consequently, there are n independent equations from which the n unknown loop currents are determined. These equations may be written as

$$I_1 Z_{11} + I_2 Z_{12} + \cdots + I_j Z_{1j} + \cdots + I_n Z_{1n} = E_1$$
$$I_1 Z_{21} + I_2 Z_{22} + \cdots + I_j Z_{2j} + \cdots + I_n Z_{2n} = E_2$$

$$I_1 Z_{n1} + I_2 Z_{n2} + \cdots + I_j Z_{nj} + \cdots + I_n Z_{nn} = E_n$$

$$(2\text{-}18)$$

The quantities E_1, E_2, . . . , E_n are the transformed driving voltages or voltage sources. The quantities Z_{ij} are impedance operators and are algebraic functions of the Laplace-transform operator p.

The self-impedance of the loop is

$$Z_{ii} = pL_{ii} + R_{ii} + \frac{1}{pC_{ii}} \qquad (2\text{-}19)$$

where L_{ii} is the self-inductance of the loop presented to the ith current flowing around the ith loop, R_{ii} is the self-resistance, and C_{ii} is the self-capacitance seen by the ith current. The common impedance terms are

$$Z_{ij} = -\left(pL_{ij} + R_{ij} + \frac{1}{pC_{ij}}\right) \qquad (2\text{-}20)$$

The quantities L_{ij}, R_{ij}, and C_{ij} are the common inductance, common resistance, and common capacitance, respectively, between the ith and jth loops. For example, the capacitance in the circuit of Fig. 2-1 is common to both loops 1 and 2.

If mutual inductance is present, a term $\pm pM_{ij}$ will appear in the Z_{ij} term [Eq. (2-20)] as follows:

$$Z_{ij} = -\left(pL_{ij} + R_{ij} + \frac{1}{pC_{ij}} \pm pM_{ij}\right) \qquad (2\text{-}21)$$

The sign of the mutual term is discussed in the next section. If i loops contain active voltage sources E_i, these are the driving functions which appear on the right side of Eqs. (2-18).

Equations (2-18) are solved by determinants; the denominator determinant is

$$\Delta = \begin{vmatrix} Z_{11} & Z_{12} & Z_{13} & \ldots & Z_{1n} \\ Z_{21} & Z_{22} & Z_{23} & \ldots & Z_{2n} \\ Z_{31} & & & \ldots & \cdot \\ \cdot & & & & \\ \cdot & & & & \\ \cdot & & & & \\ Z_{n1} & Z_{n2} & & \ldots & Z_{nn} \end{vmatrix} \qquad (2\text{-}22)$$

where, in choosing subscripts for the impedance, the first corresponds to the row and the second to the column as follows:

$$Z_{ij}$$
$$i\text{th row}\_\_\uparrow\uparrow\_\_j\text{th column}$$

If all Z_{ij} are not equal to all Z_{ji} for each pair ij, the work should be checked. For planar circuits containing only linear, bilateral, passive elements all Z_{ij} are equal to all Z_{ji} and are negative when the current directions are assumed in the manner shown.

The numerator determinant with both the ith row and jth column crossed out is written

$$
\Delta_{ij} =
\begin{vmatrix}
Z_{11} & Z_{12} & Z_{13} & \cdots & Z_{1j} & \cdots & Z_{1n} \\
Z_{21} & Z_{22} & Z_{23} & \cdots & Z_{2j} & \cdots & Z_{2n} \\
Z_{31} & Z_{32} &   & \cdots & Z_{3j} & \cdots & Z_{3n} \\
\vdots & \vdots &   &   &   &   & \vdots \\
Z_{i1} & Z_{i2} &   &   & Z_{ij} &   & Z_{in} \\
\vdots & \vdots &   &   &   &   & \vdots \\
Z_{n1} & Z_{n2} &   & \cdots & Z_{nj} & \cdots & Z_{nn}
\end{vmatrix}
\tag{2-23}
$$

This determinant is of one degree lower than the original Δ. To find the solution for any particular current, for example, the current in the jth loop i_j, the jth column of the determinant of Eq. (2-22) is replaced with the column of driving voltages. The solution can be written formally:

$$
I_j = \frac{1}{\Delta} \sum_{i=1}^{n} (-1)^{(i+j)} E_i \Delta_{ij}
\tag{2-24}
$$

This equation is simply the mathematical expression of the expansion of a determinant.

An interesting example of the use of Eq. (2-24) is in finding the input impedance Z_{jj}^{in} to a network. When all voltage sources are shorted and a voltage E_j is applied to only the jth loop, the input impedance to the jth loop is the ratio of E_j to the current I_j that flows. Since all voltage sources are zero except E_j, the summation of Eq. (2-24) reduces to one term

$$
I_j = \frac{1}{\Delta} (-1)^{j+j} E_j \Delta_{jj} = E_j \frac{\Delta_{jj}}{\Delta}
\tag{2-25}
$$

and the input impedance is

$$
Z_{jj}^{in} = \frac{E_j}{I_j} = \frac{\Delta}{\Delta_{jj}}
\tag{2-26}
$$

The input impedance for the example of Fig. 2-1 is

$$Z_{11}{}^{in} = \frac{\Delta}{\Delta_{11}} = Z_{11} - \frac{Z_{12}{}^2}{Z_{22}}$$

$$= \left(L_1p + R_1 + \frac{1}{pC}\right) - \frac{(1/pC)^2}{L_2p + R_2 + (1/pC)} \qquad (2\text{-}27)$$

2-3. Mutual Inductance. If mutual inductance is present, a similar analysis is used except that a voltage is induced in the primary of the transformer as a consequence of a change of current in the secondary, and vice versa. The term which represents the mutual inductance $\pm pM_{ij}$ is included in Eq. (2-21). The choice of the plus or minus sign

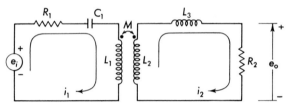

FIG. 2-8. Mutual inductance in loop circuits.

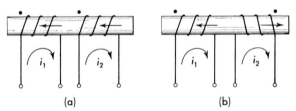

(a)   (b)

FIG. 2-9. Transformer polarity markings.

preceding the term depends upon the connection or polarity of the transformer.

As an example, consider the circuit of Fig. 2-8 where a dot is associated with each coil on the transformer. These dots indicate the winding direction of the coils. The rule associated with this convention is: If both assumed circuits I_1 and I_2 flow into or out of the dotted ends of the coils, the sign of the mutual inductance term, treated as a voltage drop, is positive. If one assumed current flows into a dotted end and the other flows out of a dotted end, the sign is negative.

The dots, or polarity markings, on a transformer indicate the winding sense of the unit. For example, consider the two transformers of Fig. 2-9, where assumed currents I_1 and I_2 flow through transformers with different winding senses. In Fig. 2-9a the assumed currents produce fluxes along the axis of the transformer which aid each other. In this case, when the fluxes aid, the mutual inductance has the same sign as the self-inductance or

$$L_1 p I_1 + M p I_2 \qquad (2\text{-}28)$$

when treated as a voltage drop. The dots, as shown in Fig. 2-9a, appear on the same ends. In Fig. 2-9b the fluxes produced by the assumed currents I_1 and I_2 are opposed and the mutual inductance has the opposite sign as the self-inductance.

$$L_1 p I_1 - M p I_2 \qquad (2\text{-}29)$$

The dots appear on opposite ends of the coils for Fig. 2-9b.

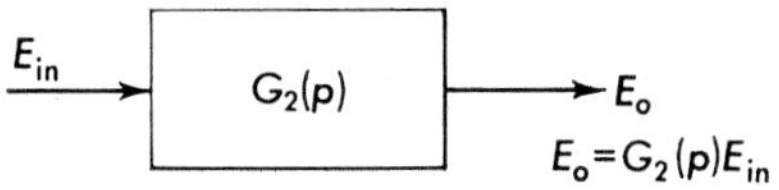

In Fig. 2-8, the current in loop 1 flows into the dotted end and I_2 flows out of the dotted end.

FIG. 2-10. Block diagram of the electrical network of Fig. 2-8.

The sign of the mutual term is negative, and the impedances for the circuit of Fig. 2-8 are

$$\begin{aligned} Z_{11} &= pL_1 + R_1 + \frac{1}{pC_1} \\ Z_{12} &= Z_{21} = -Mp \\ Z_{22} &= (L_2 + L_3)p + R_2 \end{aligned} \qquad (2\text{-}30)$$

The driving function is E_{in}, and the equations are

$$\begin{aligned} E_{in} &= Z_{11} I_1 + Z_{12} I_2 \\ 0 &= Z_{21} I_1 + Z_{22} I_2 \end{aligned} \qquad (2\text{-}31)$$

The transfer function is

$$\frac{E_o}{E_{in}} = \frac{I_2 R_2}{E_{in}} = \frac{R_2(-Z_{21})}{Z_{11} Z_{22} - Z_{12}^2} \qquad (2\text{-}32)$$

When Eqs. (2-30) are inserted into Eq. (2-32) and the result simplified, the transfer function is written

$$G_2(p) = \frac{E_o}{E_{in}}$$

$$= \frac{R_2 M C_1 p^2}{C_1[L_1(L_2 + L_3) - M^2]p^3 + [R_1(L_2 + L_3) + R_2 L_1]C_1 p^2 + (L_2 + L_3 + R_1 R_2 C_1)p + R_2} \qquad (2\text{-}33)$$

This is the transfer function from E_{in} to E_o, and the block diagram is shown in Fig. 2-10.

2-4. Nodal Analysis of Electrical Networks. The nodal method of analysis is based on Kirchhoff's second law, namely, that the sum of the currents flowing out of a node is equal to zero. The steps necessary to solve an electric network with the nodal analysis are outlined as follows:

1. Assume voltages at all nodes in the circuit. It is often convenient to choose one point or node in the circuit as ground and assume volt-

ages V_i at all other nodes. This latter method is suggested. The node voltages above ground are the dependent variables in the node solution just as the currents are the dependent variables in the loop solution. There exists no problem of finding the correct number of node voltages necessary to describe the circuit as is the case with the loop analysis.

2. Write Kirchhoff's second law; that is, the sum of the currents flowing into the node point is equal to zero. This will result in the same number of differential equations as there are assumed node-pair voltages. No equation is written for the node chosen at ground potential.

3. Laplace-transform the differential equations.

4. Solve n algebraic equations for the desired voltage.

The above procedure is used to find the transfer function E_o/E_{in} for the circuit of Fig. 2-11. The first step in the solution is to choose the

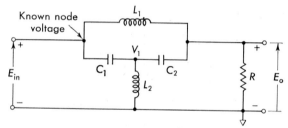

Fig. 2-11. Example of the nodal analysis method.

ground node and assume voltages for the other nodes. The lower lead on the circuit of Fig. 2-11 is conveniently taken at ground potential. E_o is the potential at the output node, and V_1 is the voltage at the center point (shown on Fig. 2-11). Since the input node is driven with a known voltage source E_{in}, only two unknown node voltages (E_o and V_1) exist in the problem so only two equations must be written. An equation is not written at E_{in}, since it is a known quantity. The next step consists of writing Kirchhoff's current equation about these two node points.

Consider first the relation that exists between current and voltage across the three electrical elements. The current through a resistor R is

$$I_R = \mathscr{L}\frac{v_1 - v_2}{R} = \frac{V_1 - V_2}{R} \tag{2-34}$$

where the current flows from V_1 to V_2 as shown in Fig. 2-12a. The current through a capacitor C is

$$I_C = \mathscr{L}C\frac{d}{dt}(v_1 - v_2) = pC(V_1 - V_2) \tag{2-35}$$

where the current flows from V_1 to V_2 as shown in Fig. 2-12b. The last portions of these equations are Laplace-transformed with zero initial conditions.   The current from V_1 to V_2 through an inductor is

$$I_L = \mathcal{L}\frac{1}{L}\int_0^t (v_1 - v_2)\, dt = \frac{1}{pL}(V_1 - V_2) \qquad (2\text{-}36)$$

The equation for the currents leaving any node, say V_1, is formed by summing currents of the form of Eqs. (2-34) to (2-36). Capitalized quantities represent Laplace-transformed functions.

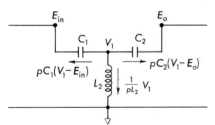

$$I_R = \frac{V_1 - V_2}{R}$$

$$I_C = Cp(V_1 - V_2)$$

$$I_L = \frac{1}{Lp}(V_1 - V_2)$$

(a)   (b)   (c)

FIG. 2-12. Current through R, L, and C elements.

Figure 2-13 shows the portion of the circuit necessary to write the first equation for the circuit of Fig. 2-11.   The sum of the currents which are shown in Fig. 2-13 flowing from the node must equal zero, or

$$pC_2(V_1 - E_o) + pC_1(V_1 - E_{in}) + \frac{1}{pL_2}V_1 = 0 \qquad (2\text{-}37)$$

The first equation is obtained by rearranging Eq. (2-37).   Since E_{in} is

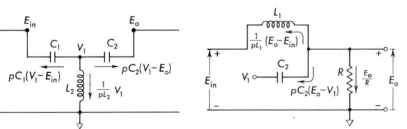

FIG. 2-13. First portion of node circuit.   FIG. 2-14. Second portion of node circuit.

the driving function, it is taken to the right side as

$$V_1\left[p(C_2 + C_1) + \frac{1}{pL_2}\right] + E_o(-pC_2) = (pC_1)E_{in} \qquad (2\text{-}38)$$

The second equation, written at the output node, is represented by the circuit of Fig. 2-14.   Again equating the sum of the currents, leaving the node to zero,

$$\frac{1}{pL_1}(E_o - E_{in}) + pC_2(E_o - V_1) + \frac{E_o}{R} = 0 \qquad (2\text{-}39)$$

The driving function E_{in} is taken to the right side, and the expression is rearranged

$$V_1(-pC_2) + E_o\left(pC_2 + \frac{1}{R} + \frac{1}{pL_1}\right) = \frac{1}{pL_1}E_{in} \qquad (2\text{-}40)$$

Equations (2-38) and (2-40) are the two necessary differential equations which define the system. These equations can be rewritten in a shorthand notation:

$$V_1Y_{11} + E_oY_{12} = I_1$$
$$V_1Y_{21} + E_oY_{22} = I_2 \qquad (2\text{-}41)$$

where Y_{11} is the sum of all admittances which tie to node 1 and in this example is

$$Y_{11} = p(C_1 + C_2) + \frac{1}{pL_2} \qquad (2\text{-}42)$$

Y_{12} is the sum of all admittances connecting nodes 1 and 2 and in this example is

$$Y_{12} = -pC_2 \qquad (2\text{-}43)$$

Since the network is formed from linear-bilateral elements,

$$Y_{21} = Y_{12} = -pC_2 \qquad (2\text{-}44)$$

Y_{22} is the sum of all admittances connected to node 2 and is

$$Y_{22} = \left(pC_2 + \frac{1}{R} + \frac{1}{pL_1}\right) \qquad (2\text{-}45)$$

The driving function for the nodal solution is a current. In this case

$$I_1 = (pC_1)E_{in} \qquad \text{and} \qquad I_2 = \frac{1}{pL_1}E_{in} \qquad (2\text{-}46)$$

The solution of Eqs. (2-41) is identical with that presented for the loop solution. For simple cases the output voltage can be found by substituting as in Eq. (2-11). A more systematic method of solution is based on the ratio of two determinants:

$$E_o = \frac{\begin{vmatrix} Y_{11} & I_1 \\ Y_{21} & I_2 \end{vmatrix}}{\begin{vmatrix} Y_{11} & Y_{12} \\ Y_{21} & Y_{22} \end{vmatrix}} = \frac{I_2Y_{11} - I_1Y_{21}}{Y_{11}Y_{22} - Y_{12}{}^2} \qquad (2\text{-}47)$$

The transfer function E_o/E_{in} is found by substituting values into Eq. (2-47) from previous equations:

$$\frac{E_o}{E_{in}} = \frac{[p(C_1 + C_2) + (1/pL_2)][(1/pL_1) - (pC_1)(-pC_2)]}{[p(C_1 + C_2) + (1/pL_2)][pC_2 + (1/R) + (1/pL_1)] - (pC_2)^2} \qquad (2\text{-}48)$$

which is reduced to

$$G_3(p) = \frac{E_o}{E_{in}}$$

$$= \frac{p^4(L_1L_2C_1C_2) + p^2[(C_1 + C_2)L_2] + 1}{p^4(L_1L_2C_1C_2) + [(1/R)(C_1 + C_2)L_1L_2]p^3 + p^2[(C_1 + C_2)L_2 + C_2L_1] + p(L_1/R) + 1} \quad (2\text{-}49)$$

The block diagram for the transfer function of Eq. (2-49) is shown in Fig. 2-15.

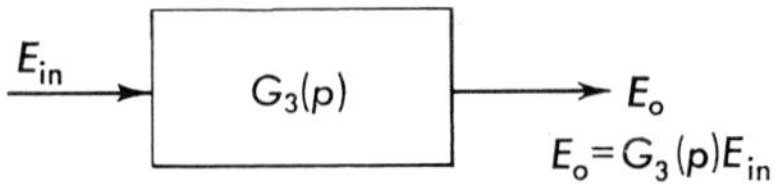

If there are $n + 1$ independent nodes, there will be n independent unknown node-pair voltages. Consequently there exist n independent equations relating these node-pair voltages to driving currents.

$$E_o = G_3(p)E_{in}$$

FIG. 2-15. Block diagram for the circuit of Fig. 2-11.

This set of Laplace-transformed equations may be written

$$\begin{aligned}
V_1Y_{11} + V_2Y_{12} + \cdots + V_nY_{1n} &= I_1 \\
V_1Y_{21} + V_2Y_{22} + \cdots + V_nY_{2n} &= I_2 \\
&\vdots \\
V_1Y_{n1} + V_2Y_{n2} + \cdots + V_nY_{nn} &= I_n
\end{aligned} \quad (2\text{-}50)$$

The driving functions $I_1, I_2, \ldots, I_n$ are active current sources or current driving functions. The general self-admittance term is written as

$$Y_{ii} = pC_{ii} + \frac{1}{R_{ii}} + \frac{1}{pL_{ii}} \quad (2\text{-}51)$$

and the general common admittance term is written

$$Y_{ij} = -\left(pC_{ij} + \frac{1}{R_{ij}} + \frac{1}{pL_{ij}}\right) \quad (2\text{-}52)$$

Mutual inductance $\pm pM_{ij}$ is purposely left out of Eq. (2-52). Although mutual inductance can be treated in a nodal solution,[*] it is usually more conveniently treated with a loop solution. When circuits which are more easily treated on the nodal basis (because there are fewer independent nodes than independent loops) involve mutual inductance, a π-equivalent circuit for the transformer can be used. The conversion to a π-equivalent circuit is shown in Fig. 2-16. This circuit is most suited for the nodal solution. A T-equivalent circuit, also shown in Fig. 2-16, can be used for the loop solution.

* Reference 18, pp. 40–43.

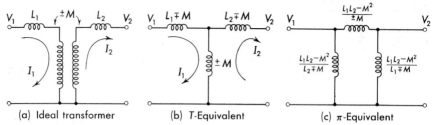

(a) Ideal transformer   (b) T-Equivalent   (c) π-Equivalent

FIG. 2-16. Two equivalent circuits for a transformer.

Equations (2-50) are solved by determinants in a similar fashion as for loop analysis:

$$V_j = \frac{1}{\Delta^N} \begin{vmatrix} Y_{11} & Y_{12} & Y_{13} & \cdots & I_1 & \cdots & Y_{1n} \\ Y_{21} & Y_{22} & \cdot & \cdots & I_2 & \cdots & Y_{2n} \\ \cdot & \cdot & \cdot & & \cdot & & \cdot \\ \cdot & \cdot & \cdot & & \cdot & & \cdot \\ \cdot & \cdot & \cdot & & \cdot & & \cdot \\ Y_{n1} & Y_{n2} & Y_{n3} & \cdots & I_n & \cdots & Y_{nn} \end{vmatrix} \tag{2-53}$$

where the symbol Δ^N is used to indicate the determinant of the coefficients

$$\Delta^N = \begin{vmatrix} Y_{11} & Y_{12} & \cdots & Y_{1j} & \cdots & Y_{1n} \\ Y_{21} & Y_{22} & \cdots & Y_{2j} & \cdots & Y_{2n} \\ \cdot & \cdot & & \cdot & & \cdot \\ \cdot & \cdot & & \cdot & & \cdot \\ \cdot & \cdot & & \cdot & & \cdot \\ Y_{n1} & Y_{n2} & \cdots & Y_{nj} & \cdots & Y_{nn} \end{vmatrix} \tag{2-54}$$

The solution for V_j can be written formally as follows:

$$V_j = \frac{1}{\Delta^N} \sum_{i=1}^{n} (-1)^{i+j} I_i \Delta_{ij}{}^N \tag{2-55}$$

where $\Delta_{ij}{}^N$ is the determinant Δ^N with the ith row and the jth column crossed out.

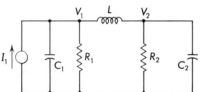

FIG. 2-17. Circuit equations found by nodal method.

The input admittance $Y_{jj}{}^{in}$ into the node is found by opening all current sources except the one that drives the jth node and finding the ratio

$$Y_{jj}{}^{in} = \frac{I_j}{V_j} = \frac{\Delta^N}{\Delta_{jj}{}^N} \tag{2-56}$$

As another example of the nodal method, consider the circuit in Fig. 2-17 for which the input admittance $Y_{11}{}^{in}$ is desired. Currents flowing out of a node are positive on the left-hand side of the equation, and currents flowing into the node are treated as sources and appear as positive on the right-hand side of the equation. The self- and common admittances are

$$Y_{11} = \frac{1}{Lp} + \frac{1}{R_1} + C_1 p$$

$$Y_{12} = Y_{21} = -\frac{1}{Lp} \tag{2-57}$$

$$Y_{22} = \frac{1}{Lp} + \frac{1}{R_2} + C_2 p$$

The equations for the network are

$$I_1 = V_1 Y_{11} + V_2 Y_{12}$$
$$0 = V_1 Y_{21} + V_2 Y_{22} \tag{2-58}$$

The input admittance is given by

$$Y_{11}{}^{in} = \frac{\Delta^N}{\Delta_{11}{}^N} = \frac{\begin{vmatrix} Y_{11} & Y_{12} \\ Y_{21} & Y_{22} \end{vmatrix}}{Y_{22}} = Y_{11} - \frac{Y_{12}{}^2}{Y_{22}} \tag{2-59}$$

When Eqs. (2-57) are used, Eq. (2-59) reduces to

$$Y_{11}{}^{in} = \frac{p^3(LC_1C_2R_1R_2) + p^2[L(C_1R_1 + C_2R_2)]}{R_1(R_2LC_2p^2 + Lp + R_2)} \tag{2-60}$$

2-5. Loop Analysis of Active Networks. The equations of the previous sections [Eqs. (2-18) and (2-50)] can be generalized to include active ele-

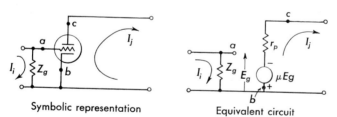

Symbolic representation   Equivalent circuit

FIG. 2-18. Equivalent circuit for a vacuum-tube triode (loop basis).

ments, that is, vacuum tubes and transistors. Such elements are not completely linear, but, over a limited range of operation, they can be considered linear and can be included in the linear analysis. Over the linear range, which is established with appropriate biasing, these elements can be replaced by an equivalent circuit.

A triode is usually* represented by the equivalent loop circuit shown on Fig. 2-18. Based upon the usual assumptions, an equivalent voltage generator in series with the plate resistance is substituted for the vacuum

* Numerous books discuss this equivalent circuit, for example, chap. 3 of Ref. 47.

tube.   The points a, b, and c in each diagram in Fig. 2-18 are inter-changeable. μ represents the amplification factor, and r_p is the plate resistance.

Suppose the vacuum tube is located in a network between the ith and jth meshes, as shown in Fig. 2-18.   The loop equation for the jth mesh is written

$$I_1Z_{j1} + I_2Z_{j2} + \cdots + I_iZ_{ji} + \cdots + I_mZ_{jm} = V_j - \mu E_g \quad (2\text{-}61)$$

where the impedances have the same significance as in Eqs. (2-19) and (2-20).   Since $E_g = I_iZ_g$, Eq. (2-57) is written

$$I_1Z_{j1} + I_2Z_{j2} + \cdots + I_i(Z_{ji} + \mu Z_g) + \cdots + I_mZ_{jm} = V_j \quad (2\text{-}62)$$

If no other loops contain this tube or any other tube, then the network determinant takes the form

$$\Delta = \begin{vmatrix} Z_{11} & Z_{12} & \ldots & Z_{1i} & & \ldots & Z_{1m} \\ Z_{21} & Z_{22} & \ldots & Z_{2i} & & \ldots & Z_{2m} \\ Z_{31} & Z_{32} & \ldots & Z_{3i} & & \ldots & Z_{3m} \\ \cdot & \cdot & & \cdot & & & \cdot \\ \cdot & \cdot & & \cdot & & & \cdot \\ Z_{j1} & Z_{j2} & \ldots & (Z_{ji} + \mu Z_g) & \ldots & Z_{jm} \\ \cdot & \cdot & & \cdot & & & \cdot \\ \cdot & \cdot & & \cdot & & & \cdot \\ \cdot & \cdot & \ldots & \cdot & & \ldots & \cdot \\ Z_{m1} & Z_{m2} & \ldots & Z_{mi} & & \ldots & Z_{mm} \end{vmatrix} \quad (2\text{-}63)$$

This determinant, Eq. (2-63), is no longer symmetrical about its principal diagonal as in the case of passive networks [Eq. (2-22)].   Addition of a bilateral element results in a nonreciprocal network; that is, $Z_{ij} \neq Z_{ji}$.

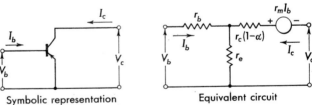

Symbolic representation   Equivalent circuit

FIG. 2-19. Equivalent circuit for a transistor used in the common-emitter connection.

If Δ^0 is defined as the value that Δ assumes when $\mu = 0$, the determinant of Eq. (2-63) can be written

$$\Delta = \Delta^0 + \mu Z_g\Delta_{ji} \quad (2\text{-}64)$$

where Δ_{ji} is the determinant found by canceling the jth row and ith column.

The inclusion of a transistor in the loop analysis modifies the network

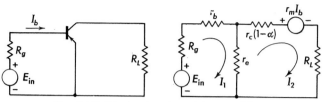

FIG. 2-20. Single-stage transistor amplifier.

determinant in a similar fashion. One equivalent circuit[42,48] for a grounded emitter stage is shown on Fig. 2-19. The resistances shown in this T network have the following physical significance:

r_e = emitter resistance or forward resistance of emitter-base diode and consequently is small in value

r_c = collector resistance or reverse resistance of collector-base diode and is therefore high in value

r_b = base resistance which represents an interaction effect between emitter and collector

r_m = mutual resistance which provides gain in the circuit

Consider the simple one-stage amplifier shown in Fig. 2-20. From the equivalent circuit, which is also shown in Fig. 2-20, the following loop equations can be written:

$$e_{in} = (R_g + r_b + r_e)i_1 + (-r_e)i_2 \qquad (2\text{-}65)$$
$$-r_m i_b = (-r_e)i_1 + [r_e + r_c(1 - \alpha) + R_L]i_2 \qquad (2\text{-}66)$$

Since i_b, the base current, is equal to i_1, Eq. (2-66) becomes

$$0 = (r_m - r_e)i_1 + [r_e + r_c(1 - \alpha) + R_L]i_2 \qquad (2\text{-}67)$$

Solution for any current (for example, i_2) proceeds in the normal fashion:

$$i_2 = \left| \frac{-e_{in}(r_m - r_e)}{\begin{array}{cc} R_g + r_b + r_e & -r_e \\ r_m - r_e & r_e + r_c(1 - \alpha) + R_L \end{array}} \right| \qquad (2\text{-}68)$$

The addition of a transistor results in a nonreciprocal network; that is, $Z_{ij} \neq Z_{ji}$. The effect of inserting a transistor is similar to that of inserting a vacuum tube. There is, however, at least one important difference—circuit loading. The input impedance to a vacuum tube is high and hence produces considerable circuit isolation. This is usually not the case with a transistor.* The entire circuit is analyzed, since each stage is not readily isolated from the rest of the circuit.

2-6. Node Analysis of Active Networks. A vacuum tube and a transistor enter into a node-basis analysis in much the same way as these active elements are included in a loop analysis.

* See Ref. 10, chap. 8, for further transistor design information.

The equivalent node circuit for a vacuum tube is given in Fig. 2-21.

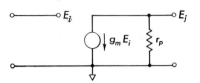

The cathode is taken as the reference node and is grounded. Voltages are assumed for all nodes; E_i is the assumed grid voltage and E_j is the output node voltage at the terminals of the tube. The operational equation for the jth node pair is

FIG. 2-21. Equivalent circuit for a vacuum-tube triode (node basis).

$$I_j = E_1 Y_{j1} + E_2 Y_{j2} + \cdots + E_i(Y_{ji} + g_m) + \cdots + E_n Y_{jn} \quad (2\text{-}69)$$

With only one tube in the circuit, the unilateral term enters the network determinant at one point:

$$\Delta^N = \begin{vmatrix} Y_{11} & Y_{12} & \cdots & Y_{1i} & \cdots & Y_{1n} \\ Y_{21} & Y_{22} & \cdots & Y_{2i} & & Y_{2n} \\ \cdot & \cdot & & \cdot & & \cdot \\ \cdot & \cdot & & \cdot & & \cdot \\ \cdot & \cdot & & \cdot & & \cdot \\ Y_{j1} & Y_{j2} & \cdots & Y_{ji} + g_m & \cdots & Y_{jn} \\ \cdot & \cdot & & \cdot & & \cdot \\ \cdot & \cdot & & \cdot & & \cdot \\ Y_{n1} & Y_{n2} & \cdots & Y_{ni} & \cdots & Y_{nn} \end{vmatrix} \quad (2\text{-}70)$$

It is sometimes inconvenient to make the cathode the reference node, since g_m would occur in several terms of Δ^N. The determinant can always be rearranged, however, without changing its value, and g_m can be made to occur only once.

The current source equivalent circuit for a grounded-emitter transistor is shown in Fig. 2-22. The node analysis of such a circuit proceeds in a similar fashion to the previous vacuum-tube solution. Node voltages are assumed for all points in the circuit and for the nodes in the tran-

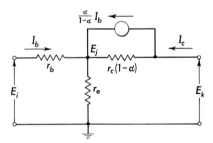

FIG. 2-22. Transistor equivalent node circuit with one current source.

sistor equivalent circuit. The emitter lead is chosen as the reference, and E_i, E_j, and E_k are the assumed node voltages for the remaining transistor nodes. The equation for node j is written

$$\frac{\alpha}{1 - \alpha} I_b = E_i \left(-\frac{1}{r_b} \right) + E_j \left[\frac{1}{r_b} + \frac{1}{r_e} + \frac{1}{r_c(1 - \alpha)} \right] + E_k \left[-\frac{1}{r_c(1 - \alpha)} \right]$$

$$(2\text{-}71)$$

Since $I_b = (E_i - E_j)/r_b$, Eq. (2-71) can be simplified:

$$0 = E_i \left[\frac{-1}{(1 - \alpha)r_b} \right] + E_j \left[\frac{1}{(1 - \alpha)} \left(\frac{1}{r_b} + \frac{1}{r_c} \right) + \frac{1}{r_e} \right] + E_k \frac{-1}{(1 - \alpha)r_c}$$

$$(2\text{-}72)$$

The current source in Fig. 2-22 depends upon the assumed node voltages. The term on the left side of Eq. (2-71) is brought to the right side and included as part of Eq. (2-72). Such a term produces a nonreciprocal network; that is, $Y_{ij} \neq Y_{ji}$. The remaining analysis proceeds in a similar fashion to that of the previous section.

2-7. Mechanical Networks—Linear Motion.[56] The analysis of mechanical networks is similar to the analysis of electrical networks. Newton's law for mechanical systems is: The algebraic sum of the forces acting on a body (mass) is equal to the product of the mass and the

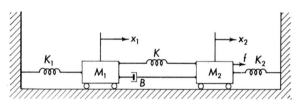

Fig. 2-23. Linear-motion mechanical system.

acceleration of the body. The method of analysis of mechanical systems is as outlined:

1. Assume displacements and directions for each mass in the system. The displacements x are the dependent variables, and the forces f are the driving functions. In assigning directions to the dependent variables, choose one direction, e.g., upward or to the right, as positive. Choose all variables in this same direction. Also assume that the positive directions of x, dx/dt, and d^2x/dt^2 are the same.

2. Write Newton's law for each mass in the system. In order to isolate the forces on each mass, a "free-body diagram" is drawn for each mass.

3. Laplace-transform the differential equations, and solve the algebraic equations for the desired linear displacement. Use of determinants provides a systematic method of solution.

The above procedure is applied to the system of Fig. 2-23. It is desired to find the Laplace-transformed transfer function X_1/F. The first step in the solution is to assign positive directions (to the right) and label these displacements x_1 and x_2. The spring constants K_i and damping constant B are described in Chap. 1. The restoring force of a linear spring is

$$f_K = K(x_1 - x_2) \qquad (2\text{-}73)$$

The force produced by the spring is opposite in direction to x_1, as shown in Fig. 2-24a. The damping force produced by a dashpot is

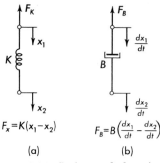

$$f_B = B \left(\frac{dx_1}{dt} - \frac{dx_2}{dt} \right) \qquad (2\text{-}74)$$

This force is shown in Fig. 2-24b.

Newton's force equation is written about each mass in the system. The free-body diagram for mass M_1 in Fig. 2-23 is shown in Fig. 2-25. As M_1 accelerates in the positive direction $(+x_1)$, the forces of the springs and dashpot oppose this motion.

(a)   (b)

FIG. 2-24. Spring and damping forces.

The sum of forces must equal the mass times the acceleration, or

$$M_1 \frac{d^2 x_1}{dt^2} = -K_1 x_1 - K(x_1 - x_2) - B \left(\frac{dx_1}{dt} - \frac{dx_2}{dt} \right) \qquad (2\text{-}75)$$

When this equation is rearranged and Laplace-transformed (with zero initial conditions), the following system equation results:

$$[M_1 p^2 + Bp + (K_1 + K)]X_1 + (-Bp - K)X_2 = 0 \qquad (2\text{-}76)$$

The dependent variable is capitalized to indicate that it is a function of p.

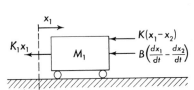

FIG. 2-25. Free-body diagram for M_1.

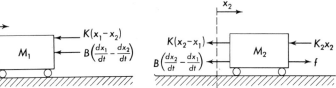

FIG. 2-26. Free-body diagram for M_2.

The free-body diagram for M_2 is shown in Fig. 2-26. As the mass accelerates in the positive direction $(+x_2$ to the right), the springs and dashpot oppose this motion. The applied force f is in the same direction as x_2 so carries a positive sign:

$$M \frac{d^2 x_2}{dt^2} = +f - K(x_2 - x_1) - B \left(\frac{dx_2}{dt} - \frac{dx_1}{dt} \right) - K_2 x_2 \qquad (2\text{-}77)$$

When this equation is transformed, the rearranged force equation on M_2 becomes

$$(-Bp - K)X_1 + [M_2 p^2 + Bp + (K + K_1)]X_2 = F \qquad (2\text{-}78)$$

Again the variables are capitalized to indicate that the equations have been Laplace-transformed.

Equations (2-76) and (2-78) are the two necessary equations for the analysis of the system of Fig. 2-22. For purposes of simplification these two equations can be written as

$$a_{11}X_1 + a_{12}X_2 = 0$$
$$a_{21}X_1 + a_{22}X_2 = F$$

(2-79)

where

$$a_{11} = [M_1p^2 + Bp + (K_1 + K)] \qquad a_{12} = a_{21} = -(Bp + K)$$

and

$$a_{22} = [M_2p^2 + Bp + (K_2 + K)]$$

(2-80)

Solution by determinants yields

$$X_1 = \frac{\begin{vmatrix} 0 & a_{12} \\ F & a_{22} \end{vmatrix}}{\begin{vmatrix} a_{11} & a_{12} \\ a_{21} & a_{22} \end{vmatrix}} = \frac{-a_{12}F}{a_{11}a_{22} - a_{12}{}^2}$$

(2-81)

The transfer function in terms of the system constants is found by inserting the expressions for a_{11}, a_{22}, a_{12}, and a_{21}. Notice that since the mechanical system is linear and bilateral, $a_{12} = a_{21}$. The transfer function is

$$\frac{X_1}{F} = G_4(p)$$

$$= \frac{Bp + K}{\begin{aligned}&M_1M_2p^4 + [B(M_1 + M_2)]p^3 + [M_1(K + K_2) \\ &\quad + M_2(K + K_1)]p^2 + [B(K_1 + K_2)]p + [K_1K_2 + K(K_1 + K_2)]\end{aligned}}$$

(2-82)

The block diagram for this system is indicated in Fig. 2-27. It is important to notice that the method of obtaining the transfer function for mechanical and electrical systems is similar.

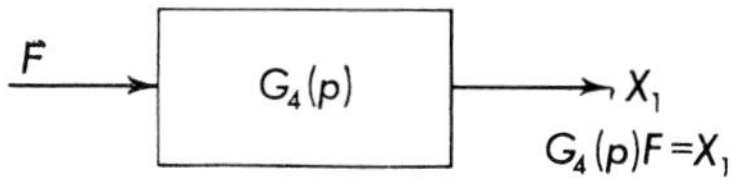

The analysis of a mechanical system of n masses follows a similar pattern

FIG. 2-27. Block diagram for the mechanical system of Fig. 2-23.

to the above example. To obtain an analogy to electrical networks, the general equations are written with velocity $V_1 = pX_1$ as the dependent variable instead of displacement. By analogy with Eq. (2-80) a set of force equations is written

$$g_{11}V_1 + g_{12}V_2 + \cdots + g_{1n}V_n = F_1$$
$$g_{21}V_1 + g_{22}V_2 + \cdots + g_{2n}V_n = F_2$$
$$\vdots \qquad \vdots \qquad \qquad \vdots \qquad \vdots$$
$$g_{n1}V_1 + g_{n2}V_2 + \cdots + g_{nn}V_n = F_n$$

(2-83)

The driving functions are forces F_i, and the quantities V_i are velocities. All variables are Laplace-transformed and hence capitalized. The self-mechanical admittances g_{ii} are of the form

$$g_{ii} = pM_{ii} + B_{ii} + \frac{K_{ii}}{p} \tag{2-84}$$

and the common-mechanical admittances g_{ij} are of the form

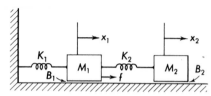

FIG. 2-28. Example of a vibration damper.

$$g_{ij} = -\left(B_{ij} + \frac{K_{ij}}{p}\right) \tag{2-85}$$

Note the absence of pM_{ij} in the common admittance term of Eq. (2-85). When all the variables are referred to one fixed coordinate system (inertial space), forces are transmitted to a particular mass only through springs and dashpots.

The solution for Eq. (2-83) is found as the ratio of two determinants

$$V_j = \frac{1}{\Delta^M} \begin{vmatrix} g_{11} & g_{12} & \cdots & F_1 & \cdots & g_{1n} \\ g_{21} & g_{22} & \cdots & F_2 & \cdots & g_{2n} \\ \cdot & \cdot & & \cdot & & \cdot \\ \cdot & \cdot & & \cdot & & \cdot \\ \cdot & \cdot & & \cdot & & \cdot \\ g_{n1} & g_{n2} & \cdots & F_n & \cdots & g_{nn} \end{vmatrix} \tag{2-86}$$

where Δ^M is the determinant of the coefficients g_{ij}.

As another example, consider the mechanical system of Fig. 2-28. The positive directions are assumed to the right for both X_1 and X_2. The Newton's force law equations for the translational system are

$$M_1 \frac{d^2x_1}{dt^2} + Kx_1 + K_2(x_1 - x_2) + B_1 \frac{dx_1}{dt} = f$$
$$M_2 \frac{d^2x_2}{dt^2} + K_2(x_2 - x_1) + B_2 \frac{dx_2}{dt} = 0 \tag{2-87}$$

Equations (2-87) are put into the form of Eq. (2-83) by writing the equations in terms of velocity rather than displacements and by rearranging

$$M_1 \frac{dv_1}{dt} + (K_1 + K_2) \int_0^t v_1 \, dt + Bv_1 - K_2 \int_0^t v_2 \, dt = f$$
$$-K_2 \int_0^t v_1 \, dt + M_2 \frac{dv_2}{dt} + K_2 \int_0^t v_2 \, dt + B_2 v_2 = 0 \tag{2-88}$$

These equations are Laplace-transformed with the result

$$g_{11}V_1 + g_{12}V_2 = F_1$$
$$g_{21}V_1 + g_{22}V_2 = F_2 \tag{2-89}$$

where the variables are capitalized to indicate that these quantities are functions of p. The coefficients are

$$g_{11} = M_1 p + B_1 + \frac{K_1 + K_2}{p} \qquad g_{12} = g_{21} = \frac{-K_2}{p}$$

$$g_{22} = M_2 p + B_2 + \frac{K_2}{p} \qquad f_1 = F \qquad f_2 = 0 \tag{2-90}$$

Figure 2-28 is an interesting example of a vibration damper. For simplicity, take $B_1 = 0 = B_2$ and find the transfer function pX_1/F:

$$\frac{pX_1}{F} = \frac{Fg_{22}}{F \begin{vmatrix} g_{11} & g_{12} \\ g_{21} & g_{22} \end{vmatrix}} = \frac{g_{22}}{g_{11}g_{22} - g_{12}{}^2} \tag{2-91}$$

Inserting values from Eq. (2-90) and simplifying,

$$\frac{X_1}{F} = \frac{M_2 p^2 + K_2}{(M_1 M_2) p^4 + [M_1 K_2 + M_2(K_1 + K_2)]p^2 + K_1 K_2} \tag{2-92}$$

If F is a sinusoidal driving function (see Sec. 5-1), the output X_1 is also sinusoidal. The magnitude is found by replacing p by $j\omega$, with the result

$$\frac{X_1}{F} = \frac{K_2 - M_2 \omega^2}{K_1 K_2 + \omega^4 M_1 M_2 - [M_1 K_2 + M_2(K_1 + K_2)]\omega^2} \tag{2-93}$$

The system is called a vibration damper because when the frequency ω is $\sqrt{K_2/M_2}$, the displacement X_1 at this frequency is zero even though a force is applied to the mass.

2-8. Mechanical Systems—Rotational Motion. The method of obtaining the differential equations for angular motion is essentially the same as for linear motion. Newton's law for angular motion can be stated: The algebraic sum of the torques acting upon an inertia is equal to the moment of inertia times the angular acceleration. The procedure for analysis is as outlined:

1. Assume angles θ_i of rotation for each inertia. Take one direction, say counterclockwise, as positive for θ_i, $d\theta_i/dt$, and $d^2\theta_i/dt^2$. The angular displacements are the dependent variables, and the torques are the driving functions.

2. Draw a free-body diagram, and write Newton's torque law for each inertia in the system.

3. Laplace-transform the differential equations, and, as in the previous cases, solve the equations by taking a ratio of determinants.

The above procedure is applied to the rotational system of Fig. 2-29. The shafts connecting the inertias act as restoring springs. The free-body diagrams for this system are included in Fig. 2-30. As the moment of inertia J_1 is accelerated in the $+\theta_1$ direction, the springs (shafts)

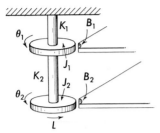

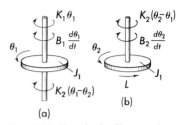

FIG. 2-29. An angular mechanical system.

FIG. 2-30. Free-body diagram for a rotational system.

oppose the motion. The damping also causes a torque which opposes the acceleration. The equation for this inertia is

$$J_1 \frac{d^2\theta_1}{dt^2} = -K_1\theta_1 - K_2(\theta_1 - \theta_2) - B_1\frac{d\theta_1}{dt} \qquad (2\text{-}94)$$

When Eq. (2-94) is transformed and the equation is rearranged,

$$(J_1p^2 + B_1p + K_1 + K_2)\bar{\theta}_1 + (-K_2)\bar{\theta}_2 = 0 \qquad (2\text{-}95)$$

In a similar fashion, the differential equation for the second moment of inertia is obtained from the free-body diagram of Fig. 2-30b. This second equation is written in simplified form:

$$(-K_2)\bar{\theta}_1 + (J_2p^2 + B_2p + K_2)\bar{\theta}_2 = \bar{L} \qquad (2\text{-}96)$$

The solution for the dependent variable, say $\bar{\theta}_2$, is found from Cramer's rule as follows:

$$\bar{\theta}_2 = \frac{\begin{vmatrix} b_{11} & 0 \\ b_{21} & \bar{L} \end{vmatrix}}{\begin{vmatrix} b_{11} & b_{12} \\ b_{21} & b_{22} \end{vmatrix}} = \frac{\bar{L}b_{11}}{b_{11}b_{22} - b_{12}{}^2} \qquad (2\text{-}97)$$

where
$$\begin{aligned} b_{11} &= J_1p^2 + B_1p + K_1 + K_2 \\ b_{22} &= J_2p^2 + B_2p + K_2 \\ b_{12} &= b_{21} = -K_2 \end{aligned} \qquad (2\text{-}98)$$

As in all previous cases, the solution for the transfer function reduces to a ratio of polynomials in p. The transfer function is found by substituting Eqs. (2-98) into Eq. (2-97).

The analysis of a rotational system containing n inertias is generalized with the equations

$$\begin{aligned} h_{11}\bar{\omega}_1 + h_{12}\bar{\omega}_2 + \cdots + h_{1n}\bar{\omega}_n &= \bar{L}_1 \\ h_{21}\bar{\omega}_1 + h_{22}\bar{\omega}_2 + \cdots + h_{2n}\bar{\omega}_n &= \bar{L}_2 \\ \vdots \qquad \vdots \qquad\qquad \vdots \qquad \vdots \\ h_{n1}\bar{\omega}_1 + h_{n2}\bar{\omega}_2 + \cdots + h_{nn}\bar{\omega}_n &= \bar{L}_n \end{aligned} \qquad (2\text{-}99)$$

The dependent variable is the angular velocity $\bar{\omega} = p\bar{\theta}$, and the driving functions are the torques $\bar{L}_i$. The self-admittances h_{ii} are of the form

$$h_{ii} = pJ_{ii} + B_{ii} + \frac{K_{ii}}{p} \tag{2-100}$$

and the common mechanical admittances h_{ii} are of the form

$$h_{ij} = -\left(B_{ij} + \frac{K_{ij}}{p}\right) \tag{2-101}$$

The solution for any $\bar{\omega}_i$ in Eq. (2-99) is found as a ratio of determinants

$$\bar{\omega}_j = \frac{1}{\Delta^M} \begin{vmatrix} h_{11} & h_{12} & \cdots & \bar{L}_1 & \cdots & h_{1n} \\ h_{21} & h_{22} & \cdots & \bar{L}_2 & \cdots & h_{2n} \\ \cdot & \cdot & & \cdot & & \cdot \\ \cdot & \cdot & & \cdot & & \cdot \\ \cdot & \cdot & & \cdot & & \cdot \\ h_{n1} & h_{n2} & \cdots & \bar{L}_n & \cdots & h_{nn} \end{vmatrix} \tag{2-102}$$

where Δ^M is the determinant of the coefficient h_{ij}.

2-9. Mechanical Coupling—Gear Trains. Mechanical systems are coupled in a number of ways; the most common is by means of gears. Consider the mechanical system shown in Fig. 2-31, where a torque L

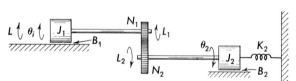

FIG. 2-31. Gear train used to couple mechanical systems.

drives a load through a gear train. The source has a moment of inertia J_1 and damping B_1; the load has a moment of inertia J_2, damping B_2, and spring constant K_2. The transformed equations for the system are

$$J_1 p^2 \bar{\theta}_1 = \bar{L} - \bar{L}_1 - Bp\bar{\theta}_1 \tag{2-103}$$
and
$$J_2 p^2 \bar{\theta}_2 = \bar{L}_2 - B_2 p\bar{\theta}_2 - K_2 \bar{\theta}_2 \tag{2-104}$$

Since θ_1 and θ_2 are related by the number of teeth on the gears, only one dependent variable exists in this problem. The relation between θ_1 and θ_2 and between L_1 and L_2 must be found. Let r_1 be the radius of the first gear and r_2 be the radius of the second gear; then, since the linear distance traveled along the surface of each gear must be the same, $\theta_1 r_1 = \theta_2 r_2$. The number of teeth on the gear surface is proportional to the radius of the gear

$$\theta_1 N_1 = \theta_2 N_2 \tag{2-105}$$

where N_1 is the number of teeth on the input gear and N_2 is the number of teeth on the load gear. But since $N = N_1/N_2$, where N is the gear ratio, Eq. (2-105) becomes

$$\theta_2 = N\theta_1 \tag{2-106}$$

Since the work done by each gear is equal,

$$L_1\theta_1 = L_2\theta_2 = L_2N\theta_1 \quad \text{or} \quad L_1 = NL_2 \tag{2-107}$$

If N is less than 1, the angular displacement of the load is less than the angular displacement of the source, whereas the torque applied to the load is greater than the torque applied by the source. Solution of Eq. (2-104) for L_2 by substituting for $\theta_2 = N\theta_1$ gives

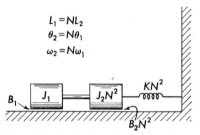

$$L_1 = NL_2$$
$$\theta_2 = N\theta_1$$
$$\omega_2 = N\omega_1$$

$$\bar{L}_2 = \frac{\bar{L}_1}{N} = (J_2p^2 + Bp + K_2)N\bar{\theta}_1 \tag{2-108}$$

FIG. 2-32. Reflecting inertia, spring, and damping constants across a gear train.

The complete expression for torque $\bar{L}$ in terms of $\bar{\theta}$ is found by substituting Eq. (2-108) into Eqs. (2-103) and (2-104)

$$\bar{L} = (J_1p^2 + B_1p)\bar{\theta}_1 + \bar{L}_2N \tag{2-109}$$
$$\bar{L} = [(J_1 + J_2N^2)p^2 + (B_1 + B_2N^2)p + K_2N^2]\bar{\theta}_1$$

Figure 2-32 summarizes the effect of a gear train by referring the inertia, damping, and spring constant to the source side of the gear train.

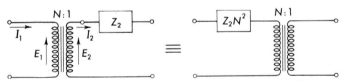

FIG. 2-33. Impedance transformed to primary of a transformer.

It is helpful to note the similarity between an ideal transformer and a gear train. In a transformer with a turns ratio of $N/1$ (step down) the voltages, currents, and impedances are transformed as follows:

$$E_1 = NE_2$$

$$I_1 = \frac{1}{N} I_2 \tag{2-110}$$

$$Z_1 = N^2Z_2 = N^2\left(Lp + R + \frac{1}{pC}\right)$$

where the symbols are defined in Fig. 2-33. In a gear train, with a gear ratio of $N/1$, the torques, velocities, and mechanical impedances are transformed across the gear train as follows:

$$L_1 = NL_2$$

$$\omega_1 = \frac{1}{N}\,\omega_2 \qquad\qquad (2\text{-}111)$$

$$h_1 = N^2 h_2 = N^2 \left(Jp^2 + B + \frac{K}{p} \right)$$

2-10. Electromechanical Networks. In many servo systems it may be necessary to find the transfer function of a system that is a combination of electrical and mechanical components. The principles of the early sections of this chapter are, of course, applicable to a problem of mixed parameters.

As an example of an electromechanical system, consider the vibration table of Fig. 2-34. The transfer function X/E is desired. The problem

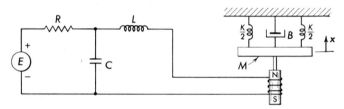

FIG. 2-34. An electromechanical system—a vibration table.

is solved by considering the electromechanical coupling between the electrical and mechanical circuit. As the mass moves in the coil, a back voltage is generated:

$$E_b = k_1 pX = k_1 V \qquad\qquad (2\text{-}112)$$

The force developed on the mass is

$$f_e = k_2 i \qquad\qquad (2\text{-}113)$$

where i is the current through the coil. The circuit is separated into two parts, as shown in Fig. 2-35. The electric circuit is solved with the loop analysis by using two loop currents. The transformed equations are written for zero initial conditions

$$E_{in} = \left(R + \frac{1}{pC} \right) I_1 + \left(-\frac{1}{pC} \right) I_2$$

$$0 = \left(-\frac{1}{pC} \right) I_1 + \left(Lp + \frac{1}{pC} \right) I_2 + k_1 V \qquad\qquad (2\text{-}114)$$

The sign of the force on the mechanical system, which depends upon the orientation of the coil, is assumed in the direction shown on Fig. 2-35.

The equation derived from the mechanical circuit is

$$0 = (0)I_1 + (k_2)I_2 + \left(Mp + B + \frac{K}{p}\right)V \qquad (2\text{-}115)$$

The denominator determinant for this system is

$$\Delta = \begin{vmatrix} R + \dfrac{1}{pC} & -\dfrac{1}{pC} & 0 \\[2ex] -\dfrac{1}{pC} & Lp + \dfrac{1}{pC} & k_1 \\[2ex] 0 & k_2 & Mp + B + \dfrac{K}{p} \end{vmatrix} \qquad (2\text{-}116)$$

Expansion yields

$$\Delta = \left(R + \frac{1}{pC}\right)\left[\left(Lp + \frac{1}{pC}\right)\left(Mp + B + \frac{K}{p}\right) - k_1k_2\right] -$$
$$\left(\frac{1}{pC}\right)^2\left(Mp + B + \frac{K}{p}\right) \qquad (2\text{-}117)$$

The transfer function is

$$\frac{pV}{E_{in}} = \frac{X}{E_{in}} = \frac{p}{\Delta}\left(\frac{-k_2}{pC}\right) = -\frac{k_2}{\Delta C} \qquad (2\text{-}118)$$

where Δ is given by Eq. (2-117). Solution of Eq. (2-118) results in a ratio of polynomials in p.

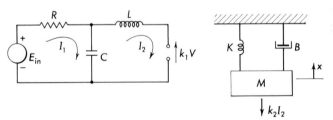

FIG. 2-35. Two parts of electromechanical problem.

2-11. Analogies. The derivation of equations of motion for lumped-parameter, linear systems, whether electrical, mechanical, or electro-mechanical, is similar. The procedure, the use of basic laws, and the solution are carried out alike. Because of the similarities among these systems, it is possible to construct electrical analogies, both nodal and loop, for mechanical circuits. The electrical analogue is found by determining an electric network which has a differential equation with the same form as the equation for the mechanical system. Although the analogous electric circuit is often determined intuitively, the following procedure is suggested:

1. Write the equations for the mechanical system.

2. Substitute electrical quantities using electric-network constants and variables. These substitutions are given subsequently.

3. Interpret these equations to yield the analogue network.

a. Nodal Analogue. To obtain a nodal analogue for a mechanical equation, compare the admittance of the mechanical circuit [Eq. (2-83)]

$$\left(pM_{ii} + B_{ii} + \frac{K_{ii}}{p}\right) V_i \cdots = F_i \tag{2-119}$$

or Eq. (2-99)

$$\left(pJ_{ii} + B_{ii} + \frac{K_{ii}}{p}\right) \bar{\omega}_i \cdots = \bar{L}_i \tag{2-120}$$

with the admittance of Eq. (2-50)

$$\left(pC_{ii} + \frac{1}{R_{ii}} + \frac{1}{pL_{ii}}\right) V_i \cdots = I_i \tag{2-121}$$

Comparison of the coefficients of these equations indicates the following analogous quantities:

Mass (M) or moment of inertia (J)....... Analogous to capacitance C
Damping constant (B)................. Analogous to electrical conductance $1/R$
Spring constant K.................... Analogous to inverse inductance $1/L$
Forces or Torques.................... Analogous to current
Velocity............................ Analogous to voltage

$$K \sim \frac{1}{L} \quad \left.\begin{matrix} M \\ J \end{matrix}\right\} \sim C \quad B \sim \frac{1}{R} \quad \left.\begin{matrix} F \\ L \end{matrix}\right\} \sim I \quad \left.\begin{matrix} V \\ \bar{\omega} \end{matrix}\right\} \sim E \tag{2-122}$$

b. Loop Analogue. Comparison of Eqs. (2-119) and (2-120) with Eq. (2-18) indicates

$$\left(pL_{ii} + R_{ii} + \frac{1}{pC_{ii}}\right) I_i \cdots = E_i \tag{2-123}$$

which yields the following analogies:

Mass or moment of inertia........... Analogous to inductance
Damping constant.................. Analogous to resistance
Spring constant.................... Analogous to capacitance
Forces or torques.................. Analogous to voltages
Velocity.......................... Analogous to current

which are summarized below:

$$K \sim \frac{1}{C} \quad \left.\begin{matrix} M \\ J \end{matrix}\right\} \sim L \quad B \sim R \quad \left.\begin{matrix} F \\ L \end{matrix}\right\} \sim E \quad \left.\begin{matrix} V \\ \bar{\omega} \end{matrix}\right\} \sim I \tag{2-124}$$

As might be noted from Sec. 2-11*a* and *b* there is a possibility of more than one electric analogue existing for a given mechanical circuit. As an example, an analogue for the mechanical system of Fig. 2-28 is found. Figure 2-36 shows the nodal analogue which is found from Eqs. (2-122).

Equations (2-124) are used to find the loop analogue of Fig. 2-37. Usually electric networks have "duals."* The two networks thus derived are duals, since node pair voltages in Fig. 2-36 are analogous to loop currents in Fig. 2-37.

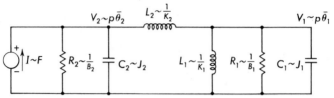

FIG. 2-36. Node analogue of Fig. 2-27.

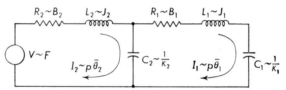

FIG. 2-37. Loop analogue of Fig. 2-28.

2-12. Separable and Nonseparable Networks. Block diagrams and transfer functions are found for most of the examples in this chapter. The input to the block is multiplied or operated on by the quantity in the block to equal the output.

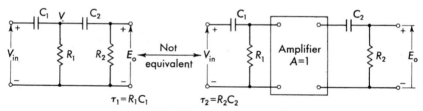

FIG. 2-38. Nonseparable networks.

In general it is desirable, from the point of view of simplicity, to write transfer functions for small sections of the system. A common error in writing transfer functions results when networks or components are analyzed separately when the network cannot be separated. For example, consider the network of Fig. 2-38. The student is often tempted to write this network as two blocks each with the same over-all transfer function. This leads to

$$\frac{E_o}{E_{in}} = \frac{(\tau_1 p)(\tau_2 p)}{(\tau_1 p + 1)(\tau_2 p + 1)} = \frac{\tau_1 \tau_2 p^2}{\tau_1 \tau_2 p^2 + (\tau_1 + \tau_2)p + 1} \quad (2\text{-}125)$$

The transfer function for this network is actually found by solving

* Additional information on duality of electric networks is found in Ref. 18, chap. 2, sec. 15.

two nodal equations

$$V\left[p(C_1 + C_2) + \frac{1}{R_1}\right] + E_o(-pC_2) = pC_1 V_{in}$$

$$V(-pC_2) + E_o\left(pC_2 + \frac{1}{R_2}\right) = 0 \tag{2-126}$$

The transfer function is found by solving these equations

$$\frac{E_o}{V_{in}} = \frac{p^2\tau_1\tau_2}{p^2\tau_1\tau_2 + p(\tau_1 + a\tau_2) + 1} \tag{2-127}$$

where $\tau_1 = R_1C_1$, $\tau_2 = R_2C_2$, and $a = 1 + (R_1/R_2)$.   Notice that in this case the form of the equation is similar but differs by the inclusion of the factor a.

Generally two networks can be separated if the second network does not load the first, that is, if the impedance which is presented the first network is high in comparison with the impedance of the first network. A vacuum tube provides good isolation, since the input impedance of a tube is very high.   Because of the loading effects of transistors (as pointed out earlier) similar isolation is not always provided.

PROBLEMS

2-1. Write Laplace-transformed differential equations for the electrical networks of Fig. 2P-1.   Assume zero initial conditions.

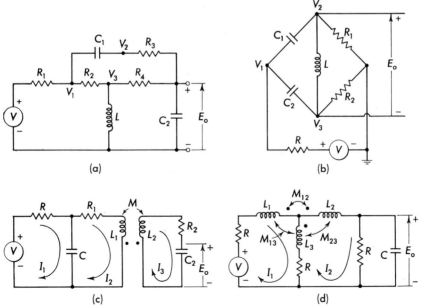

(a)   (b)

(c)   (d)

Fig. 2P-1

2-2. Write transfer functions for the electrical networks of Fig. 2P-2. All networks are driven from zero source impedance and into infinite load impedance. Assume zero initial conditions.

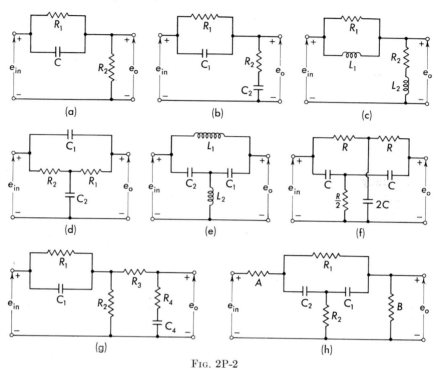

(a)   (b)   (c)

(d)   (e)   (f)

(g)   (h)

FIG. 2P-2

2-3. Find the transfer function E_o/E_{in} and block diagram for the network of Prob. 2-1d.

2-4. Write Laplace-transformed differential equations for the mechanical networks of Fig. 2P-4. Assume zero initial conditions.

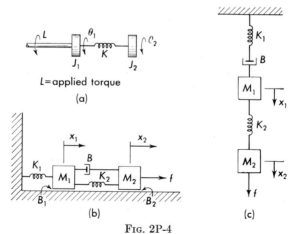

L = applied torque

(a)

(b)   (c)

FIG. 2P-4

2-5. Write transfer functions X_2/F or $\bar{\theta}_2/L$ for the mechanical networks of Prob. 2-4.

2-6. Write the Laplace-transformed differential equations for the mechanical system shown in Fig. 2P-6. Assume zero initial conditions. Find the transfer function

$$\frac{X_1}{V} = G_1(p)$$

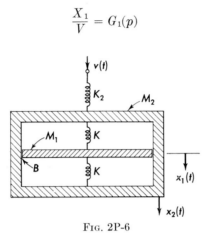

Fig. 2P-6

2-7. Find the transfer function for the fluid coupling shown in Fig. 2P-7,

$$\frac{\bar{\theta}_3}{L} = G_2(p)$$

assume zero initial conditions.

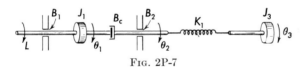

Fig. 2P-7

2-8. Find the transfer function for the electromechanical system of Fig. 2P-8. Assume linear torque-speed curves for the motor. The potentiometer rotates through 10 turns. e_{in} is a zero impedance source.

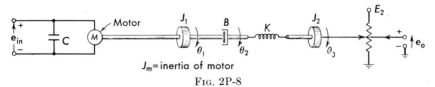

J_m = inertia of motor

Fig. 2P-8

2-9. A torsion rod is frequently used to measure the effective moment of inertia of gear trains and inertia loads. Such a rod is fitted as shown in Fig. 2P-9a. When the system is disturbed, the time required for 20 cycles of oscillation is found to be 10 sec. The torsion rod is then coupled to a shaft of a gear train and load moment of inertia as shown in Fig. 2P-9b. When the system is shocked, the time required for

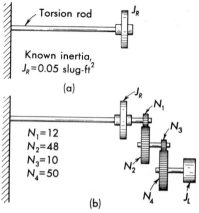

(a)

(b)

Fig. 2P-9a and b

10 cycles of oscillation is found to be 18 sec.   What is the effective moment of inertia of the combined gear train and load moment of inertia?   Assume $\zeta \ll 1$ for both cases, and assume all shafts rigid with the exception of the torsion rod.

2-10. Find the transfer function E_o/Y of the system of Fig. 2P-10 used to measure high-frequency displacements of a shake table.   The potentiometer measures the

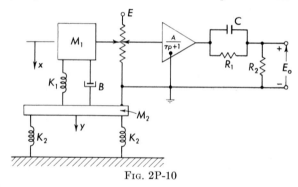

Fig. 2P-10

difference in displacement between M_1 and M_2.   The driving function is a position $y(t)$.   Ignore the acceleration produced by gravity, and assume infinite input and zero output impedance of the amplifier.   The maximum travel of the linear motion potentiometer is l.

CHAPTER 3

STEADY-STATE ERRORS

3-1. The Steady-state Component. The solution of a linear differential equation which has constant coefficients can be divided into two parts. The transient component is the general solution to the homogeneous equation (derived from the given differential equation obtained by setting the driving function equal to zero). The steady-state component is any particular solution not contained in the transient and is found from the nonhomogeneous differential equation. It is the aim of this chapter to find the steady-state components for servo systems which are subjected to particular types of inputs. In the case of feedback control systems it is desirable to find the steady-state error which results for particular types of input. This error, which is the difference between the input and the output variables, is one of the measures of servo performance.

The design specification for a feedback control system may include noise reduction, sensitivity, stability, low-frequency errors, accuracy, steady-state errors, and many others.* The starting points in the basic design of servo systems are usually the steady-state error and the stability requirement. The stability information is contained in the transient solution or the weighting function (impulse response). Chapters 4 and 5 treat the stability problem. The steady-state errors that result for various types of inputs are found in this chapter.

3-2. Steady-state Errors Due to Input Disturbances. To determine the nature of the stability of a system the characteristic equation alone is necessary. However, when investigating the steady-state errors or the steady-state components of the solutions of differential equations, it is necessary to know the type of driving function which is applied to the system. Three types of input driving functions are chosen in this text. These are usually adequate for basic servo design applications: a step function in position, a ramp function in position which is a step function in velocity, and a step function in acceleration. These are written analytically

* Many of these words are defined throughout the text.

$$r = A \tag{3-1}$$

$$r = vt \tag{3-2}$$

$$r = \tfrac{1}{2}at^2 \tag{3-3}$$

where A, v, and a are constants. The functions are applied at $t = 0$ and are valid for positive t only. The servo is assumed to be stable when the steady-state errors are computed.

Consider the steady-state error that results in a system if a step function of position is applied. The system under consideration is shown in the block diagram of Fig. 3-1. $KG(p)$ is the forward loop gain, where K is a constant independent of p and $G(p)$ is the frequency-dependent quantity. As a first case, suppose the feedback transfer function $H(p)$ is taken equal to unity. In this case the steady-state error, the difference between the desired output (R) and the actual output (C)

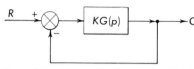

Fig. 3-1. Generalized servo block diagram for $H = 1$.

$$\varepsilon = R - C \tag{3-4}$$

is equal to the actuating signal. Reference to Eq. (1-81), where $H = 1$ yields the error ε in terms of the input R,

$$\varepsilon = \frac{1}{1 + KG(p)} R \tag{3-5}$$

Equation (3-5) may be written alternatively as

$$[1 + KG(p)]\varepsilon = R \tag{3-6}$$

If $v(t)$ is constant A, as given by Eq. (3-1), the steady-state component is also a constant if the system is stable. From a physical point of view, if the input r to the position servo of Chap. 1 is a constant, then after all transient terms die out, the output c is a constant. All output derivatives, velocity, acceleration, etc., are zero. In the steady state, the error may also be constant (this constant can be zero).

The final value theorem, which is discussed in Appendix I, is basic to the problem of finding steady-state errors. This theorem is written

$$\lim_{t \to \infty} y(t) = \lim_{p \to 0} pY(p) \tag{3-7}$$

provided

1. $Y(p) = \mathcal{L}y(t)$.
2. $y(t)$ is stable [i.e., all poles of $pY(p)$ lie in the left half plane].

Notice that the value of the time function at infinite time is found directly from the transformed function at $p = 0$.

As an example, suppose it is desired to find the steady-state ($t \to \infty$)

value for the function $\varepsilon(t)$ if the transformed function has the form

$$\varepsilon(p) = \frac{1}{1 + KG(p)}\, R(p) \tag{3-8}$$

Suppose the system transfer function has the form

$$KG = \frac{K(p + 3)(p + 2)}{(p + 10)(p^2 + p + 1)} \tag{3-9}$$

where, for simplicity in this equation and elsewhere in the book, G is written for $G(p)$. In this case, the limit as p approaches zero of KG is given by a constant or stated mathematically

$$\lim_{p \to 0} KG = \frac{K(3)(2)}{(10)(1)} = \frac{3}{5}\, K \tag{3-10}$$

Since the Laplace transform of a unit step function is $R = 1/p$, the steady-state error for a unit step function applied to a closed-loop system is

$$\lim_{t \to \infty} \varepsilon(t) = \lim_{p \to 0} p\, \frac{1/p}{1 + KG} = \frac{1}{1 + \lim\limits_{p \to 0} KG} \tag{3-11}$$

When Eq. (3-10) is substituted into Eq. (3-11),

$$\lim_{t \to \infty} \varepsilon(t) = \frac{1}{1 + \frac{3}{5}K} \tag{3-12}$$

Equation (3-12) is presented pictorially in Fig. 3-2. When a step in position is applied to the system, the output tends to follow this step;

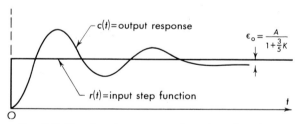

Fig. 3-2. Step-function response for a type 0 system.

however, a steady-state position difference ε_0 between r and c results. This difference is reduced by increasing the gain K of the servo. Although the error can be made small, it will always be present, since infinite gain ($K \to \infty$) is not practical.

The example just cited shows how the steady-state error is found in servo systems. Most feedback control systems can be classed into a few types according to the form of the open-loop transfer function KG. The steady-state errors resulting from step inputs in position, velocity, and acceleration are found for each type of system. As a result, certain general error coefficients are derived, and the steady-state errors in systems are readily found.

3-3. Classification of Feedback Control Systems According to Type. In order to classify a servo system according to its type, consider the block diagram given in Fig. 3-1. The quantity G in this diagram is an operational transfer function, which appears in the forward loop. K is a constant independent of the operator p. The transfer function relating error to R is given by the following expression:

$$\varepsilon = \frac{R}{1 + KG} \tag{3-13}$$

In general, the product KG, which is termed the open-loop transfer function and which is found by multiplying all the transfer function operators around the particular loop, can be expressed by the following typical transfer function:

$$KG = \frac{K'[p + (1/\tau_1)][p + (1/\tau_3)]}{p^n[p + (1/\tau_2)][p + (1/\tau_4)]} \tag{3-14}$$

where $K = K'\tau_2\tau_4/\tau_1\tau_3$.

That is, KG is the ratio of two factored polynomials. All the values of τ are time constants for various components. If one should go through a system and compute the transfer functions for each of the items in a loop, the product is called the open-loop transfer function. When these transfer functions are multiplied together and all terms collected, there usually will be an excess of ps in the denominator.

The excess ps in the denominator are termed poles at the origin of the open-loop transfer function. The values of $p(p_i = -1/\tau_i,\ i$ even) which make the denominator of KG zero are termed "poles." The values of $p(p_i = -1/\tau_i,\ i$ odd) which make the numerator zero are termed "zeros."

Because of the form of this transfer function, the system has a definite steady-state response to various types of inputs depending upon the value of n. Hence the steady-state error for various types of inputs is specified by knowing the value of n. It is convenient, then, to classify feedback control systems in terms of Eq. (3-14). This will be done before discussing other steady-state conditions in order to simplify terminology.

Type 0 system, one for which $n = 0$, in Eq. (3-14)
Type 1 system, one for which $n = 1$, in Eq. (3-14)
Type 2 system, one for which $n = 2$, in Eq. (3-14)
Type 3 system, one for which $n = 3$, in Eq. (3-14)

3-4. Error Constants.[54] Based upon a system which has unity feedback ($H = 1$) the error coefficients are defined

$$\text{Positional-error constant} = K_0 = \lim_{p \to 0} KG(p) \qquad (3\text{-}15)$$

$$\text{Velocity-error constant} = K_v = \lim_{p \to 0} pKG(p) \qquad (3\text{-}16)$$

$$\text{Acceleration-error constant} = K_a = \lim_{p \to 0} p^2 KG(p) \qquad (3\text{-}17)$$

where K is the constant portion and $G(p)$ the variable portion of the forward-loop transfer function. These functions are shown on Fig. 3-1. For the case of $H = 1$ the actuating signal $\varepsilon(p)$ is the error ($= R - C$).

The error constants are found for various types of systems (i.e., types 0, 1, and 2). Each of the inputs of Eqs. (3-1) to (3-3) are applied to a system whose transfer function is given by Eq. (3-14). In this manner the significance of the various error constants becomes apparent.

Position-error Constant. The error, which also corresponds to the actuating signal for the case $H = 1$, is given by

$$\varepsilon(p) = \frac{R(p)}{1 + KG} \qquad (3\text{-}18)$$

Suppose it is desired to find the steady-state or final value of $\varepsilon(t)$ when $r(t)$ is a step function in position. From the final value theorem,

$$\lim_{t \to \infty} \varepsilon(t) = \lim_{p \to 0} p \, \frac{R(p)}{1 + KG(p)} \qquad (3\text{-}19)$$

But $R(p) = A/p$ for a unit step function. This term cancels with the p in the numerator

$$\varepsilon_0 = \lim_{t \to \infty} \varepsilon(t) = \frac{A}{1 + \lim_{p \to 0} KG(p)} = \frac{A}{1 + K_0} \qquad (3\text{-}20)$$

For a type 0 system $n = 0$

$$\frac{\varepsilon_0}{A} = \frac{1}{1 + K' \dfrac{(1/\tau_1)(1/\tau_3)}{(1/\tau_2)(1/\tau_4)}} = \frac{1}{1 + K_0} \qquad (3\text{-}21)$$

K_0 is the position constant and, as can be noticed from Eq. (3-21), has a finite value.

For type 1 system (or higher) $n \geq 1$

$$\frac{\varepsilon_0}{A} = \lim_{p \to 0} \frac{1}{1 + K' \dfrac{(1/\tau_1)(1/\tau_3)}{p^n (1/\tau_2)(1/\tau_4)}} = 0 \qquad (3\text{-}22)$$

Notice that the steady-state error in response to a step function for systems of type 1 or greater is equal to zero. The time response for systems with $n \geq 1$ has zero steady-state error (i.e., after all transients have died out). The difference between r and c, which is the error, is zero.

The time response for $n = 0$ systems is that of the example given in Fig. 3-2. The ratio of position error to magnitude of the applied step function is $1/(1 + K_0)$.

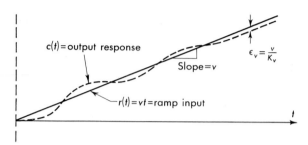

FIG. 3-3. Ramp-function response for a type 1 system.

Velocity-error Constant. Consider next the response to systems with a ramp input, that is, for $r = vt$. Again the transfer function is written, and the final value theorem invoked

$$\lim_{t \to \infty} \epsilon(t) = \lim_{p \to 0} p \frac{v/p^2}{1 + KG(p)} \tag{3-23}$$

where $R(p) = v/p^2$ is the Laplace transform of $r(t) = vt$. Equation (3-23) is simplified by canceling:

$$\lim_{t \to \infty} \frac{\epsilon(t)}{v} = \lim_{p \to 0} \frac{1}{p + pKG(p)} = \frac{1}{\lim\limits_{p \to 0} pKG} = \frac{1}{K_v} \tag{3-24}$$

This limit for $n = 0$; that is, a type 0 system has infinite value, since, setting $n = 0$, the p in the denominator can be factored:

$$\frac{\epsilon_v}{v} = \frac{1}{\lim\limits_{p \to 0} p \dfrac{K'[p + (1/\tau_1)][p + (1/\tau_3)]}{[p + (1/\tau_2)][p + (1/\tau_4)]}} = \frac{1}{\lim\limits_{p \to 0} p \dfrac{K'\tau_2\tau_4}{\tau_1\tau_3}} \to \infty \tag{3-25}$$

For a type 1 system, $n = 1$, and Eq. (3-24) has a constant, finite value given by

$$\frac{\epsilon_v}{v} = \frac{1}{\lim\limits_{p \to 0} \left\{ p \dfrac{K'[p + (1/\tau_1)][p + (1/\tau_3)]}{p[p + (1/\tau_2)][p + (1/\tau_4)]} \right\}} = \frac{\tau_1\tau_3}{K'\tau_2\tau_4} \tag{3-26}$$

The expression ϵ_v/v is the ratio of position error to input velocity and is defined by the reciprocal of the velocity constant $1/K_v$ as follows:

$$\frac{1}{K_v} = \frac{\epsilon_v}{v} \quad \text{or} \quad K_v = \frac{v}{\epsilon_v} \tag{3-27}$$

Comparison of Eq. (3-27) with (3-26) indicates that K_v is the limit as p

approaches zero of pKG, or

$$K_v = \lim_{p \to 0} pKG \qquad (3\text{-}28)$$

If a type 1 system is subjected to a ramp input, the output has the form of the curve of Fig. 3-3. The position error ϵ_v is the difference between input r and output c. As an example, suppose a gun turret is to track a target with a maximum rate of 20 radians/min = $\frac{1}{3}$ radian/sec with a maximum position error of $\frac{1}{2}°$ = 0.0087 radian. The velocity constant obtained from this specification is equal to the tracking rate ($\frac{1}{3}$ radian/sec) divided by the tracking position error (0.0087 radian), or

$$K_v = \frac{v}{\epsilon_v} = \frac{\frac{1}{3}}{0.0087} = 38.2 \text{ sec}^{-1} \qquad (3\text{-}29)$$

A type 1 system with a K_v of at least 38.2 is required to meet this specification.

For a type 2 system (or higher) $n \geq 2$ and

$$\lim_{p \to 0} \frac{p[p + (1/\tau_1)][p + (1/\tau_3)]}{p^2[p + (1/\tau_2)][p + (1/\tau_4)]} = \infty \qquad (3\text{-}30)$$

and the steady-state position error is zero.

In summary, if a ramp function is applied to a type 0 system, the error becomes infinite, which means that a type 0 system cannot follow a ramp function. A type 1 system follows with the same velocity but has a finite position error. This case is shown in Fig. 3-3. For type 2 and higher, the steady-state error is zero, and these types of systems follow with no steady-state error.

Acceleration-error Constant. To determine the acceleration constant, consider the input to be a step function of acceleration, or

$$r(t) = \frac{1}{2}at^2 \qquad (3\text{-}31)$$

The Laplace transform of this driving function is found in Table I-1.

$$R(p) = \frac{a}{p^3} \qquad (3\text{-}32)$$

The position error due to an acceleration input is

$$\epsilon_a = \lim_{t \to \infty} \epsilon(t) = \lim_{p \to 0} p \frac{a/p^3}{1 + KG} = \frac{a}{\lim_{p \to 0} p^2 KG(p)} \qquad (3\text{-}33)$$

Replacing the expression for KG from Eq. (3-14),

$$\frac{\epsilon_a}{a} = \frac{1}{\lim_{p \to 0} p^2 \dfrac{K'[p + (1/\tau_1)][p + (1/\tau_3)]}{p^n[p + (1/\tau_2)][p + (1/\tau_4)]}} \qquad (3\text{-}34)$$

The position error due to an acceleration input is symbolized by ϵ_a. This error is infinite for both types 0 and 1 systems since $\lim_{p \to 0} p^2 KG = 0$ appears in the denominator. For type $n = 2$ systems, the error is a finite constant

$$\frac{\epsilon_a}{a} = \frac{1}{K \tau_2 \tau_4 / \tau_1 \tau_3} = \frac{1}{K_a} \tag{3-35}$$

The finite constant is defined as the reciprocal of the acceleration constant K_a, which is the ratio of the amplitude of the step in acceleration to the position error. In the steady state, types 0 and 1 systems cannot follow an acceleration input and a type 2 system follows with a constant position error. This last case is shown in the sketch of Fig. 3-4.

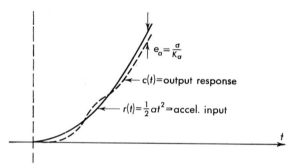

FIG. 3-4. Acceleration response for a type 2 system.

From the above consideration, it is seen that a servo has zero steady-state error in response to a unit step function only if $n \geqslant 1$. With velocity inputs (ramp inputs) into a type 0 system, the output velocity is different from the input velocity, and in the limit the error becomes infinitely large. For a type 1 system, the output velocity is equal to the input velocity; however, there is a constant position error between output and input. For types 2 and 3 and higher type systems, the servo operates with the input and the output in exact correspondence. When the system is excited with a parabolic function for types 0 and 1 systems, the acceleration is not reproduced and the error increases continuously to infinity. For type 2 systems, the acceleration is reproduced but there is a constant position error. For systems of type 3 or higher, the error is zero and there is an exact correspondence between input and output. The information regarding error coefficients is summarized in Table 3-1.

Of all the aforementioned constants, the velocity constant is most commonly encountered. Written in terms of an equation, the velocity constant is the ratio of the input velocity to the position error. When the transfer function is written as

$$KG = \frac{K_v(\tau_1 p + 1)(\tau_3 p + 1)}{p(\tau_2 p + 1)(\tau_4 p + 1)} \tag{3-36}$$

the limit of pKG as p approaches zero is K_v. Hence, the constant multiplier of the transfer function, if written in the form shown here, is the velocity constant when there is a single p in the denominator.

From a consideration of Table 3-1, it might appear without further

TABLE 3-1. SUMMARY OF ERROR COEFFICIENTS

n	K_0	ϵ_0	K_v	ϵ_v	K_a	ϵ_a
0	Finite constant	$\dfrac{1}{1 + K_0}$	0	∞	0	∞
1	∞	0	Finite constant	$\dfrac{1}{K_v}$	0	∞
2	∞	0	∞	0	Finite constant	$\dfrac{1}{K_a}$

investigation that the higher the type system, the better the servo. For systems of type 2 there is zero error for either a step in position or a step in velocity and only a finite error for a step in acceleration. However, when the stability of servo systems is under consideration, those systems with two or more poles at the origin (ps occurring alone in the denominator), corresponding to type 2 and higher, are increasingly more difficult to stabilize. Systems with one pole or less at the origin are more easily stabilized. As with most other engineering problems, the design of feedback control systems is usually a compromise between the steady-state

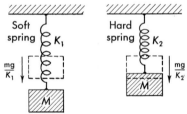

FIG. 3-5. Comparison of a soft and hard spring.

error that results in a system and the stability, or the damping, that may be obtained with a particular type of system.

Although all systems with good steady-state behavior are not necessarily hard to stabilize, often it is true. In this case a compromise must be achieved.

The compromise between steady-state errors and stability can be seen from a physical consideration of the mechanical system of Fig. 3-5. When a soft spring supports the mass, the steady-state deflection of the mass under its own weight is large. The vibrations of the system are sluggish, i.e., have a low resonant frequency, but it has a relatively large damping ratio. This system would correspond to a low-gain servo.

When a tight (hard) spring supports the mass, the steady-state deflection (steady-state error) is small, and the system responds more rapidly. Although the natural frequency is higher, the damping ratio is smaller— less stable. This corresponds to a high-gain servo.

3-5. Generalized Steady-state Errors. If the block diagram has the more general form of Fig. 3-6, that is, if $H \neq 1$ and an input transfer function G_2 is added, the steady-state errors take on a different significance. The input to the summing point is G_2R, and the feedback to the

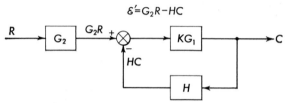

FIG. 3-6. Generalized block diagram.

summing point is HC. The actuating signal ε' is no longer the difference between the input R and the output C but is

$$\varepsilon' = G_2R - HC \qquad (3\text{-}37)$$

In this form the transfer function is written as

$$\frac{\varepsilon'}{R} = \frac{G_2}{1 + KG_1H} \qquad (3\text{-}38)$$

For step inputs of position $r = A$, the steady-state actuating signal is given by

$$\epsilon'_0 = \lim_{p \to 0} p \frac{G_2(A/p)}{1 + KG_1H} = \lim_{p \to 0} \frac{AG_2}{1 + KG_1H} \qquad (3\text{-}39)$$

For step inputs of velocity $r = vt$, the actuating signal is found from the transfer function

$$\frac{\epsilon'}{v} = \lim_{p \to 0} p \frac{G_2}{1 + KG_1H} \frac{1}{p^2} = \lim_{p \to 0} \frac{G_2}{pKG_1H} \qquad (3\text{-}40)$$

Similarly, for step inputs of acceleration $r = \frac{1}{2}at^2$, the actuating signal is given by

$$\frac{\epsilon'_a}{a} = \lim_{p \to 0} \frac{G_2}{p^2KG_1H} \qquad (3\text{-}41)$$

Although the actuating signal ε' does not correspond to the error $R - C$, its magnitude may be a measure of performance of the servo. Quite often the input and feedback blocks G_2 and H, respectively, of Fig. 3-6 are constants which change the variable from mechanical position to an electrical voltage, pressure to angle, etc. In this case direct subtraction of input and output would have no meaning. For example, if the input R is a pressure and the output C a position, the difference $R - C$ would be meaningless. Before subtraction is possible, an appropriate constant ($K = $ pressure/position) must be included so the actuating signal can be obtained. If R and C are comparable quantities, and if the error ε, equal to the difference between the input R and output C, is desired, the transfer function is found from Fig. 3-6:

$$\varepsilon = R - \frac{KG_1G_2R}{1 + KG_1H} = R\left(1 - \frac{KG_1G_2}{1 + KG_1H}\right) \qquad (3\text{-}42)$$

3-6. Steady-state Errors Due to Output Load Disturbances. Steady-state errors also result from disturbances applied at the output of a servo. Consider the example of a simple position servo of the type considered in

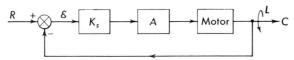

FIG. 3-7. Servo subjected to output torque.

Chap. 1. The input is a position $r(t)$, and the output $c(t)$ is positioned by a motor driven with an amplifier whose input is the error or the actuating signal $\epsilon = r - c$. This system, with $H = 1$, is shown in the block diagram of Fig. 3-7, where K_s is the constant transfer function of the input and output potentiometers and A is the constant amplifier gain.

The motor transfer function $K_m/p(\tau p + 1)$ is applicable only when driving an inertia load. Since a constant torque is also applied to the output shaft of this motor, the differential equation of a motor must be reconsidered. This equation is written as follows:

$$\bar{L}_m = K_1 E_{in} - K_2 pC \qquad (3\text{-}43)$$

where Eq. (3-43) is taken directly from the linearized torque-speed curves of the motor, as presented in Chap. 1. K_1 and K_2 are constants taken from the linearized torque-speed curves. For the present application, the motor torque $\bar{L}_m$ is balanced by an inertial torque Jp^2C, together with the output torque $\bar{L}$:

$$\bar{L}_m = Jp^2C - \bar{L} \qquad (3\text{-}44)$$

where $\bar{L}$ is the Laplace-transformed disturbing torque on the output shaft. The shaft angle C, the disturbing torque $\bar{L}$, and the motor torques are all taken in the same direction. Equating Eqs. (3-43) and (3-44),

$$C = \frac{K_1 E_{in} + \bar{L}}{p(Jp + K_2)} \qquad (3\text{-}45)$$

The voltage input to the motor is related to the error as follows:

$$E_{in} = K_s A \varepsilon = K_s A (R - C) \qquad (3\text{-}46)$$

When Eq. (3-46) is used in conjunction with Eq. (3-45), the differential equation of motion of the system is

$$(Jp^2 + K_2 p + K_1 K_s A)C = K_1 K_s A R + \bar{L} \qquad (3\text{-}47)$$

Equation (3-47) is a system with two inputs—the reference signal R and the output torque $\bar{L}$. If $\bar{L}$ is now considered as the input to the servo system, then the transfer function $C/\bar{L}$ for $R = 0$ is written

$$\frac{C}{\bar{L}} = \frac{1}{Jp^2 + K_2 p + K_1 K_s A} \qquad (3\text{-}48)$$

Equation (3-48) represents the transfer function for a linear system whose driving function is the torque $\bar{L}$. Both transient and steady-state effects result from the application of such a torque. If the form of $\bar{L}$ is known, the output C can be found by ordinary methods (Laplace transforms or classical solution).

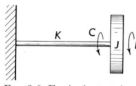

FIG. 3-8. Equivalent spring constant of a feedback control system.

Since the servo was at rest before the application of L, no generality is lost by taking $r = 0$. Whether $r = 0$ or any other constant, the variations from this steady-state condition would be represented by Eq. (3-48). It is easier, however, to consider $r = 0$; then $c = -\epsilon$. The transfer function expressed by Eq. (3-48) is the error in response to an applied output-shaft torque and is written, with Laplace transforms, for a step function in torque (of magnitude L)

$$\varepsilon = \frac{-L/p}{Jp^2 + K_2 p + K_1 K_s A} \qquad (3\text{-}49)$$

The steady-state error ϵ_0 is found with the final value theorem

$$\lim_{t \to \infty} \varepsilon(t) = \lim_{p \to 0} p \, \frac{-L/p}{Jp^2 + K_2 p + K_1 K_s A} = \frac{-L}{K_1 K_s A} \qquad (3\text{-}50)$$

where L/p is the Laplace transform of a step function in torque which is applied to the output shaft.

Physically, a position servo can be considered as a rotational spring. If an error exists, the motor will develop a torque to cancel this error. In particular, if a torque is applied to the output shaft, an error will result ($\epsilon = -c$) which will produce a voltage at the motor terminals and hence develop a torque to cancel this applied torque. Similarly, if a rotational spring system is torqued, as shown in Fig. 3-8, the spring rotates through an angle c until the torque developed by the spring Kc

equals the torque applied. The spring constant K is the torque per unit angle. For the feedback system, the torque per unit angle is $L/\epsilon = K_1K_sA$. If L were any function other than a constant, the error resulting from the application of the load torque L is obtained in a similar manner to that used in finding the steady-state errors due to standard types of inputs.

The work of this example is extended to a general servo system such as that shown in Fig. 3-9, where K_1 is the constant portion of G_2 and is removed from K_1G_2, since $\bar{L}$ is transferred through G_2 only. The output

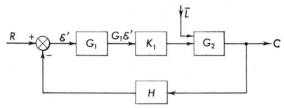

FIG. 3-9. General block diagram subjected to output disturbances.

disturbance, indicated by $\bar{L}$ in Fig. 3-9, enters directly into the final block G_2. The equations for the system of Fig. 3-9 are

$$(K_1G_1\varepsilon' + \bar{L})G_2 = C \tag{3-51}$$

$$\varepsilon' = R - HC \tag{3-52}$$

The two arrows going into the G_2 block indicate that the sum $\bar{L} + K_1G_1\varepsilon'$ is the input to G_2. Combining Eqs. (3-51) and (3-52),

$$G_2[K_1G_1(R - HC) + \bar{L}] = C \tag{3-53}$$

which when rearranged becomes

$$(1 + K_1G_1G_2H)C = G_2(\bar{L} + K_1G_1R) \tag{3-54}$$

If the system is originally at rest, no generality is lost by taking $r = 0$ and the actuating signal ε' is

$$\varepsilon' = -HC \tag{3-55}$$

Equation (3-55) is substituted into Eq. (3-54), and the differential equation relating the actuating signal ε' to the applied disturbing torque is written

$$(1 + K_1G_1G_2H)\varepsilon' = -HG_2\bar{L} \tag{3-56}$$

If $r = 0$, the block diagram of Fig. 3-9 may be redrawn, as shown in Fig. 3-10, so as to correspond in an input-output form to Eq. (3-56). The normal servo is given by Fig. 3-9. A fictitious servo, which is given in Fig. 3-10, is useful for the purposes of analysis. The subtraction, indicated in Fig. 3-9, is replaced by a block with a -1 gain, which is incorporated in the H block. If the standard subtractor (output subtracted from input) is used in Fig. 3-10, another -1 gain block must be included in the feedback path. If the original diagram is redrawn (Fig. 3-9), a new block diagram which represents Eq. (3-56) is obtained. The error in response to any type of disturbing torque L at the output of the original system is determined from either Eq. (3-56) or the block diagram of Fig. 3-10.

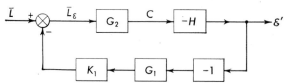

FIG. 3-10. Inverted block diagram with output torque as input.

3-7. Servo Specifications. Since the specification of a closed-loop system must be interpreted by the servo designer, a review of the more commonly encountered requirements is presented. The specifications as generally given are divided into those which are specified with quantities in the frequency domain, i.e., stated in terms of frequency, and those specified in the time domain, i.e., stated in terms of time response. Often a combination of both is given.

Frequency-domain Specifications. A servo specification is commonly written in the same sense as an electronic amplifier or as a filter. "Hi Fi"

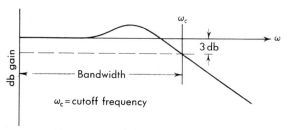

FIG. 3-11. Definition of bandwidth.

enthusiasts will recall that their amplifiers are specified and compared on the basis of their bandwidth, that is, flat from 30 to 15,000 cps. Most filters, i.e., bandpass, low pass, band reject, etc., are specified in terms of the amplitude response versus frequency. The *bandwidth*, which is shown in Fig. 3-11, is the frequency range between which the amplitude response does not drop 3 db (0.707 amplitude ratio) below the amplitude at the center of the passband. Decibel is defined as $20 \log_{10} A_2/A_1$, where A_2/A_1 is an amplitude ratio. The bandwidth indicates to some degree the speed of response of the system. In filter theory the bandwidth measures the ability of the system to reproduce the shape of the input signal. For example, if a square pulse is applied to the input of a low-pass filter which has a bandwidth limit, at a finite cutoff frequency* ω_c, the output will no longer be a square pulse but might be distorted as shown in Fig. 3-12. In some specifications not only the bandwidth but also the characteristics of the cutoff are given. For example, the rate of cutoff beyond the cutoff frequency may be specified as 12 db/octave. An octave is a factor of 2 change in frequency.

The d-c performance specification of a control system is frequently given. It is included as a frequency specification, since direct current is the limiting case of zero frequency. The various error constants, and especially the velocity constant K_v, provide a simple method of d-c system specification.

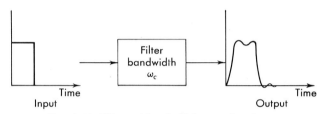

FIG. 3-12. Effect of bandwidth on pulse shape.

A variety of other frequency-domain specifications may be encountered in practical control system design. For example, if a control system is used in an aircraft which has a resonance due to the structure or aerodynamics at a particular frequency, then it may be necessary to design a system which blocks the transmission of signals in this band of frequencies but passes both higher and lower frequencies. Otherwise the aircraft may be subjected to severe vibration or erratic flight. If noise which is limited to a particular band is present, a special bandpass characteristic must be specified to block these undesirable frequencies.

Time-domain Specifications. Often the desired characteristics of the system performance are specified in terms of time-domain quantities, that is, by the response to a step function or a ramp function. A complete transient component is required to satisfy exactly the time-domain requirements. It is, however, impossible to find the transient component until most of the design has been completed. As an aid in bridging the gap between specifications given in the time domain and useful design quantities (such as damping ratio ζ, natural resonant frequency ω_n, etc.) the second-order solution may prove useful. Care must be exercised in more complex systems, since the extension of the second-order system to these can be misleading. At least the second-order system is a starting point.

---

* The cutoff frequency is the limit of the passband. It is the frequency where the amplitude is down 3 db as shown in Fig. 3-11.

The response of a second-order system to a step function is considered in Chap. 1.   From the transient component of the second-order system it is observed that the design based on the calculation of time-domain specifications can be rather cumbersome because of the amount of work involved.   The charts which relate the various time-domain specifications, such as per cent overshoot, damping ratio, and the like, are presented in Chap. 1.   For higher-order systems, beyond the second, these charts are used only as a guide and a starting point.

A typical response to a unit step function for a particular damping ratio is shown in Fig. 3-13.   The curve is conveniently described in terms

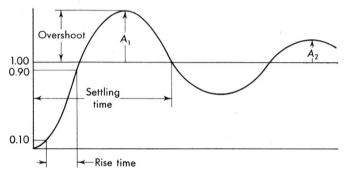

Fig. 3-13. Time-domain specifications shown on a typical response curve.

of three quantities: the per cent overshoot, the rise time, and the settling time (which is related to the damping ratio).

The *overshoot*, in per cent of the final value, measures the amount the output overshoots the steady-state response for a unit step input.   For Fig. 3-13, the overshoot is $A_1/1$ per cent.

The *rise time* is defined as the time required for the response to a unit step function to rise from 10 to 90 per cent of the final value.   An alternate and substantially equivalent definition may be used: The reciprocal of the slope of the response at the instant the response is half the final value.   The first definition seems preferable.

The *settling time* is defined as the time required for the response to a unit step function to decrease, to reach, and thereafter to stay within a specified percentage of its final value.   Often it is the time required for the response to again cross unit amplitude after overshooting the first time.   (See, for example, Fig. 3-13.)

The damping ratio, discussed in Chap. 1, is the ratio of the damping which exists in a second-order system divided by the system critical damping.   This quantity may be calculated from the time response when the ratio of two successive positive overshoots is known: A_1 and A_2 shown in Fig. 3-13.   The damping ratio ζ for a second-order system is given by the equation

$$\zeta = \frac{1/2\pi \ln A_1/A_2}{\sqrt{1 + (1/2\pi \ln A_1/A_2)^2}} \qquad (3\text{-}57)$$

Besides the difficulty of relating these given time-response quantities directly to frequency-response information or frequency-domain data, another difficulty arises in the specification of servo systems on the basis of the time-domain information: No common definition has been accepted for time-domain quantities. For example, often the rise time is the time from 10 to 90 per cent; however, it is also expressed as the time from 5 to 95 per cent or, alternately, the reciprocal of the slope at 50 per cent. The definitions of the quantities given in this chapter correspond as closely as possible to present accepted servo definitions.

PROBLEMS

3-1. Find position, velocity, and acceleration coefficients for the following forward-loop transfer functions ($H = 1$ for all systems):

(a) $KG = \dfrac{K}{(p + 10)(p + 100)}$

(b) $KG = \dfrac{K}{p(p + 10)(p + 100)}$

(c) $KG = \dfrac{Kp}{(p + 1)(p + 10)(p + 100)}$

(d) $KG = \dfrac{K}{p^2(p^2 + 2\zeta\omega_n p + \omega_n{}^2)}$

(e) $KG = \dfrac{100}{(p^2 + 2\zeta\omega_n p + \omega_n{}^2)}$

(f) $KG = \dfrac{100(p + 10)(p + 50)}{p^3(p^2 + 2\zeta\omega_n p + \omega_n{}^2)}$

3-2. Find the actuating signal ε' for the system shown in Fig. 3P-2. Find the position, velocity, and acceleration constants, and determine their significance in this general case.

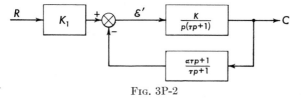

Fig. 3P-2

3-3. Determine the actuating signal ε' and the difference $R - C$ for the problem of Fig. 3P-3. Which is the best measure of servo performance? How are these related to the error constants?

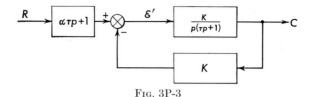

FIG. 3P-3

3-4. Derive the relation between ζ, the damping ratio, and the amplitudes of two successive overshoots A_1 and A_2 of Fig. 3-13. The result is given by Eq. (3-57).

✓ **3-5.** For the systems of Prob. 3-1 find the steady-state error for a unit step input and a unit ramp input.

✓ **3-6.** For the system of Fig. 3P-6, find the steady-state error for

(a) A unit step position input
(b) A unit step velocity input
(c) A unit step acceleration input

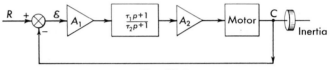

FIG. 3P-6

✓ **3-7.** For the following open-loop transfer function,

$$KG = \frac{K(p + p_1)}{p^2(p + p_2)(p + p_4)}$$

(a) What type system is it?
(b) Find K_0, K_v, and K_a.

3-8. For the system of Fig. 3P-6, find the steady-state error for a constant output torque applied to the system. Assume zero input.

3-9. Repeat Prob. 3-8 with an output load torque given by the equation

$$L = bt$$

3-10. Repeat Prob. 3-8 with the second amplifier changed from a constant to

$$A_2 = K\frac{1}{p}$$

3-11. Repeat Prob. 3-8 with the second amplifier changed from a constant to

$$A_2 = Kp$$

CHAPTER 4

THE ROOT-LOCUS METHOD[14,15,16]

4-1. Introduction. It is indicated in Chap. 1 that the design of closed-loop systems requires repetitive analysis. The engineer observes by analysis the effect on the system of a particular change, and after several trials a fairly optimum system results. It is important for the servo engineer to be able to analyze rapidly each successive trial. The importance of the root-locus method can be fully appreciated when the rapidity of completing each solution is realized. The root locus pictures the entire character (transient behavior) of the system as a result of changes of loop gain, component time constants, and stabilizing-network configurations.

4-2. The Second-order System. In Chap. 1, the second-order system, shown in the block diagram of Fig. 4-1, is studied. The complete time solution is found for this system (cf. Secs. 1-4 and 1-5). The value of amplifier gain A necessary to produce a stable system is an important quantity that must be found in the design.

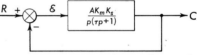

FIG. 4-1. Second-order position servo.

The motor transfer function $K_m/p(\tau p + 1)$, the time constant τ, and motor constant K_m are fixed when the motor is chosen. The motor* is chosen from a knowledge of the load power requirements. How does the transient response, which is directly related to the location of the roots of the system characteristic equation, change as the variable quantities A and K_s are altered? For the system of Fig. 4-1 the answer can be obtained analytically.

The transfer function relating output to input is easily found to be

$$\frac{C}{R} = \frac{KG}{1 + KG} = \frac{A K_m K_s / p(\tau p + 1)}{1 + [A K_m K_s / p(\tau p + 1)]} \tag{4-1}$$

where p is the Laplace-transform operator. Equation (4-1) is multiplied out as follows:

$$\frac{C}{R} = \frac{A K_m K_s}{\tau p^2 + p + A K_m K_s} \tag{4-2}$$

* See Chap. 9 for further information on motors.

The impulse response is found from Eq. (4-2) by setting $R(p) = 1$ (the Laplace transform of a unit impulse is 1) and solving for

$$c(t) = \mathcal{L}^{-1} \frac{A K_m K_s}{\tau p^2 + p + A K_m K_s} \qquad (4\text{-}3)$$

This is evaluated by finding the roots of the denominator

$$p^2 + \frac{1}{\tau} p + \frac{A K_m K_s}{\tau} = 0 \qquad (4\text{-}4)$$

The location of the two roots of this equation determines the transient behavior and hence yields information with regard to the degree of stability of the system.   If the roots lie in the right half plane, the response has the following form:

$$c(t) = e^{+\alpha t}(A \sin \omega t + B \cos \omega t) \qquad (4\text{-}5)$$

and if the roots should lie along the j axis, the response is

$$c(t) = A \sin \omega t + B \cos \omega t \qquad (4\text{-}6)$$

In either case, the system would be unsatisfactory, since Eq. (4-5) is an increasing transient response and Eq. (4-6) is an undamped transient response.   Location of all the roots determines the stability of the system.   The damping ratio, the undamped natural frequency, and the frequency of oscillation are all found from the root location.

Identical information is obtained from the classical solution.   The transient part is found for the system of Eq. (4-1) by setting the driving function to zero and assuming a solution $c_0 e^{pt}$.   When this is substituted

TABLE 4-1. CALCULATION OF ROOTS OF SECOND-ORDER SYSTEM AS GAIN VARIES

$A K_s$	Root location	
	p_1	p_2
0.1	-99.5	$- 0.5$
1.0	-94.7	$- 5.3$
2.0	-88.7	-11.3
3.0	-81.6	-18.4
4.0	-72.4	-27.6
5.0	-50.0	-50.0
6.0	$-50 + j22.4$	$-50 - j22.4$
7.0	$-50 + j31.6$	$-50 - j31.6$
8.0	$-50 + j38.7$	$-50 - j38.7$
9.0	$-50 + j44.7$	$-50 - j44.7$
10.0	$-50 + j50$	$-50 - j50$
50.0	$-50 + j150$	$-50 - j150$
100.0	$-50 + j217.9$	$-50 - j217.9$

into the homogeneous equation,

$$\tau c_0 p^2 \epsilon^{pt} + c_0 p \epsilon^{pt} + A K_m K_s c_0 \epsilon^{pt} = 0 \qquad (4\text{-}7)$$

which reduces to

$$p^2 + \frac{1}{\tau} p + \frac{A K_m K_s}{\tau} = 0 \qquad (4\text{-}8)$$

Equation (4-8) is identical with Eq. (4-4).

The two roots of Eq. (4-4) are found from the binomial expression

$$p_i = -\frac{1}{2\tau} \pm \sqrt{\frac{1}{4\tau^2} - \frac{A K_m K_s}{\tau}} \qquad (4\text{-}9)$$

For definiteness the following numerical values are taken: $\tau = 0.01$, and $K_m = 5.0$. The computations necessary to find the variation of p_i as

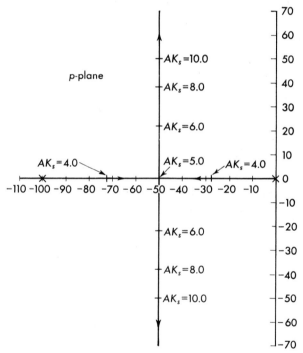

FIG. 4-2. Plot of roots of second-order system.

$A K_s$ varies are shown in Table 4-1. The plot of these root variations is given in Fig. 4-2. As the gain $A K_s$ is varied, the roots move along a continuous curve or locus. The values of gain that produce particular roots are indicated along the plot. From the "root-locus," or the location of the roots versus gain, diagram, the form of the transient solution is completely known for all values of gain.

For example, if $AK_s = 8.00$, the roots are located at

$$p_i = -50 \pm j38.7 \qquad (4\text{-}10)$$

and the impulse response (transient component) is written

$$c(t) = e^{-50t}(A \cos 38.7t + B \sin 38.7t) \qquad (4\text{-}11)$$

where A and B are constants that depend upon the initial conditions. The stability of a system, however, depends upon the location of the roots of the system and not upon the driving function or initial conditions. Since the roots of this second-order system do not cross the j axis, the system is stable for any value of amplifier gain.

The plot of the root location as the system gain is varied is analytically calculated only to demonstrate the method. The root locus is a graphical method which enables the engineer to plot the positions of the roots as the gain is varied.

4-3. The Locus of Roots. The root-locus method is based upon knowledge of the location of the roots of the system with zero gain, that is, with the feedback loop open.

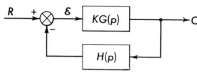

FIG. 4-3. Generalized block diagram.

In most cases these are easily determined from the open-loop transfer function KGH. K is the constant portion of the loop gain, $G(p)$ is the forward-loop transfer function, and $H(p)$ is the feedback-loop transfer function. These quantities are defined in the block diagram of Fig. 4-3 and for the example of Fig. 4-1 have the values

$$K = \frac{AK_mK_s}{\tau} \qquad G(p) = \frac{1}{p[p + (1/\tau)]} \qquad H(p) = 1 \qquad (4\text{-}12)$$

In subsequent expressions, the "function of p" is understood; that is, G is written for $G(p)$ and H for $H(p)$.

Consider the expression which relates output to input and is derived from the block diagram of Fig. 4-3:

$$\frac{C}{R} = \frac{KG}{1 + KGH} \qquad (4\text{-}13)$$

where $1 + KGH$ is the characteristic equation. The stability of a system depends only upon the impulse response (transient component). The location of the roots of $1 + KGH$ determines the degree of system stability.

In the example of this section the roots of the characteristic equation, for a gain of 8.00, are found to be complex numbers:

$$p_1 = -50 + j38.7 \qquad p_2 = -50 - j38.7 \qquad (4\text{-}14)$$

Any complex quantity written in rectangular form $a + jb$ is expressed in polar form as follows:

$$\sqrt{a^2 + b^2}\, e^{j\phi} = \sqrt{a^2 + b^2}\, \angle \phi \qquad (4\text{-}15)$$

where $\phi = \tan^{-1} b/a$. The roots of Eq. (4-14) can also be expressed in polar form

$$p_1 = \sqrt{50^2 + 38.7^2}\, e^{j\,\tan^{-1}\frac{38.7}{-50}} = 63.2 e^{j142.3°}$$

$$= 63.2\angle + 142.3° \qquad (4\text{-}16)$$

$$p_2 = 63.2 e^{-j142.3°} = 63.2\angle - 142.3°$$

In polar form these roots are located by a magnitude (63.2) and an angle ($\pm 142.3°$). In general, the roots of the characteristic equation are complex numbers and can be written in polar form

$$p_i = A_i e^{j\phi_i} \qquad (4\text{-}17)$$

where A_i is the magnitude and ϕ_i is the angle of the root which is expressed in polar form. In a similar fashion, any term of the form $p_1 + a$ can be written in polar form as a magnitude at a phase angle $A e^{j\phi}$.

The open-loop transfer function KGH is a ratio of factored polynomials, for example,

$$KGH = \frac{K_1(p\tau_1 + 1)(p\tau_3 + 1)}{p^n(p\tau_2 + 1)(p\tau_4 + 1)} \qquad (4\text{-}18)$$

Equation (4-18) can be rewritten in the following form (this form should always be used for root-locus analysis):

$$KGH = \overbrace{\frac{K_1\tau_1\tau_3}{\tau_2\tau_4}}^{K}\; \overbrace{\frac{[p + (1/\tau_1)][p + (1/\tau_3)]}{p^n[p + (1/\tau_2)][p + (1/\tau_4)]}}^{GH} \qquad (4\text{-}19)$$

Each factor in the KGH function is considered as a complex number and is written in polar form as follows:

$$p + \frac{1}{\tau_1} = A_1 e^{j\phi_1} \qquad (4\text{-}20)$$

Hence, the entire KGH function is a complex quantity and can be written in polar form:

$$KGH = \frac{K\,(A_1 e^{j\phi_1})(A_3 e^{j\phi_3})}{(A_0{}^n e^{jn\phi_0})(A_2 e^{j\phi_2})(A_4 e^{j\phi_4})} \qquad (4\text{-}21)$$

$$= \frac{KA_1 A_3}{A_0{}^n A_2 A_4}\, e^{j[(\phi_1 + \phi_3 + \cdots\,) - (n\phi_0 + \phi_2 + \cdots\,)]} \qquad (4\text{-}22)$$

The algebraic equation from which the roots are determined,

$$1 + KGH = 1 + A e^{j\phi} = 0 \qquad (4\text{-}23)$$

can be written as two expressions:

$$\text{Angle of } KGH = \arg KGH = \phi = (2k + 1)180° \qquad (4\text{-}24)$$

where $k = 0, 1, 2, 3, \ldots$

$$\text{Magnitude of } KGH = |KGH| = A = 1 \qquad (4\text{-}25)$$

Equations (4-24) and (4-25) are the result of setting $1 + KGH = 0$, that is, the angle or the argument of KGH equal to odd multiples of 180° and the magnitude of KGH equal to 1. These equations are the basis for the root-locus method.

To avoid confusion, the various singularities are defined as follows:

A *Zero* is a value of p which causes the numerator of KGH to equal zero.

A *Pole* is a value of p which causes the denominator of KGH to equal zero.

A *Root* is a value of p which causes $1 + KGH$ to equal zero.

Notice that if p_j is a pole of KGH, it is also a pole of $1 + KGH$, since the addition of 1 does not affect the infinite magnitude of $KGH(p_j)$.

The formal definition of the root-locus criterion follows from a comparison of Eq. (4-22) with Eqs. (4-24) and (4-25). The angle criterion yields

$$(\phi_1 + \phi_3) - (n\phi_0 + \phi_2 + \phi_4) = (2k + 1)180° \qquad (4\text{-}26)$$

where $k = 0, 1, 2, \ldots$
The magnitude criterion yields

$$\frac{KA_1A_3}{A_0{}^n A_2 A_4} = 1 \qquad (4\text{-}27)$$

The root locus is plotted by finding all points p_i in the p plane which satisfy Eq. (4-26). When the locus is completely plotted, Eq. (4-27) is used to scale it in terms of the values of gain K that correspond to particular roots along the locus.

Consider the example of Fig. 4-1 which is cited earlier in this chapter. In this example the transfer function is

$$KGH = \frac{AK_mK_s}{\tau}\,\frac{1}{p[p + (1/\tau)]} = 500AK_s\,\frac{1}{p(p + 100)} \qquad (4\text{-}28)$$

Since Eq. (4-26) (the angle criterion) is first used to make the plot, only the GH function is examined. The system has a pole at the origin, a pole at -100, and no zeros. These are first put on the diagram of Fig. 4-4. An X designates a pole, a 0 designates a zero, and a dot, ., designates a root.

A point p_1 is guessed for a root of $1 + KGH = 0$. If p_1 is a root, then the angles of GH must sum to 180°.   The angle or argument of GH is

$$\arg GH = -(\theta_0 + \theta_2) = -\left(\tan^{-1}\frac{\beta_1}{-\alpha_1} + \tan^{-1}\frac{\beta_1}{100 - \alpha_1}\right) \quad (4\text{-}29)$$

θ_0 and θ_2 are the angles subtended at the poles of GH and are shown in Fig. 4-4.   The sign is negative because the angles subtended by poles which are positive in the denominator become negative in the numerator.

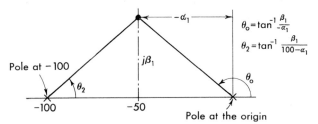

$$\theta_0 = \tan^{-1}\frac{\beta_1}{-\alpha_1}$$

$$\theta_2 = \tan^{-1}\frac{\beta_1}{100 - \alpha_1}$$

FIG. 4-4. Location of the poles of $500AK_s/p(p + 100)$.

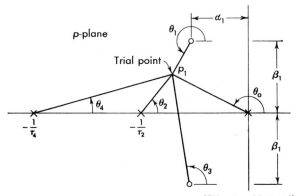

FIG. 4-5. Location of zeros and poles for $\dfrac{K[(p + \alpha_1)^2 + \beta_1{}^2]}{p[p + (1/\tau_2)][p + (1/\tau_4)]}$.

The locus of all points at which the angles subtended to the zeros and poles sum to an odd multiple of 180° is the root locus.   The reader can verify from the plot of Fig. 4-2 that the sum of the angles subtended to the poles from any root is 180°.   (This particular transfer function has no zeros.)

Figure 4-5 shows the zero and pole locations for the transfer function

$$KGH = \frac{K(p + \alpha_1 + j\beta_1)(p + \alpha_1 - j\beta_1)}{p[p + (1/\tau_2)][p + (1/\tau_4)]} \quad (4\text{-}30)$$

The characteristic equation $(1 + KGH)$ for this system is solved graphically for the roots by locating a trial point p_1 in the p plane and moving it until the angle criterion [Eq. (4-24)] is satisfied.   Application of Eqs. (4-24) and (4-25) to the situation depicted in Fig. 4-5 indicates that if

p_1 is a root of the characteristic equation, then the algebraic sum of all the angles (positive for zeros and negative for poles) must equal 180° and the magnitude must equal unity, or written in equation form

$$\Sigma\theta_i = \theta_1 + \theta_3 + (-\theta_0 - \theta_2 - \theta_4) = (2k+1)180° \quad (4\text{-}31)$$

$$A = \frac{K|p_1 + \alpha_1 + j\beta_1|\ |p_1 + \alpha_1 - j\beta_1|}{|p_1|\ |p_1 + (1/\tau_2)|\ |p_1 + (1/\tau_4)|} = 1 \quad (4\text{-}32)$$

Each angle in $\Sigma\theta_i$ is the angle of the vector $p_1 + (1/\tau_i)$ measured from the horizontal. Each term in A is the distance from the respective pole or zero to the point p_i. The root-locus diagram is plotted by using the condition of Eq. (4-31). A point p_i is moved about in the p plane until the angle criterion is satisfied.

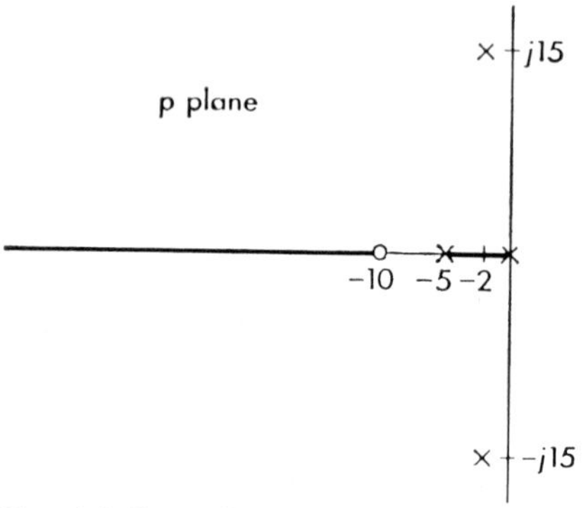

The gain K of the system for particular operating points along this locus is found by application of the condition of Eq. (4-32). Usually the procedure of first finding the root locus and then finding the gain at particular points along the locus is easier than trying to satisfy both the angle and the magnitude conditions simultaneously. Often, for the purposes of certain problems, it is unnecessary to plot all branches of the locus or to determine K.

FIG. 4-6. Example of Rules 1 and 2 applied to the system

$$KGH = \frac{K(p+10)}{p(p+5)[(p+2)^2 + 15^2]}$$

The essence of the root-locus method has been described; however, the next section presents a set of useful rules which reduces the time consumed in a completely trial-and-error procedure.

4-4. Rules for Rapid Construction of Root-locus Diagrams. The rules which are stated and demonstrated in this section enable the engineer to sketch rapidly the locus diagrams. The proofs for the rules are postponed to Sec. 4-7. The following open-loop transfer function is used to demonstrate the method:

$$KGH = \frac{K(p+10)}{p(p+5)(p+2+j15)(p+2-j15)} \quad (4\text{-}33)$$

The zeros and poles are shown in Fig. 4-6. Notice that the scales on the real and imaginary axes of the p plane are identical.

Rule 1: Continuous curves, which comprise the locus, start at each pole of KGH for $K = 0$. The branches of the locus, which are single-valued functions of gain, terminate on the zeros of KGH for $K = \infty$. The zeros and poles of KGH are first located on the p plane, an X for each pole and a 0 for each zero. According to Rule 1, the locus starts at the poles and terminates at the zeros. Each locus is a continuous curve between a pole and a zero. Each branch of the locus is a single-valued function of gain along the curve. For the example [Eq. (4-33)] shown in Fig. 4-6, there exist four branches, starting from the four poles, which are located at $p = 0$, $p = -5$, $p = -2 + j15$, $p = -2 - j15$. Since there is only one finite zero, located at $p = -10$, three of the branches must terminate at infinity. The rule then can be expanded to read: The locus starts at the poles and terminates on either finite zeros or $(\#P - \#Z)$ zeros located at infinite p. $\#P$ is the number of poles and $\#Z$ is the number of finite zeros of KGH. The number of separate branches equals the number of poles if, as is usually the case, $\#P \geqslant \#Z$.

The gain K is usually positive and varies from zero to infinity. On occasion it may be necessary to work with negative K. In this case, the angle criterion is changed so that the angles are summed to $\pm 2k(180°)$. Since this is an unusual case, only positive K will be considered in this text.

Rule 2: The locus exists at any point along the real axis where an odd number of poles plus zeros is found to the right of the point. To determine if the locus exists in a given region along the real axis, count the number of zeros plus poles which lie to the right of the trial point. If there is an odd number of these, then a branch of the locus does exist. For the example of Fig. 4-6 the locus exists along the real axis from the origin to the point $p = -5$ and from $p = -10$ to $-$infinity. These regions along the real axis are shown darkened on Fig. 4-6. Any complex zeros or poles, such as $p = -2 \pm j15$, are ignored in applying this rule.

Rule 3: For large values of gain the locus is asymptotic to the angles

$$\frac{(2k + 1)180°}{\#P - \#Z} \qquad \text{for } k = 0, 1, 2, \ldots \qquad (4\text{-}34)$$

where $\#P$ is the number of poles and $\#Z$ is the number of zeros.

If the number of poles exceeds the number of finite zeros, some of the branches terminate on zeros which are located at infinity. Rule 1 states that the number of roots which terminate at infinity is the number of poles minus the number of zeros. As the gain becomes large, these branches tend to become asymptotic to straight lines whose angles are given by Eq. (4-34).

For the example of Fig. 4-6, $\#P = 4$ and $\#Z = 1$ and the asymptotic angles are computed as follows:

$$\theta_k = \frac{(2k + 1)180°}{+3} \qquad (4\text{-}35)$$

$k = 0$	$k = 1$	$k = 2$
$\theta_0 = +60°$	$\theta_1 = +180°$	$\theta_2 = +300°$

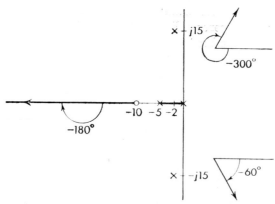

Fig. 4-7. Asymptotic directions determined by Rule 3.

Since only three branches go to infinity, all the angles are computed, and these are plotted on Fig. 4-7. No error would result if different consecutive values of k had been chosen, since the angles repeat after any three consecutive ks have been inserted into Eq. (4-35). This rule gives the asymptotic directions or angles. The point from which these asymptotes radiate is given by the next rule.

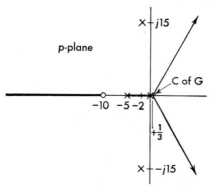

Fig. 4-8. Location of center of gravity of roots (Rule 4).

Rule 4: *The starting point for the asymptotic lines is given by*

$$CG = \frac{\Sigma \text{ poles} - \Sigma \text{ zeros}}{\#P - \#Z} \quad (4\text{-}36)$$

which is called the center of gravity of the roots. The angular directions to which the branches of the locus are asymptotic are given by Rule 3. The asymptotic lines start at the center of gravity of the zero-pole configuration. This point is found from Eq. (4-36). For the example of Fig. 4-6, the CG (center of gravity) is found as follows:

$$\Sigma \text{ poles} = (-5) + (-2 + j15) + (-2 - j15) + 0 = -9$$
$$\Sigma \text{ zeros} = -10$$
$$\#P = \#\text{poles} = 4$$
$$\#Z = \#\text{zeros} = 1$$

and
$$CG = \frac{(-9) - (-10)}{4 - 1} = \frac{1}{3} \quad (4\text{-}37)$$

The asymptotic lines, found in Eq. (4-35), start from the center of gravity. These lines are placed on the p plane as shown on Fig. 4-8.

Since both complex zeros and complex poles always appear in conjugate pairs, that is, equal vertical distances from the real axis, the center of gravity will always lie along the real axis.

Rule 5: The breakaway point p_b is found from the equation

$$\frac{-1}{|p_b + (1/\tau_2)|} + \frac{-1}{|p_b + (1/\tau_4)|} + \frac{+1}{|p_b + (1/\tau_1)|}$$
$$= \frac{-1}{|p_b + (1/\tau_6)|} + \frac{1}{|p_b + (1/\tau_3)|} \quad (4\text{-}38)$$

where $p_b + 1/\tau_i$ is the magnitude of the distance from the assumed breakaway point p_b and the real axis zeros and poles. The distances are read graphically. From Rule 2 the regions where the locus exists along the real axis are determined. If an acceptable region on the real axis lies between a single-order zero and a single-order pole (single order means one zero or one pole located at a point), the locus usually moves from the pole to the zero along the real axis. If an acceptable region along the real axis lies between two single-order poles, the two roots which start from these poles usually approach each other along the axis. As the gain is increased, these roots form a double-order root at the point at which they coalesce (come together). As the gain is further increased, the branches of the locus break away from the real axis and form a complex conjugate pair of roots.

The point p_b, at which the roots come together and break away, is found as follows:

1. Guess a point p_b.

2. Measure the distances between the guessed point and the real axis zeros and poles.

3. Equate the sum of the reciprocals of the distances from p_b to the zeros and poles to the left of p_b to the sum of the reciprocals of the distances to the right of p_b. These are added with a negative sign for the poles and a positive sign for the zeros.

4. If the sum to the left does not equal the sum to the right, guess another value of p_b and repeat.

The above procedure should be performed by trial and error. If, in an attempt to find an analytical solution, Eq. (4-38) is multiplied out, a polynomial in p_b will result. The solution for p_b would then require finding the roots of a polynomial—an arduous task that the root-locus method is supposed to obviate. In many cases, it is not even necessary to find p_b, an intelligent guess being suitable. For difficult cases (zeros and poles close to the real axis) it may be necessary to find p_b to aid in sketching the locus.

The zero-pole configuration of Fig. 4-6 indicates that a locus exists between 0 and −5. To find the point at which the two roots break away from the axis guess a point $p_b = -2.5$, as shown in Fig. 4-9.   The sum of the reciprocals to the left of p_1 equated to the sum of the reciprocals to the right of p_1 results in the numerical expression

$$-\frac{1}{2.5} \;+\; \frac{1}{7.5} \stackrel{?}{=} -\frac{1}{2.5} \tag{4-39}$$
$$\downarrow \qquad\qquad \downarrow \qquad\qquad \downarrow$$
$$p_1 + 5 \qquad p_1 + 10 \qquad p_1 + 0$$

This equation is not quite satisfied, since

$$-0.400 + 0.133 = -0.267 \neq -0.400 \tag{4-40}$$

As a second guess take $p_2 = -3.0$ and obtain

$$-\frac{1}{2.0} + \frac{1}{7.0} \stackrel{?}{=} -\frac{1}{3.0}$$
$$-0.500 + 0.143 = -0.357 \neq -0.333 \tag{4-41}$$

As a third guess take $p_3 = -2.9$

$$-\frac{1}{2.1} + \frac{1}{7.1} \stackrel{?}{=} -\frac{1}{2.9} \tag{4-42}$$
$$-0.476 + 0.141 = -0.335 = -0.345$$

Probably this value of $p_3 = -2.9$ would be satisfactory.   The process can be repeated until the desired accuracy is achieved.   The result is shown in Fig. 4-9.

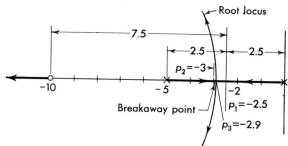

Fig. 4-9. Location of the breakaway point from the real axis (Rule 5).

In this example and in all cases where complex poles or zeros are located relatively far from the real axis, that is, their distance from the real axis is more than five times the distance to the real axis poles and zeros, the complex poles or zeros can be ignored in the computation of the breakaway point.   When the complex poles or zeros are near the real axis, their effect must be included.   Also, if the number of real axis poles and zeros is small, the net change in angle contributed from complex poles or zeros must be included. Figure 4-10 shows a method of computing the net change in angle contributed from complex singularities. The angles θ_1 and θ_2 in this figure are given by

$$\tan \theta_1 = \frac{\omega_1}{p_b - \alpha_1} \quad \text{and} \quad \tan \theta_2 = \frac{\omega_1 - \Delta\omega}{p_b - \alpha_1} \qquad (4\text{-}43)$$

where p_b is the guessed breakaway point. α_1 is the real component of the complex pole, ω_1 is the imaginary component of the complex pole, and $\Delta\omega$ is the vertical distance from the real axis. For small $\Delta\omega$, θ_1 and θ_2 are approximately equal. The difference is expressed with the small-

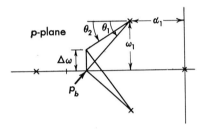

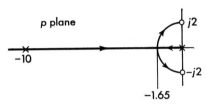

FIG. 4-10. Net change in angle from complex poles.

FIG. 4-11. Breakaway from real axis with complex zeros included.

angle approximation

$$\theta_1 - \theta_2 \approx \tan(\theta_1 - \theta_2) = \frac{\tan \theta_1 - \tan \theta_2}{1 + \tan \theta_1 \tan \theta_2} \qquad (4\text{-}44)$$

The total angular contribution is given by

$$2(\theta_1 - \theta_2) = \frac{2[\omega_1/(p_b - \alpha_1) - (\omega_1 - \Delta\omega)/(p_b - \alpha_1)]}{1 + \omega_1(\omega_1 - \Delta\omega)/(p_b - \alpha_1)^2} \approx \frac{2\Delta\omega(p_b - \alpha_1)}{(p_b - \alpha_1)^2 + \omega_1^2} \qquad (4\text{-}45)$$

As an example, consider the zero-pole configuration of Fig. 4-11, which has a transfer function

$$GH = \frac{p^2 + 4}{p(p + 10)} \qquad (4\text{-}46)$$

Two roots leave the poles which are located at the origin and at -10 and approach each other. The breakaway point p_b is computed from the equation

$$\frac{-\Delta\omega}{|p_b + 10|} = \frac{-\Delta\omega}{|p_b|} + \frac{2\Delta\omega p_b}{|p_b^2 + 2^2|} \qquad (4\text{-}47)$$

Guess $p_b = -2$

$$-\frac{1}{8} \stackrel{?}{=} -\frac{1}{2} + \frac{(2)(2)}{4 + 4} \qquad (4\text{-}48)$$

$$-0.125 \neq -0.5 + 0.5$$

Guess $p_b = -1.7$

$$-\frac{1}{8.3} \stackrel{?}{=} -\frac{1}{1.7} + \frac{(2)(1.7)}{(1.7)^2 + 4} \tag{4-49}$$

$$-0.1205 \neq -0.588 + 0.494 = -0.094$$

Guess $p_b = -1.65$

$$-\frac{1}{8.35} \stackrel{?}{=} -\frac{1}{1.65} + \frac{(2)(1.65)}{(1.65)^2 + 4} \tag{4-50}$$

$$-0.1197 = -0.606 + 0.492 = -0.113$$

The breakaway point is at $p = -1.65$, and the root-locus sketch is approximately that shown in Fig. 4-11. This rule is also applicable in

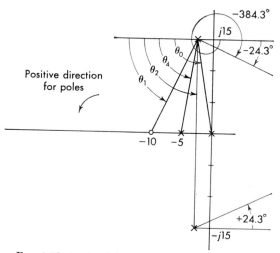

Fig. 4-12. Angle of departure from complex poles.

the same manner for locating the point where two complex roots strike the axis as the gain is increased.

Rule 6: Two roots leave or strike the axis at the breakaway point at an angle of $\pm 90°$. The two roots of Figs. 4-9 and 4-11 approach each other along the real axis, coalesce, and break away. The angle which the locus makes with the real axis is $\pm 90°$. This is shown in Figs. 4-9 and 4-11.

Rule 7: The angle of departure from complex poles and the angle of arrival to complex zeros are found by summing the angles to all the singularities. The angle is found by subtracting $180°$ *from this sum.* Knowledge of the initial angle of departure of the roots from complex poles is helpful in sketching root-locus diagrams. The zero-pole configuration of Fig. 4-6 is redrawn in Fig. 4-12 for the purpose of finding the angle of departure from the complex poles at $p = -2 \pm j15$. The angles subtended by the poles and zeros to the pole in question are added (positive for zeros and negative for poles):

$$-(\theta_0 + \theta_2 + \theta_4) + \theta_1 \qquad (4\text{-}51)$$

A protractor is used to measure these angles

$$-(97.6° + 90° + 78.7°) + 62° = -204.3° \qquad (4\text{-}52)$$

When 180° is subtracted from this angle, an angle of departure of $-204.3° - 180° = -384.3°$ is found. This angle is shown on Fig. 4-12.

The Spirule, which is discussed later, is convenient for finding the angle of departure. Its application to this rule is presented in Sec. 4-9.

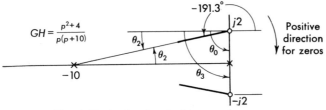

FIG. 4-13. Angle of arrival to complex zeros.

The angle at which the roots arrive at complex zeros is also found from this rule. As an example, consider the zero-pole configuration of Fig. 4-13. The angles subtended at $j2$ are added:

$$\theta_3 - \theta_0 - \theta_2 = 90° - 90° - 11.3° = -11.3° \qquad (4\text{-}53)$$

The angle of arrival is found by subtracting 180° from this angle:

$$-180° - 11.3° = -191.3° \qquad (4\text{-}54)$$

The method of finding the departure angle is similar to finding the arrival angle except for the direction of positive angles. For a pole, the positive direction is counterclockwise, as shown in Fig. 4-12. For a zero, the positive angle is clockwise, as shown in Fig. 4-13.

The above seven rules are fundamental to the rapid sketching of root-locus diagrams. In general, when a new problem is approached, the rules are used in the given order. Practice should enable the student to apply these rules efficiently and rapidly.

The root-locus procedure is based upon the location of the poles and zeros of KGH in the p plane. These points do not move. They are merely the terminal points for the branches of the locus of the roots of $1 + KGH$. If a branch of the locus crosses the imaginary axis and goes into the right half plane for some gain K, the system becomes unstable at this value of K. The degree of stability is determined largely by the roots near the imaginary axis. Even when more exact plotting aids (i.e., Spirule) are used, the root locus is first sketched with the aid of the preceding rules.　The sketch gives an idea as to the form of the locus and hence is helpful in making a more accurate plot.

4-5. Example of the Application of the Above Rules.　As an aid in understanding the above seven rules, consider the following open-loop

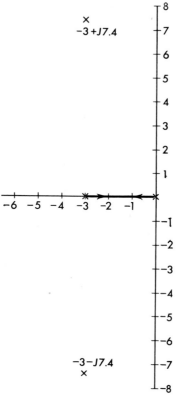

FIG. 4-14. Pole location for the transfer function $KGH = \dfrac{K}{p(p+3)(p^2+6p+64)}$

transfer function:

$$KGH = \frac{K}{p(p+3)(p^2+6p+64)} \tag{4-55}$$

The sketches of Figs. 4-14 and 4-15 demonstrate the use of the rules to sketch root locus for Eq. (4-55).

The procedure is outlined as follows:

1. Location of zeros and poles

　Zeros: none
　Poles: 0, -3, $-3 + j7.4$, $-3 - j7.4$

2. Locus exists along real axis between 0 and -3.

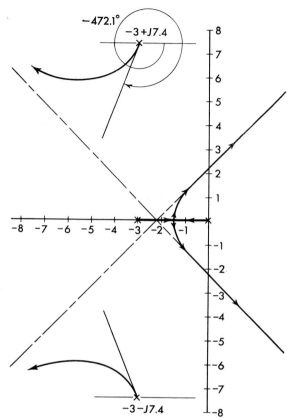

FIG. 4-15. Root-locus sketch for the system $KGH = \dfrac{K}{p(p+3)(p^2+6p+64)}$

3. Asymptotic angles

$$\theta = \frac{2k+1}{4-0}\,180° = \begin{cases} +45° & k = 0 \\ +135° & k = 1 \\ +225° & k = 2 \\ +315° & k = 3 \end{cases} \qquad (4\text{-}56)$$

4. Center of gravity—starting point of asymptotes

$$CG = \frac{0 - 3 - 3 + j7.4 - 3 - j7.4}{4 - 0} = \frac{-9}{4} = -2.25 \qquad (4\text{-}57)$$

5. Breakaway point from real axis. Since the complex poles are at some distance from the axis, the breakaway point p_b will be taken midway between the two real axis poles, or at -1.5.

6. The breakaway angle from the real axis is $\pm 90°$.

7. Breakaway angle from complex poles.

$$-\theta_0 - 2\theta_2 = -112.1 - 180 = -292.1$$

Subtracting 180°,

$$-292.1 - 180 = -472.1 \qquad (4\text{-}58)$$

For many problems all the rules are not needed. In these cases, of course, only those which are applicable are chosen. A collection of common root-locus diagrams is included in Fig. 4-16.

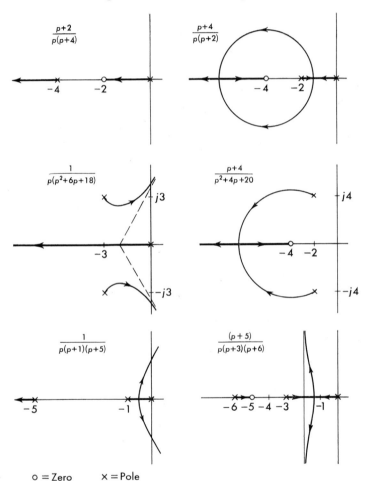

o = Zero   x = Pole

FIG. 4-16. Collection of root-locus diagrams.

4-6. Measurement of Gain. The rules of Sec. 4-4 center about the angle criterion [Eq. (4-24)]

$$\arg KGH = (2k + 1)180° \qquad (4\text{-}59)$$

After the locus has been sketched and certain points located more accurately with the Spirule (Sec. 4-8), the values of gain which occur at certain points along the locus must be found. This gain K is evaluated from the criterion of Eq. (4-25):

$$|KGH| = 1 \qquad \text{or} \qquad K = \frac{1}{|GH|} \qquad (4\text{-}60)$$

where $|GH|$ is the product of the magnitudes of the distances from the point at which the gain is to be evaluated to the zeros divided by the product of the magnitude of the distances to the poles:

$$K = \frac{\text{product of pole distances}}{\text{product of zero distances}} \qquad (4\text{-}61)$$

The magnitudes are measured directly from the root-locus plot.

The example of Sec. 4-5, which is plotted in Fig. 4-15, is used to demonstrate the measurement of gain. From Eq. (4-61)

$$\frac{1}{|GH|} = K = |p|\,|p+3|\,|p+3+j7.4|\,|p+3-j7.4| \qquad (4\text{-}62)$$

The gain at the point where the locus crosses the j axis is to be found. The magnitudes in Eq. (4-62) are read from Fig. 4-15, and the gain is

$$K = (2.22)(3.74)(10.1)(5.92) = 490 \qquad (4\text{-}63)$$

In this example and in many practical servo problems, the distances can be read directly with a pair of dividers as found in most drafting sets. The distances can also be measured with the Spirule.

4-7. Proof of the Root-locus Construction Rules. Each of the rules is verified in the same order, as presented in Sec. 4-4.

Rule 1: A continuous locus starts at each pole of KGH for $K = 0$. The locus terminates on the zeros of KGH for $K = \infty$.

The proof of this rule follows from a consideration of the characteristic equation. The KGH function of Eq. (4-19) is substituted into $1 + KGH$

$$\frac{p^n[p+(1/\tau_2)][p+(1/\tau_4)] + K[p+(1/\tau_1)][p+(1/\tau_3)]}{p^n[p+(1/\tau_2)][p+(1/\tau_4)]} = 0 \qquad (4\text{-}64)$$

where K replaces the product $K_1\tau_1\tau_3/\tau_2\tau_4$. The zeros of KGH are represented by an odd subscript on τ, and the poles of KGH by an even subscript on τ. The system stability is determined from the numerator of $1 + KGH$

$$p^n\left(p+\frac{1}{\tau_2}\right)\left(p+\frac{1}{\tau_4}\right) + K\left(p+\frac{1}{\tau_1}\right)\left(p+\frac{1}{\tau_3}\right) = 0 \qquad (4\text{-}65)$$

For small values of K ($K = 0$), the second part of Eq. (4-65) is zero and the roots for $K = 0$ are

$$p^n \left(p + \frac{1}{\tau_2}\right)\left(p + \frac{1}{\tau_4}\right) \tag{4-66}$$

The roots of $1 + KGH$ are equal to the poles of KGH for $K = 0$, or the locus for $1 + KGH$ starts on the poles of KGH.

As K becomes very large, the second portion of Eq. (4-65) becomes larger than the first, and as K approaches infinity, the roots of $1 + KGH$ become

$$\left(p + \frac{1}{\tau_1}\right)\left(p + \frac{1}{\tau_3}\right) \tag{4-67}$$

As K becomes large, the locus terminates on the zeros of KGH.

When the number of finite zeros is less than the number of poles, the rule is best proved by considering the value of KGH for large values of p

$$KGH = K\frac{p^{\#Z}}{p^{\#P}} = \frac{K}{p^{\#P - \#Z}} \tag{4-68}$$

where $\#P$ is the number of poles and $\#Z$ is the number of zeros of KGH. For large p, there exist $\#P - \#Z$ zeros at infinity, a $(\#P - \#Z)$-order zero at infinity. It follows that the locus terminates on these zeros at infinity when the number of poles exceeds the number of finite zeros.

The locus is a single-valued function of K, since $1 + KGH = 0$ is a linear function of K.

Rule 2: *The locus exists at any point along the real axis where an odd number of poles plus zeros is found to the right of the point.*

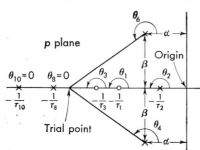

FIG. 4-17. Proof of Rule 2.

The validity of this rule is based upon the angle criterion

$$\arg GH = \angle GH = (2k + 1)180° \tag{4-69}$$

where $k = 0, 1, 2, 3, \ldots$. In Fig. 4-17 the zero-pole configuration is shown for the function

$$KGH = \frac{K[p + (1/\tau_1)][p + (1/\tau_3)]}{[p + (1/\tau_2)][p + (1/\tau_8)][p + (1/\tau_{10})][(p + \alpha)^2 + \beta^2]} \tag{4-70}$$

The angle criterion of Eq. (4-69) is written as a sum of angles subtended by the poles and zeros

$$\theta_1 + \theta_3 - (\theta_2 + \theta_4 + \theta_6 + \theta_8 + \theta_{10}) = (2k + 1)180° \tag{4-71}$$

where $k = 0, 1, 2, 3 \ldots$

The sum of the angles subtended by the complex poles, $\theta_4 + \theta_6$ in Fig. 4-17, is 360°, since complex zeros and poles for systems described by linear differential equations with constant coefficients are symmetrical about the real axis. Any poles or zeros to the left of the trial point contribute nothing ($\theta_8 = 0$ and $\theta_{10} = 0$). The angles to the right of the trial point contribute either $+180°$ or $-180°$

$$\theta_1 - \theta_3 - \theta_2 = 180° + 180° - 180° = 180°$$

At any point where an odd number of zeros plus poles exists to the right of the trial point, the sum is $(2k + 1)180°$, and the locus exists.

Rule 3: For large values of gain the locus is asymptotic to the angles

$$\left(\frac{2k + 1}{\#P - \#Z}\right) 180° \qquad k = 0, 1, 2, 3, \ldots \qquad (4\text{-}72)$$

where #P is the number of poles and #Z is the number of zeros.

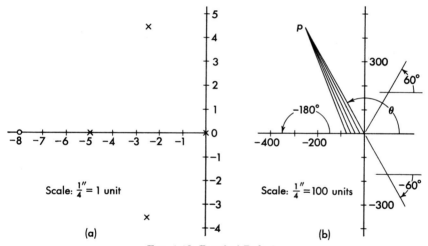

Fig. 4-18. Proof of Rule 3.

This rule is proved by reference to Fig. 4-18a and b. The scale of the axes in Fig. 4-18b is increased over that of Fig. 4-18a. The scale change reduces the zeros and poles almost to a point. Figure 4-18b shows the zero-pole configuration for large gain K which corresponds to large values of the roots. The angle subtended to a point p_1 by all zeros or poles is the same. The sign of the angles from zeros is opposite to the sign from the poles. The sum of the angles $\Sigma\theta_i$ for Fig. 4-18b is $-(\#P - \#Z)\theta$, where #P equals the number of poles and #Z equals the number of zeros. If p_1 is a point on the locus, that is, if p_1 is a root of $1 + KGH = 0$, then the sum of the angles must equal $(2k + 1)180°$, $k = 0, 1, 2, 3, \ldots$

and

$$-(\#P - \#Z)\theta = (2k + 1)180°$$

$$\theta = \frac{(2k + 1)180°}{\#P - \#Z} \tag{4-73}$$

where θ is the asymptotic angle, and the negative sign is included in $2k + 1$, since usually $\#P > \#Z$.

Rule 4: The starting point for the asymptotic lines is the center of gravity of the zero-pole configuration.

Proof of this rule is based upon the theory of polynomial equations. A factored polynomial can be multiplied out as

$$(p + a)(p + b)(p + c) = p^3 + (a + b + c)p^2 + (ab + ac + bc)p + abc \tag{4-74}$$

where a, b, and c are the roots of the unfactored polynomial on the right. Even when the polynomial is unfactored, a certain amount of information can be obtained about the roots. For example, the negative algebraic sum of the roots $a + b + c$ is the coefficient of the second term in the polynomial. Although Eq. (4-74) is only a third-order equation, it can be shown to be true for any order equation.

The application to this rule follows from a consideration of the characteristic equation

$$1 + KGH = 0 \tag{4-75}$$

where GH is a ratio of polynomials

$$GH = \frac{N(p)}{D(p)} = \frac{p^l + \cdots + a_l}{p^{l+r} + b_1 p^{l+r-1} + \cdots + b_{l+r}} \tag{4-76}$$

where l and r are integers, a_i and b_i are constants, and N and D are the numerator and denominator polynomials, respectively. Substituting Eq. (4-76) into Eq. (4-75),

$$1 + KGH = \frac{D(p) + KN(p)}{D(p)} \tag{4-77}$$

The root locus is found by setting the numerator of Eq. (4-77) to zero, or

$$-K = \frac{D(p)}{N(p)} = \frac{p^{l+r} + b_1 p^{l+r-1} + \cdots + b_{l+r}}{p^l + a_1 p^{l-1} + \cdots + a_l} \tag{4-78}$$

A polynomial, which can be compared with Eq. (4-74), results when the denominator is divided into the numerator:

$$p^r + (b_1 - a_1)p^{r-1} + \cdots = -K \tag{4-79}$$

When rearranged, Eq. (4-79) becomes

$$p^r + (b_1 - a_1)p^{r-1} + \cdots + K = 0 \tag{4-80}$$

When the magnitude of p is large (which corresponds to large-gain K), Eq. (4-80) is an rth-degree polynomial with the sum of the roots given by $b_1 - a_1$. $b_1 - a_1$ is a constant, which is independent of gain as long as r is greater than 2. This is no limitation, since the rule is of value only when $r \geqslant 2$, that is, when $\#P - \#Z \geqslant 2$. When $r = 1$, the asymptote lies along 180° and the point is of no interest. When $r = 0$, no asymptotes exist, since all roots terminate on finite zeros.

Since $b_1 - a_1$ is independent of gain, the sum of the roots remains at one point for any value of gain. Because the roots occur in complex conjugate pairs, the sum of the roots of Eq. (4-79) is a real number; that is, $b_1 - a_1$ lies on the real axis. Hence, the asymptotic lines radiate from the point on the real axis given by

$$CG = \frac{b_1 - a_1}{r} \qquad (4\text{-}81)$$

This point is termed the center of gravity of the roots. In terms of the original polynomial,

b_1 = algebraic sum of poles
a_1 = algebraic sum of zeros
r = difference between degree of denominator and numerator, $\#P - \#Z$

Equation (4-81) is written in words as

$$CG = \frac{\Sigma \text{ poles} - \Sigma \text{ zeros}}{\# \text{ poles} - \# \text{ zeros}} \qquad (4\text{-}82)$$

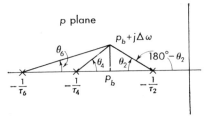

FIG. 4-19. Proof of Rule 5.

Rule 5: The breakaway point p_b is found by equating the sum of reciprocals to the left and to the right of the trial point p_b.

The proof of this rule is demonstrated by Fig. 4-19. If the trial point p_b is moved a small vertical distance $\Delta\omega$ off the real axis, the net change in angle contributed from all singularities must be zero. From the example shown in Fig. 4-19, the following expression is written:

$$-(\theta_6 + \theta_4 + 180° - \theta_2) = (2k + 1)180°$$
$$-(\theta_6 + \theta_4) = -\theta_2 \qquad (4\text{-}83)$$
$$\frac{-\Delta\omega}{|p_b + (1/\tau_6)|} + \frac{-\Delta\omega}{|p_b + (1/\tau_4)|} = \frac{-\Delta\omega}{|p_b + (1/\tau_2)|}$$

where $\tan \theta$ has been replaced by θ. The point p_b is determined from Eq. (4-83). It should be emphasized that a graphical, trial-and-error solution should be used when determining the breakaway point.

If complex zeros or poles occur in the KGH function, the net change in angle is included with Eq. (4-45)—the proof is the same.

Rule 6: *Two roots leave or strike the axis at the breakaway point at an angle of* $\pm 90°$.

Before verifying this rule, it is important to show that the locus leaves a double real axis pole at $\pm 90°$. Suppose a pair of poles is at a point along the real axis where an even number of poles plus zeros exists, as shown in Fig. 4-20. According to Rule 2 the locus does not exist to the

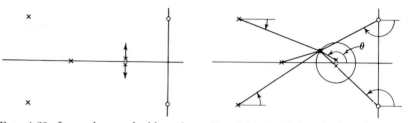

Fig. 4-20. Locus leaves double-real axis poles at $\pm 90°$.

Fig. 4-21. Proof that the locus leaves a double-real axis pair of poles at $\pm 90°$.

right or left of the double poles. To find the angle of departure from these real axis poles, draw a small circle around this pair of poles, as shown on Fig. 4-21. The angles from a point p_i on the circle to the zeros and poles are summed. As the radius of the circle is made small, the contribution to this sum from all real axis zeros and poles is zero (for those to the left) or $k360°$ (for those to the right). If there is an odd number of zeros plus poles to the right, the locus does not leave the axis at that point but goes along the real axis.

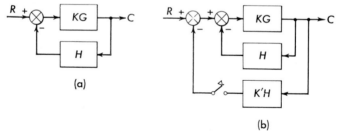

Fig. 4-22. Block diagrams used to prove Rule 6.

The contribution from all complex zeros and poles cancels, since these always appear as complex conjugate pairs. The entire angular contribution, then, comes from the pair of poles within the small circle. The locus exists at points on the small circle where the sum of these angles is 180°, or

$$2\theta = 180° \qquad \text{or} \qquad \theta = 90° \tag{4-84}$$

Hence the locus leaves a pair of real axis poles at $\pm 90°$.

This present rule is verified by breaking the KGH function, as indicated on Fig. 4-22a, into the multiple-loop system of Fig. 4-22b. The over-all transfer function of the original system (Fig. 4-22a) is given by

$$\frac{KG}{1 + KGH} \tag{4-85}$$

and for the modified system (Fig. 4-22b)

$$\frac{KG/(1 + KGH)}{1 + KGK'H/(1 + KGH)} = \frac{KG}{1 + (1 + K')KGH} \tag{4-86}$$

The denominators of Eqs. (4-85) and (4-86) have the same form. The constant in the latter equation is made up of a product of two constants

$$K(1 + K') \tag{4-87}$$

As K is varied, with $K' = 0$, the root locus is plotted in the normal fashion. The value of K is set so that two roots of $1 + K_1GH$ coalesce. With this value of gain $K = K_1$, the outer loop is closed and the roots of $1 + KGH$ become poles of the new function that is to be plotted as K' varies from zero:

$$1 + \left(\frac{K_1G}{1 + K_1GH}\right)K'H \tag{4-88}$$

The two roots of $1 + K_1GH = 0$ which are at the same point are now two identical poles. As shown above, when K' is increased, two loci leave these at $\pm 90°$.

If the complete locus had been plotted for the original equation $1 + KGH$, the locus would have the same shape as for the second equation $1 + (1 + K')KGH$. It must be concluded, then, that the locus breaks away from the real axis at $\pm 90°$.

Rule 7: The angle of departure from complex poles and the angle of arrival to complex zeros is found by summing the angles to all the singularities. The angle is found by subtracting 180° from the sum.

Rule 7 defines the initial angle of departure of the roots leaving complex poles. The angle subtended by the complex conjugate pole to a test point located a small distance Δp removed from the complex conjugate pole is the angle of departure of the root from the pole. This angle is determined by drawing a small circle about the pole as shown in Fig. 4-23. The angles subtended by all the singularities, including the complex conjugate poles under consideration, are summed at a point p_1 along the small circle:

$$+ \theta_1 + \theta_3 - (\theta_2 + \theta_4 + \theta_6 + \theta_8) = (2k + 1)180° \tag{4-89}$$

Equation (4-89) is solved for θ_8:

$$\theta_8 = [\theta_1 + \theta_3 - (\theta_2 + \theta_4 + \theta_6)] - (2k + 1)180° \qquad (4\text{-}90)$$

As the small circle about the point is reduced to zero ($\Delta p \to 0$), the angles θ_i are simply the angles subtended between the various singularities and the particular complex pole in question. The angles to all the singularities from the complex poles are summed in the usual fashion (poles taken negative and zeros taken positive). The angle of departure θ_8 differs from this sum by 180°. In Sec. 4-9 on the use of the Spirule, a simpler method is given for finding the angle of departure.

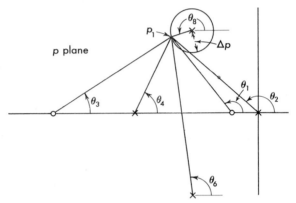

FIG. 4-23. Proof of Rule 7.

When the rule is applied to find the angle of arrival at complex zeros, only a change in sign is required. This is seen by reference to Eq. (4-90). If θ_8 were the angle from a zero, the opposite sign is taken in the sum.

4-8. The Spirule. Use of the root-locus technique requires the measurement and summation (or subtraction) of angles and the measurement and multiplication (or division) of lengths.

These graphical constructions can be performed with a protractor to measure the angles of the vectors to the trial point and a ruler to determine the gain from the magnitude of these vectors. If the locus is constructed on graph paper, the magnitude may also be measured with dividers and the lengths compared with the scales of the paper. For greater accuracy the coordinates of the trial point can be obtained from the known pole and zero positions to give the real and imaginary parts of the various vectors. A desk calculator and a table of tangents permit the determination, to any degree of accuracy, of particular points on the locus.

Most servo problems do not require the accuracy made possible with this latter method. In fact, the real advantage in the root-locus technique rests in the ability to sketch the root-locus plots rapidly and hence to analyze the servo system quickly. For this latter reason a device called the "Spirule"* has been developed. The Spirule performs three functions:

1. Adds the angles from a point to the zeros and subtracts the angles from a point to the poles

2. Multiplies the distances from a point to the poles and divides by the distances to the zeros

3. Gives the damping ratio ζ for applicable points on the locus

The Spirule, which is shown in the sketch of Fig. 4-24, comprises a transparent protractor for addition of the angles and a logarithmic spiral

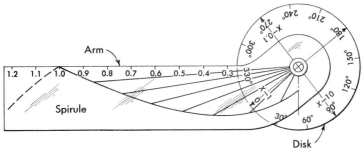

FIG. 4-24. The Spirule.

for multiplication of vector lengths. It consists of a circular disk and an arm which is held to the disk with an eyelet that provides light friction between the disk and arm. A pivot, in the form of a pin or a movable insert, is provided on the eyelet to locate the Spirule over the trial point.

The instrument is used to locate points on a locus which has been previously sketched. The Spirule is used to find the angle of KGH at a trial point p_1 by linear addition of angles. The Spirule finds the magnitude at a point on the locus by adding the logarithms of the vectors and then taking the antilog.

Several "dynamic root-locus plotters" have also been devised.[19] These units utilize potentiometers to represent the zeros and poles. The voltages from the potentiometer arms are summed to represent the sum of the angles.

4-9. Use of the Spirule to Sum Angles. The first requirement in plotting root-locus diagrams is to choose equal scales on the plot. It is convenient to choose a scale on the chart that corresponds to an even multiple of the scale on the top edge of the arm (a distance of 0.1 on the scale equals $\frac{1}{2}$ in.).

* The Spirule was developed by Mr. Walter Evans and is available from the Spirule Company, 9728 El Venado, Whittier, Calif.

To find angles with the Spirule

1. Align the upper side of the arm with the 0° mark on the disk.

2. Place the center of the disk over the point where the angles are to be measured, and set the arm horizontal, pointing to the left; that is, the $1 - X$ arrow is pointing to the left.

3. *For a zero* hold the disk and rotate the arm from the horizontal until the upper edge of the arm passes through the zero. Read the positive angle opposite the arrow on the arm.

4. *For a pole* rotate both the arm and the disk so the upper edge of the arm passes through the pole. Hold the disk, and rotate the arm back to horizontal. Read the negative angle from the circular disk.

5. When adding angles, proceed as in 1 and 2. Add zeros by applying 3 successively, then subtract the poles by applying 4 successively.

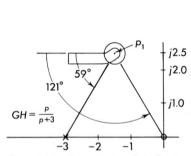

Fig. 4-25. Use of the Spirule for plotting root-locus diagrams.

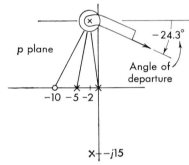

Fig. 4-26. Use of the Spirule to find the angle of departure from complex poles.

The net angle must equal $(2k + 1)180°$ to satisfy the angle condition of Eq. (4-31).

As an example, in Fig. 4-25, use the Spirule to check the angle criterion at point p_1. The Spirule is placed at the point p_1, as shown in the figure. The disk is held, and the arm is rotated down to the zero at the origin. Both arm and disk are rotated back to the original position. To add the angle to the pole, both arm and disk are rotated until the upper edge of the arm passes through the pole. The disk is held, and the arm is rotated back to the horizontal. The Spirule reads 62°. The angle condition is not satisfied. Use the Spirule to see if the angle condition is satisfied when the zero at the origin is replaced by a pole. (Answer: it is.)

As a second example, return again to the problem of finding the breakaway angle from the complex pole of Fig. 4-12. Place the Spirule on the point $-2 + j15$. The 0° line is aligned with the top edge of the arm. Follow the procedure outlined above. Hold the disk, and move the arm to the zero. Return the disk, and successively subtract the angles at the poles located at 0, −5, and −2 − j15. The Spirule should read 156°. To find the angle of departure set the Spirule, with the arm remaining in position, so that the 0° mark on the disk is horizontal to the left. The Spirule is in the position shown on Fig. 4-26. The angle of departure is read to the right as −24°.

4-10. The Spirule Used to Find Lengths. The logarithmic curve on the arm of the Spirule permits the multiplication of lengths. The angle between the arm and the curve is proportional to the logarithm of the distance from the center of the rule to the log curve.

To multiply lengths:

1. Align the upper side of the arm with the 0° mark on the disk.

2. Place the center of the disk over the point where the lengths are to be measured.

3. *For a zero* rotate both disk and arm until the log curve passes through the zero. Hold the disk, and move the arm until the top of the arm passes through the zero. The reciprocal of the magnitude $p + (1/\tau_1)$ is read on the log-spiral curve opposite the arrow on the disk. If the $X − 1$ arrow is pointing to the log curve, the number along the curve is the reciprocal magnitude. If the $X − 0.1$ arrow is pointing to the log curve, the reciprocal magnitude is 0.1 times the number read along the log spiral.

4. *For a pole* put the top of the arm (i.e., rule) on the pole. Hold the disk, and move the arm until the log curve passes through the pole. The length of the vector $p + (1/\tau_2)$ is read opposite the arrow. The length is found by multiplying the number found on the log curve by the $X − 1$, the $X − 10$, or the $X − 0.1$ number which is on the disk and which is pointing to the log curve.

5. *The net length*, or the gain, is found by applying Rule 3 successively for the zeros and Rule 4 for the poles. The gain K is the number found on the log curve times the $X −$ number found on the disk, both multiplied by the scale factor, or is

$$K = (\text{scale factor})(\text{number on log curve})(X − \text{number}) \quad (4\text{-}91)$$

6. *Scale Factor.* The scale of the problem does not necessarily agree with the scale on the Spirule. The scale factor for Eq. (4-91) is

$$\text{Scale factor} = \sigma^{\#P-\#Z} \quad (4\text{-}92)$$

where σ is the number on the problem scale read opposite the 1.0 on the Spirule arm. $\#P$ is the number of poles, and $\#Z$ is the number of zeros.

As an example, consider the *KGH* function of Fig. 4-27. To find the gain at p_1 place the Spirule at the position shown on the figure. Place the arm on the pole at the origin, hold the disk, and rotate the arm until the curve is on the pole.   The $X - 1$ arrow on the disk is pointing to 0.29.   Repeat again for the pole at $p = -3$.   The $X - 0.1$ arrow is now pointing to 0.84.   Place the pivot of the Spirule at the origin; the number

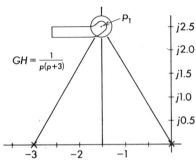

read opposite the 1 on the arm is 10. The scale factor is $(10)^2 = 100$. The gain, which is equal to the product of the two lengths, is

$$(0.84)(X - 0.1)(100) = 8.4$$

The dotted portion of the log curve is an extension of the logarithmic spiral for vectors whose lengths are greater than 1.   Since the curve in this region has been reversed in sense (so the curve does not run off the rule), step 3 is used for poles

FIG. 4-27. Use of the Spirule to measure gain.

and step 4 for zeros; i.e., the rules are reversed.

4-11. The Spirule Used to Find Damping Ratio.   The damping ratio ζ is derived in Chap. 1 for the second-order characteristic equation

$$p^2 + 2\zeta\omega_n p + \omega_n{}^2 = 0 \qquad (4\text{-}93)$$

Any pair of complex conjugate roots is located as in Fig. 4-28.   The horizontal distance from the axis is $\zeta\omega_n$, and the vertical distance is $\omega_n \sqrt{1 - \zeta^2}$.   This is verified by finding the roots of Eq. (4-93),

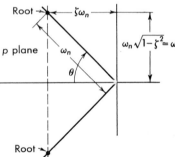

$$p_1 = -\zeta\omega_n \pm j\omega_n \sqrt{1 - \zeta^2} \qquad (4\text{-}94)$$

The angle θ is computed from Fig. 4-28 to be

$$\cos \theta = \frac{\zeta\omega_n}{\omega_n} = \zeta \qquad (4\text{-}95)$$

The damping ratio is read directly from the p plane with the Spirule.   Set the arrow on the rule opposite 180° on the disk, and place the center of the disk at

FIG. 4-28. Use of the Spirule to find damping ratio.

the origin of the p plane so that 180° on the disk lies along the negative real axis.   Move the arm to the root where the damping ratio is to be determined.   The damping ratio ζ is read from the intersection of the arm and the scale on the disk.

4-12. Root-locus Plots with Variable Other than Gain.   All examples presented thus far in this chapter deal with location of the roots of a closed-loop system as the loop gain is varied.   Often it is necessary to optimize a system with respect to another variable. The root-locus method is basically a method of determining the position of the roots of a polynomial as a quantity K is varied whenever the polynomial can be written

$$1 + K \frac{N(p)}{D(p)} = 0 \qquad (4\text{-}96)$$

In general, any problem, servo or otherwise, that can be put into the form of Eq. (4-96) can be solved with the aid of the root-locus method.

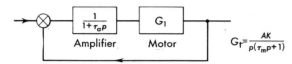

FIG. 4-29. Effect of τ_a, time constant, on servo stability.

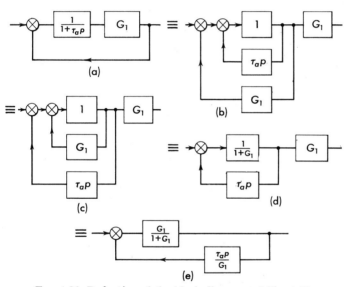

FIG. 4-30. Reduction of the block diagrams of Fig. 4-29.

The parameter K must not be a function of p, and it must appear as a multiplicable quantity. The problem is simplified if the polynomials $N(p)$ and $D(p)$ are factored.

As an example, consider the problem of determining the effect of amplifier time constant τ_a upon the control system pictured in Fig. 4-29. The problem has been solved and the gain AK set for a particular value of τ_a and τ_m. To determine the effect upon the system of variations of τ_a, the block diagram is altered as shown in Fig. 4-30. The $1/(1 + \tau_a p)$ term is made into two blocks. The G_1 block, which represents the amplifier constant A and motor transfer function

$$G_1 = \frac{AK}{p(\tau_m p + 1)} \qquad (4\text{-}97)$$

is divided as shown in Fig. 4-30b. The two loops are interchanged as shown in Fig. 4-30c. The inner loop is combined into one block, $1/(1 + G_1)$, and the outer loop is closed around the entire system with the final block taking the form of Fig. 4-30e. Use is made of block-diagram algebra presented in Chap. 1 (Sec. 1-8) for these manipulations. The KGH function for this diagram is

$$KGH = \frac{\tau_a p}{1 + G_1} = \frac{\tau_a p}{1 + [AK/p(\tau_m p + 1)]} \qquad (4\text{-}98)$$

This equation is simplified to

$$KGH = \tau_a \frac{p^2[p + (1/\tau_m)]}{p^2 + (1/\tau_m)p + (AK/\tau_m)} \qquad (4\text{-}99)$$

Equation (4-99) satisfies the requirements for use in a root-locus construction with τ_a as the variable. The poles and zeros are fixed for given

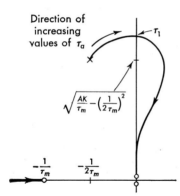

values of A, K, and τ_m. The system has three zeros, one located at $-1/\tau_m$ and two at the origin, and two poles located at

$$-\frac{1}{2\tau_m} \pm j \sqrt{\frac{AK}{\tau_m} - \left(\frac{1}{2\tau_m}\right)^2} \qquad (4\text{-}100)$$

The locus, which is a plot of the system roots as the amplifier time constant is increased, is shown in Fig. 4-31. The form of the locus is different from that found in a conventional servo problem. In this problem there are more zeros than poles. Rather than a root going to infinity, here the root starts at infinity

FIG. 4-31. Locus of third-order system as time constant is varied.

and comes in from infinity along the negative real axis. All the root-locus rules are applicable—only the variable has changed from loop gain to time constant.

The nonconventionality of this root locus, i.e., more zeros than poles, can be avoided if the following inverse function be plotted:

$$1 + \frac{1}{K}\frac{1}{GH} = 1 + K'\frac{1}{GH} \qquad (4\text{-}101)$$

In this form the zeros and poles are interchanged and a conventional plot is obtained.

In either case, the significance of a root in the right half plane is still the same. For the system of Fig. 4-31 the amplifier time constant can become no larger than τ_1, at which value the locus crosses into the right half plane.

Electrical and mechanical circuit problems are also amenable to solution with the root-locus method. Consider the shock mount problem indicated in Fig. 4-32. This system is driven with a position input $y(t)$, and the following values are given:

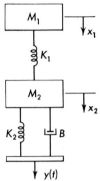

$W_1 = 50$ lb ($M_1 = 1.55$ slugs)
$W_2 = 20$ lb ($M_2 = 0.62$ slugs)
$K_1 = 100$ lb/in. $= 1{,}200$ lb/ft
$K_2 = 70$ lb/in. $= 840$ lb/ft

The value of B, in pound-seconds per foot, is to be optimized for maximum possible damping on the upper mass. From a practical point of view, it is interesting to ascertain if an optimum does exist. If $B = 0$, the system is undamped. If $B = \infty$, M_2 is fastened rigidly to the base and again the system is undamped. Since energy is dissipated for values between $B = 0$ and $B = \infty$, it is reasonable to assume that an optimum value of damping does exist.

Fig. 4-32. Shock mount which is optimized with root-locus method.

The problem is solved by arranging the characteristic equation so that B is the variable of a root-locus plot. The equations of motion for the system are

$$(M_2 p^2 + Bp + K_1 + K_2)X_2 + (-K_1)X_1 = (Bp + K_2)Y \quad (4\text{-}102)$$
$$(-K_1)X_2 + (M_1 p^2 + K_1)X_1 = 0$$

Solution of these equations for X_1 yields

$$\frac{X_1}{Y} = \frac{(K_1 K_2 / M_1 M_2)[1 + p(B/K_2)]}{p^4 + (B/M_2)p^3 + [(K_1 + K_2)/M_2 + (K_1/M_1)]p^2 + (BK_1/M_1 M_2)p + (K_1 K_2 / M_1 M_2)} \quad (4\text{-}103)$$

The characteristic equation, which is in the denominator of Eq. (4-103), contains B in only two terms. To solve the shock mount problem with B as a parameter, the characteristic equation must be written in the form $1 + B[N(p)/C(p)]$. With this form as a goal, the characteristic equation is rearranged as follows:

$$\left[p^4 + \left(\frac{K_1 + K_2}{M_2} + \frac{K_1}{M_1}\right)p^2 + \frac{K_1 K_2}{M_1 M_2}\right] + \frac{Bp}{M_2}\left(p^2 + \frac{K_1}{M_1}\right) \quad (4\text{-}104)$$

when Eq. (4-104) is divided by the first term in parentheses, the correct form results:

$$1 + B \frac{N(p)}{D(p)} = 1 + \frac{(B/M_2)p[p^2 + (K_1/M_1)]}{p^4 + [(K_1 + K_2)/M_2 + (K_1/M_1)]p^2 + (K_1K_2/M_1M_2)}$$
$$(4\text{-}105)$$

When the numerical values of the problem are substituted into Eq. (4-105), the characteristic equation reduces to

$$1 + B \frac{1.61p(p^2 + 773)}{(p^2)^2 + 4.06 \times 10^3(p^2) + 1.05 \times 10^6} \qquad (4\text{-}106)$$

which is factored (with the binomial equation) to

$$1 + B \frac{1.61p(p^2 + 773)}{(p^2 + 3,780)(p^2 + 274)} \qquad (4\text{-}107)$$

Equation (4-107) has two imaginary zeros at $\pm j27.8$, one zero at the origin, two imaginary poles at $\pm j16.5$, and two imaginary poles at $\pm j61.5$.

The root locus, which is shown in Fig. 4-33, is plotted in the normal manner. The variable is the damping constant B. The system has four roots; however, the least damped roots correspond to p_1 and p_2. The maximum damping is found by drawing a line tangent to the inner locus from the origin. The damping ratio at this point is $\zeta = 0.42$. The value of B which produces this root is found in the same manner as the gain is found (cf. Sec. 4-6). The product of the pole distances divided by the zero distance yields

$$B = 62.7 \text{ lb-sec/ft} \qquad (4\text{-}108)$$

At this value of B, the other two roots p_3 and p_4 are located at $\zeta = 0.91$ and $\omega_n = 43.5$. These roots are sufficiently damped and far removed to have negligible effect.

The method of this example can be applied whenever the parameter to be investigated can be isolated and the transformed characteristic equation written in the form

$$1 + K \frac{N(p)}{D(p)} \qquad (4\text{-}109)$$

where K is the parameter, N and D are polynomials in p but independent of K. If the effect of varying several parameters is to be studied, more than one diagram may be required.

4-13. Root Locus Used to Factor a Polynomial. The root-locus method can be applied to any problem that can be put into servo form, that is, the form of Eq. (4-96). Consider the problem of finding the roots of the polynomial

$$p^4 + 5p^3 + 22p^2 + 80p + 96 = 0 \qquad (4\text{-}110)$$

This equation is rewritten in the following form:

$$p^2(p^2 + 5p + 22) + 80(p + {}^{96}\!\!/_{80}) = 0 \qquad (4\text{-}111)$$

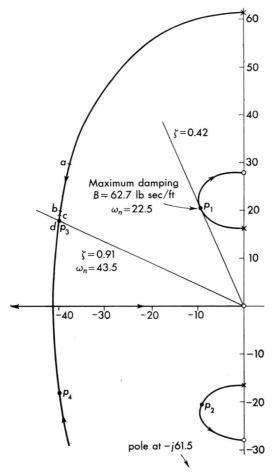

FIG. 4-33. Root locus plot for $\dfrac{1.61 Bp(p \pm j27.8)}{(p \pm j16.54)(p \pm j61.5)}$.

The two bracketed terms are factored:

$$p^2[(p + \tfrac{5}{2} + j3.96)(p + \tfrac{5}{2} - j3.96)] + 80(p + 1.2) = 0 \quad (4\text{-}112)$$

This equation is now rewritten in the following form:

$$1 + \frac{80(p + 1.2)}{p^2(p + \tfrac{5}{2} + j3.96)(p + \tfrac{5}{2} - j3.96)} = 0 \quad (4\text{-}113)$$

The equation is now in servo form, with one zero at -1.2 and four poles located as follows:

Two at the origin
One at $-\tfrac{5}{2} + j3.96$
One at $-\tfrac{5}{2} - j3.96$

The root locus is plotted, as shown in Fig. 4-34, as a function of a variable K. The roots of Eq. (4-113), which are the roots of the original
equation, are found from the plot of Fig. 4-34 for the value of $K = 80$.
At this value of gain the four roots are found from the four branches

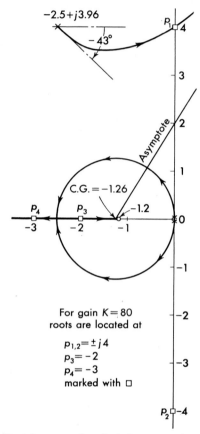

FIG. 4-34. Root locus used to find the roots of a polynomial.

of the locus to be

$$p_{1,2} = \pm j4 \qquad p_3 = -2 \qquad p_4 = -3 \qquad (4\text{-}114)$$

and are marked in Fig. 4-34 with a small square.

In general the procedure for factoring an nth-order polynomial consists of splitting the original equation

$$x^n + a_1 x^{n-1} + a_2 x^{n-2} + \cdots + a_{n-1} x + a_n = 0 \qquad (4\text{-}115)$$

as follows:

$$\left\{\left[(x^2 + a_1x + a_2)x^2 + a_3\left(x^2 + \frac{a_4}{a_3}x + \frac{a_5}{a_3}\right)\right]x^2\right.$$
$$\left. + a_5\left(x^2 + \frac{a_7}{a_6}x + \frac{a_8}{a_6}\right)\right\}x^2 + \text{etc.} \dots \quad (4\text{-}116)$$

The quadratics are solved with the binomial expression, and the roots for each bracketed term are found from a root-locus plot. For definiteness, take $n = 6$ in Eq. (4-115). The equation

$$x^6 + a_1x^5 + a_2x^4 + a_3x^3 + a_4x^2 + a_5x + a_6 = 0 \quad (4\text{-}117)$$

is arranged as follows:

$$\left[(x^2 + a_1x + a_2)x^2 + a_3\left(x + \frac{a_4}{a_3}\right)\right]x^2 + a_5x + a_6 = 0 \quad (4\text{-}118)$$

The quadratic is factored:

$$\left[(x + r_1)(x + r_2)x^2 + a_3\left(x + \frac{a_4}{a_3}\right)\right]x^2 + a_5x + a_6 = 0 \quad (4\text{-}119)$$

Equation (4-119) is rewritten and solved with two root-locus plots. The first is for the system

$$1 + a_3\frac{x + a_4/a_3}{x^2(x + r_1)(x + r_2)} = 0 \quad (4\text{-}120)$$

The roots r_3, r_4, r_5, and r_6 of this equation are found from a root-locus plot with the following conditions:

Zero at $-a_4/a_3$
Poles at $-r_1$ and $-r_2$ and two at the origin
Gain $= a_3$

Equation (4-119) is now written

$$[(x + r_3)(x + r_4)(x + r_5)(x + r_6)]x^2 + a_5x + a_6 = 0 \quad (4\text{-}121)$$

A second root-locus plot is used to find the roots of Eq. (4-121), which is rearranged

$$1 + \frac{x + a_6/a_5}{a_5x^2(x + r_3)(x + r_4)(x + r_5)(x + r_6)} \quad (4\text{-}122)$$

The root locus has one zero and six poles, four located at $-r_3$, $-r_4$, $-r_5$, and $-r_6$ and two at the origin. The six roots of Eq. (4-122), which are the six roots of the original equation, Eq. (4-117), are found for a gain of a_5.

Several methods[14] exist of using the root locus to factor polynomials.

For example, the characteristic equation could be split into cubics instead of quadratics. The method presented, however, seems easier.

4-14. Root Locus Applied to Multiple-loop Systems. A multiple-loop control system consists of several feedback paths. Figure 4-35 indicates a block diagram for a typical multiple-loop system. The inner loop can be replaced by a single block with transfer function

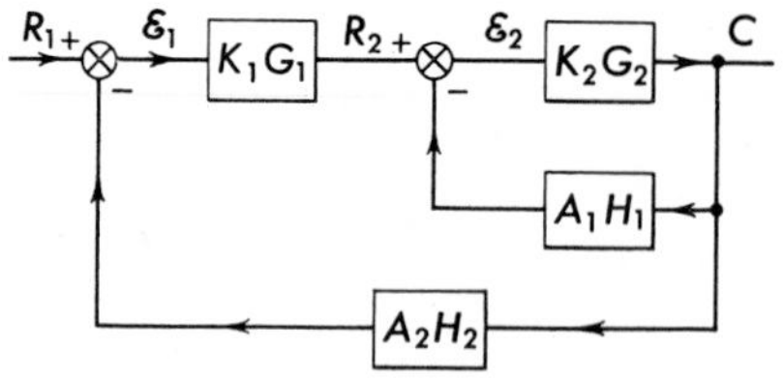

$$\frac{C}{R_2} = \frac{K_2 G_2}{1 + A_1 K_2 H_1 G_2} \qquad (4\text{-}123)$$

This equation is solved by root-locus methods to find the roots of the characteristic equation for a particular value of $A_1 K_2$. These roots become poles in the over-all system, so the outer loop system is plotted with the equation

$$KGH = K_1 A_2 G_1 H_2 \frac{K_2 G_2}{1 + A_1 K_2 H_1 G_2} \qquad (4\text{-}124)$$

Fig. 4-35. A multiple-loop control system.

Besides the roots of $1 + A_1 K_2 H_1 G_2$, which are poles of KGH, the zeros and poles of G_1, H_2, and G_2 are added and a complete plot is made. The

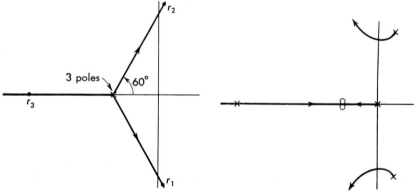

Fig. 4-36. Root-locus plot for inner loop of a multiple-loop servo.   Fig. 4-37. The second root-locus plot for a multiple-loop system.

application of the root locus is identical with that for single-loop systems. The difficulty that exists for multiple-loop systems is that as $A_1 K_2$ varies, the roots of $1 + A_1 K_2 H_1 G_2$ and hence the poles of KGH vary. Hence two plots are necessary to determine the response.

As an example, take

$$K_1 G_1 = \frac{K_1}{p} \qquad\qquad K_2 G_2 = \frac{K_2}{0.5p + 1} \qquad (4\text{-}125)$$

$$A_1 H_1 = \frac{1}{(0.5p + 1)^2} \qquad A_2 H_2 = 1$$

The root-locus sketch for the inner loop is shown in Fig. 4-36. For a particular gain, K_2, the roots are located, as shown in Fig. 4-36, at r_1, r_2, and r_3. The outer-loop locus consists of the transfer function

$$\frac{K_1 K_2 (0.5p + 1)^2}{p[(0.5p + 1)^3 + K_2]} \qquad (4\text{-}126)$$

The locus for this system is shown in Fig. 4-37, where the variable along the curve of this second locus is K_1 since K_2 is fixed.

The optimization of a multiple-loop system requires that two plots be made, one for the inner loop and one for the outer. A variation of the inner-loop gain changes the location of the poles of the outer-loop transfer function. Hence, the design of a multiple-loop system requires more plots than for a single-loop system.

PROBLEMS

Except where noted, in the problems of this chapter $KG(p)$ represents the forward transfer function in a system with unity feedback. $H = 1$.

4-1. $KG(p) = \dfrac{K_1}{p + 1}$

(a) Plot the root of the above equation as K_1 varies.
(b) Determine the phase angle at

    (1) $(-2 + j0)$
    (2) $(0 + j1)$
    (3) $(-3 + j2)$

4-2. $KG(p) = K_1(p + 3)$

(a) Plot the root of the above equation as K_1 varies.
(b) Determine the phase angle at

    (1) $(-2 + j0)$
    (2) $(-5 + j0)$
    (3) $(-5 + j2)$

4-3. For each of the following transfer functions locate the zeros and poles and make root-locus *sketches*. Discuss the stability of each case.

(a) $KG(p) = \dfrac{K_1}{p(2p + 1)}$

(b) $KG(p) = \dfrac{K_1(3p + 1)}{p(2p + 1)}$

(c) $KG(p) = \dfrac{K_1(p + 1)}{p(2p + 1)}$

(d) $KG(p) = \dfrac{K_1}{p(p + 1)(2p + 1)}$

(e) $KG(p) = \dfrac{K_1}{p^2 + 10p + 100}$

(f) $KG(p) = \dfrac{K_1(p + 1)}{p^2 + p + 10}$

(g) $KG(p) = \dfrac{K_1 p}{(p + 1)(p + 10)}$

(h) $KG(p) = \dfrac{K_1}{p(p + 1)(p^2 + p + 10)}$

4-4. $KG(p) = \dfrac{K_1}{p(p + 1)(p + 3.5)(p + 3 + j2)(p + 3 - j2)}$

(a) Plot the roots of the above equation as K_1 varies.

(b) Determine the net phase angle from point p_0 located at $-2 + j1$.   Is this point on the locus?

4-5. $KG(p) = \dfrac{K_1 p(p + 2)}{(p + 5)(p + 3 + j4)(p + 3 - j4)}$

(a) Plot the roots of the above equation as K_1 varies.

(b) Determine the net phase angle from the point p_0 located at $(-4 + j2)$.   Is this point on the locus?

4-6. $KG(p) = \dfrac{K_1(p + 2 + j2)(p + 2 - j2)}{(p + 1)(p + 3)}$

(a) Plot the roots of the above equation as K_1 varies.

(b) Determine the net phase angle from point p_0 located at $-3 + j2$.   Is this point on the locus?

4-7. $KG(p) = \dfrac{K_1}{p(p + 1)(p + 10)}$

(a) Plot the roots of the above equation as K_1 varies.

(b) Find the distance between point $p = -\frac{1}{2}$ and the following points:

   (1) $(-2.414 + j1.414)$

   (2) $(-4 + j0)$

   (3) $(2 + j0)$

4-8. For any of the systems in Prob. 4-3 that are unstable, estimate the gain K_1 when the roots cross the imaginary axis.

4-9. In the following systems, find the gain when the damping ratio is $\zeta = 0.2$:

(a) $\dfrac{K}{p(p + 1)(1/2p + 1)}$

(b) $\dfrac{K_1(p + 0.2)}{p(p + 1)(1/2p + 1)(p + 20)}$

(c) $\dfrac{K_1(p + 2)}{p(p + 1)(1/2p + 1)(p + 200)}$

(d) $\dfrac{K_1(p + 5)}{p(p + 1)(1/2p + 1)(p + 500)}$

4-10. Sketch the root-locus diagrams for the following functions, and discuss stability.   The quantities K, G, and H are defined in Fig. 4-3.

(a) $KG = \dfrac{K_1(1 + 3p)}{p^2 + 2p + 100}$ $H = \dfrac{1}{p^2}$

(b) $KG = \dfrac{K_1}{p^2 + 2p + 100}$ $H = \dfrac{1}{p}$

(c) $KG = \dfrac{K_1(p + 2)}{p(p + 20)}$ $H = \dfrac{p + 4}{p^2}$

4-11. For any of the systems of Prob. 4-10 that are unstable, estimate the gain K_1 of the system when the roots cross the imaginary axis.

4-12. For each of the following KG functions, plot the root-locus diagram and determine the roots of the characteristic equation for values of K_1 equal to 1, 10, 100, and 1,000.

(a) $KG = \dfrac{K_1}{p(p+1)}$

(b) $KG = K_1(p+1)$

(c) $KG = \dfrac{K_1}{p^2(p+1)^2}$

(d) $KG = K_1\dfrac{p^2 + 2p + 20}{(0.5p+1)^3}$

(e) $KG = \dfrac{K_1}{p(0.5p+1)(0.05p+1)}$

(f) $KG = \dfrac{K_1 p(p^2+10)}{(p^2+5)(p^2+30)}$

4-13. If K_1 equals 10, are there any roots of $1 + KG(p)$ in the right half plane for the function

$$KG(p) = \frac{K_1}{p(0.1p+1)(0.5p+1)(p+1)}$$

Find all four roots of this equation for $K = 10$.

4-14. For what value of K_1 does the following system become unstable:

$$KG(p) = \frac{K_1}{p^2(p+1)(p+10)}$$

4-15. Determine the velocity constant K_v and the resonant frequency ω_r when the gain in the following system

$$KG = \frac{K_1}{p(1+0.5p)(1+0.2p)} \qquad H = 1$$

is set for a damping ratio ζ equal to 0.40.

4-16. Repeat Prob. 4-15 when a series lead network is added. The system functions become

$$KG = \frac{0.25K_1(1+0.3p)}{(1+0.075p)p(1+0.5p)(1+0.2p)} \qquad H = 1$$

4-17. Repeat Prob. 4-15 with position plus rate feedback. The system functions become

$$KG = \frac{K_1}{p(1+0.5p)(1+0.2p)} \qquad H = 1 + 0.3p$$

4-18. Repeat Prob. 4-15 with two series-parallel lead networks. The system functions become

$$KG = \frac{K_1(1+1/6p)}{(1+1/60p)p(1+0.5p)(1+0.2p)} \qquad H = \frac{1+1/6p}{1+1/60p}$$

4-19. Use the Spirule to find the root-locus diagrams for

$$G = \frac{K}{p(\tau_1 p + 1)(\tau_2{}^2 p^2 + \tau_2 p + 1)(\tau_3 p + 1)}$$

$$G = \frac{K}{p(\tau_1 p + 1)(\tau_2 p + 1)^2(\tau_3 p + 1)}$$

where $\tau_1 = 2\tau_2$ and $\tau_1 = 3\tau_3$. Determine accurately the initial direction of the motion of the roots, the asymptotic direction, and the center of gravity.

4-20. For the system with an open-loop transfer function of the form

$$KG = \frac{(p + \alpha)[p + (\alpha/2)]}{p^2(p + 10)^2} K_1$$

sketch on one diagram a root locus for each of the following values of $\alpha = 1, 4, 6.67,$ 9, 12.

4-21. Determine the initial angle of departure from the complex poles and sketch the root-locus diagrams for the following transfer functions:

(a) $\dfrac{1 + \tau_1 p}{\tau_2^2 p^2 + 2\zeta \tau_2 p + 1}$ $\dfrac{\zeta}{\tau_2} < \dfrac{1}{\tau_1}$

(b) $\dfrac{1 + \tau_1 p}{\tau_2^2 p^2 + 2\zeta \tau_2 p + 1}$ $\dfrac{\zeta}{\tau_2} > \dfrac{1}{\tau_1}$

(c) $\dfrac{p(p + 10)}{(p^2 + 4)(p + 20)}$

4-22. For the systems of Prob. 4-9, find accurately the critical damping points.

4-23. A simple position servo is expressed in block-diagram form as shown in the figure.

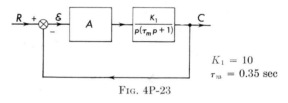

$K_1 = 10$
$\tau_m = 0.35$ sec

Fig. 4P-23

(a) Is the system unstable for any value of gain A?

(b) Upon construction of the above servo, it is found to have zero damping for a value of gain $A = 30$. The instability is due to parasitic time lags in the synchros, amplifier, and motor. Lump these effects together in the form of an additional time lag in the forward transfer function, i.e., as a factor $1/(1 + \tau_a p)$. What is the value of τ_a?

4-24. Use the root-locus method to find the roots of the following equations:

(a) $p^7 + 2p^6 - p^5 - 2p^4 + 4p^3 + 8p^2 - 4p - 8 = 0$
(b) $p^4 - 4p^3 - 7p^2 + 22p + 24 = 0$
(c) $2p^5 + 17p^4 + 78p^3 + 167p^2 + 246p + 90 = 0$

4-25. For the vibration damper of Fig. 4-32, assume the following values:

$W_1 = 50$ lb
$W_2 = 20$ lb
$K_1 = 100$ lb/in.
$B = 63$ lb-sec/ft

Optimize the system, with root-locus techniques, by varying the lower spring constant K_2.

4-26. One of the amplifiers in the system of Fig. 4P-26 is inverted so that it yields a negative gain instead of a positive gain. The resulting system, without compensation, is unstable.

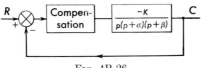

Fig. 4P-26

(a) Show, by means of a root-locus plot, why this system is unstable.

(b) The system can be made stable by appropriate compensation. What form of compensation should be used?

Note: When a negative gain is present, the angles must be summed to 0° instead of 180°. The principles of locus plotting otherwise remain the same.

CHAPTER 5

STABILITY, THE FREQUENCY-ANALYSIS METHOD

5-1. The Impedance Concept. The concept of impedance in electrical circuits is familiar to most engineers. Early in their electrical engineering training, engineers learn to find the steady-state component of differential equations that are driven with a sinusoidal function by means of the impedance method. For example, consider the circuit of Fig. 5-1 where a simple series circuit is shown. If e_1 is a sinusoidal driving voltage, that is, $e_1 = \sqrt{2}\,E_1 \sin \omega t$, then the complex amplitude of the current through the circuit is given by

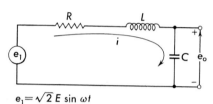

$e_1 = \sqrt{2}\,E \sin \omega t$

FIG. 5-1. A simple electrical circuit.

$$I(j\omega) = \frac{E_1}{R + j\omega L + (1/j\omega C)} \qquad (5\text{-}1)$$

where ωL is the "inductive reactance" of the circuit and $1/\omega C$ is the "capacitive reactance" of the circuit. The units of $|I|$ are amperes (rms),* and E_1 is the rms amplitude of the applied voltage. If it were desired to find the complex amplitude of the output voltage $E_o(j\omega)$, then Eq. (5-1) is multiplied by the impedance $1/j\omega C$ and the rms output voltage is written

$$E_o(j\omega) = \frac{E_1}{(1 - \omega^2 LC) + j\omega CR} \qquad (5\text{-}2)$$

Because of the appearance in these equations of the complex quantity j, the output voltage E_o is a complex quantity. E_o can be written in polar form as a magnitude at a particular angle. For the circuit of Fig. 5-1 the complex output voltage, written in polar form, is

$$E_o(j\omega) = \frac{E_1}{\sqrt{(1 - \omega^2 LC)^2 + (\omega CR)^2} \; \angle + \tan^{-1} \omega CR/(1 - \omega^2 LC)} \qquad (5\text{-}3)$$

A ratio of complex quantities is put into polar form by writing the numerator and the denominator separately in polar form. The expres-

---

* rms is defined as the root mean square voltage and, for sinusoidal functions, is equal to $1/\sqrt{2}$ times peak value.

sion is written completely in polar form by dividing the magnitudes and by subtracting the angles.   The symbol $\angle\phi$ means the angle or argument of the complex quantity and has the same meaning as $e^{j\phi}$.

The expression for the output voltage for Eq. (5-3) is written as follows:

$$E_o(j\omega) = \frac{E_1}{\sqrt{(1 - \omega^2 LC)^2 + (\omega RC)^2}} \angle - \tan^{-1} \frac{\omega RC}{1 - \omega^2 LC} = A(\omega)\angle\phi(\omega)$$

$$(5\text{-}4)$$

This expression represents the output voltage as a function of frequency ω. The complex expression for E_o [Eq. (5-4)] has a magnitude designated by $A(\omega)$ and an angle $\phi(\omega)$.   When a variable-frequency signal generator is applied to the input, it is theoretically possible to plot the magnitude and the phase angle of the output voltage E_o as the input frequency is varied. These plots comprise the so-called "frequency response" of the network.

It is important to notice that $E_o(j\omega)$, as given in Eq. (5-4), is independent of time.   In reality, however, the input voltage is a function of time and as written in Fig. 5-1 is

$$e_1(t) = \sqrt{2}\, E_1 \sin \omega t$$

where $\sqrt{2}$ converts the rms voltage E_1 to peak value.   The output voltage expressed as a function of time is found from the complex expression of Eq. (5-4).   The magnitude of E_o, as given in Eq. (5-4), is the amplitude of the output sine wave, and the phase angle ϕ is the phase shift which must be added to the sinusoid as follows:

$$e_o(t) = \frac{\sqrt{2}\, E_1}{\sqrt{(1 - \omega^2 LC)^2 + (\omega CR)^2}} \sin \left(\omega t - \tan^{-1} \frac{\omega CR}{1 - \omega^2 LC}\right) \quad (5\text{-}5)$$

Although a differential equation is required to describe the circuit of Fig. 5-1, the engineer who is familiar with the impedance concept can quickly solve and obtain the steady-state component of the solution of these equations.   If it is necessary, the steady-state time component can be obtained by appropriate interpretation of the amplitude and phase angle of the complex solution [as is indicated in going from Eq. (5-4) to Eq. (5-5)].

The impedance concept can be applied with equal success and with equal reduction of labor to any linear system whether it be electrical, mechanical, or electromechanical.   To understand better the nature of the process involved, write the two differential equations for Fig. 5-1 as follows:

$$e_1 = R_1 i + L \frac{di}{dt} + \frac{1}{C} \int i\, dt \qquad (5\text{-}6)$$

and

$$C \frac{de_o}{dt} = i \qquad (5\text{-}7)$$

where i is the instantaneous current in the loop of Fig. 5-1. When Eq. (5-7) is substituted into Eq. (5-6), the following differential equation relating e_1 to e_o results:

$$e_1 = RC \frac{de_o}{dt} + LC \frac{d^2 e_o}{dt^2} + e_o \qquad (5\text{-}8)$$

The impedance concept is based upon the following principle: *If e_1 is a sinusoidal voltage, then, in the steady state, the current that flows in a linear network and hence all voltages that appear in the network are also sinusoidal quantities of the same frequency, but possibly with different amplitudes and different phase angles.* Using this basic principle of linear systems, let e_1 be expressed by the equation

$$e_1 = \sqrt{2}\, E_1 e^{j\omega t} \qquad (5\text{-}9)$$

where $e^{j\omega t}$ is the complex form of a sinusoid and can be written

$$e^{j\omega t} = \cos \omega t + j \sin \omega t \qquad (5\text{-}10)$$

Application of the above-cited principle to Eq. (5-8) indicates that e_o is a sinusoidal signal of the same frequency but of different amplitude and phase; hence

$$e_o = \sqrt{2}\, E_o e^{j\phi} e^{j\omega t} = \sqrt{2}\, \bar{E}_o e^{j\omega t} \qquad (5\text{-}11)$$

where $\bar{E}_o$ is the complex magnitude of the output voltage and equals $E_o e^{j\phi}$. When Eqs. (5-9) and (5-11) are substituted into Eq. (5-8), the following expression is obtained:

$$\sqrt{2}\, E_1 e^{j\omega t} = RC \frac{d}{dt} \sqrt{2}\, \bar{E}_o e^{j\omega t} + LC \frac{d^2}{dt^2} \sqrt{2}\, \bar{E}_o e^{j\omega t} + \sqrt{2}\, \bar{E}_o e^{j\omega t} \quad (5\text{-}12)$$

Since $\bar{E}_o$ is independent of time, the differentiations indicated in Eq. (5-12) can be carried out, with the result

$$E_1 \sqrt{2}\, e^{j\omega t} = RC\bar{E}_o j\omega \sqrt{2}\, e^{j\omega t} + LC\bar{E}_o (j\omega)^2 \sqrt{2}\, e^{j\omega t} + \bar{E}_o \sqrt{2}\, e^{j\omega t} \quad (5\text{-}13)$$

Since the expression $\sqrt{2}\, e^{j\omega t}$ occurs in each term of Eq. (5-13), it is canceled and Eq. (5-13) is simplified:

$$E_1 = E_o e^{j\phi}[jRC\omega + LC(j\omega)^2 + 1] \qquad (5\text{-}14)$$

It is important to compare Eq. (5-8) with Eq. (5-14). These two equations are identical except that in Eq. (5-14) $j\omega$ is substituted for the differentiation with respect to time d/dt that appears in Eq. (5-8). This substitution can be formalized:

$$\frac{d}{dt} \to j\omega \qquad \frac{d^2}{dt^2} \to (j\omega)^2 \qquad \int dt \to \frac{1}{j\omega} \qquad (5\text{-}15)$$

5-2. Generalized Impedance Functions. The principle that is demonstrated in the solution of the example of Fig. 5-1 can be generalized to any linear system. When the derivative operator d/dt in the differential equation of any linear system is replaced by $j\omega$, an algebraic equation results. This equation can be solved for the dependent variable, and the solution yields a steady-state value of the dependent variable in response to a sinusoidal driving function input.

For the example of Fig. 5-1, Eq. (5-14) is solved for $E_o e^{j\phi}$, resulting in the following expression:

$$E_o e^{j\phi} = \frac{E_1}{(1 - \omega^2 LC) + j\omega RC} = \frac{E_1}{\sqrt{(1 - \omega^2 LC)^2 + (\omega RC)^2}} \angle - \tan^{-1} \frac{\omega RC}{1 - \omega^2 LC} \quad (5\text{-}16)$$

Equation (5-16) is identical with Eq. (5-4), hence demonstrating the validity in this example of substituting $j\omega$ for d/dt.

As an example of the impedance method for finding the sinusoidal steady-state solution to servo systems, consider the system of Chap. 1 which also is shown in the block diagram of Fig. 5-2.

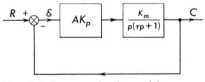

FIG. 5-2. An example of a position servo.

The differential equation relating the input position r to the output position c is written as follows:

$$\frac{d^2 c}{dt^2} + 2\zeta\omega_n \frac{dc}{dt} + \omega_n^2 c = \omega_n^2 r \quad (5\text{-}17)$$

To find the steady-state response $C(j\omega)$ when $R(j\omega)$ is a sinusoidal signal, substitute $j\omega$ for d/dt in Eq. (5-17) and solve for $C(j\omega)$:

$$C(j\omega) = \frac{\omega_n^2 R(j\omega)}{(\omega_n^2 - \omega^2) + j2\zeta\omega_n\omega} \quad (5\text{-}18)$$

where capital C and R are used to indicate that these are complex amplitudes and not functions of time. Dividing through by the undamped natural resonant frequency ω_n^2

$$\frac{C(ju)}{R(ju)} = \frac{1}{(1 - u^2) + j2\zeta u} \quad (5\text{-}19)$$

where u is the frequency ratio ω/ω_n and ζ is the damping ratio. Equation (5-19) is written in polar form as follows:

$$\frac{C(ju)}{R(ju)} = \frac{1}{\sqrt{(1 - u^2)^2 + (2\zeta u)^2}} \angle - \tan^{-1} \frac{2\zeta u}{1 - u^2} = A(u)\angle\phi(u) \quad (5\text{-}20)$$

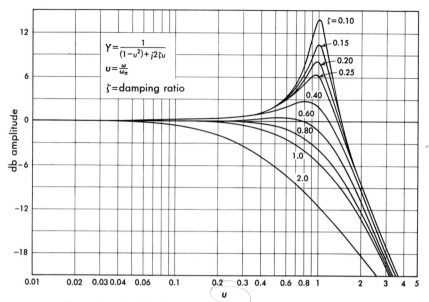

FIG. 5-3a. Amplitude of the second-order transfer function.

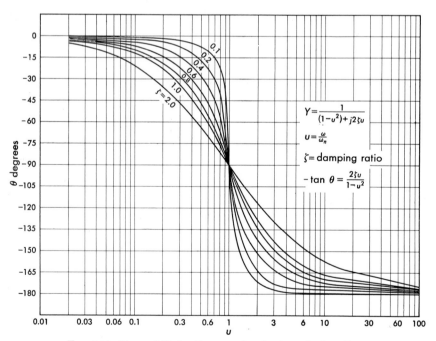

FIG. 5-3b. Phase shift for the second-order transfer function.

The output C is a sinusoid of the same frequency as the applied input R. As shown in Eq. (5-20) the amplitude is multiplied by A and the phase is shifted by an angle ϕ.   If the frequency of the sinusoidal driving signal is varied, the closed-loop frequency response of the servo, pictured in Fig. 5-2, is obtained.   The amplitude and phase curves which are shown in Figs. 5-3a and b are plotted against the logarithmic frequency ratio for values of damping ratio in the range 0.1 to 2.0.   Figure 5-3a is the db amplitude of $C(ju)/R(ju)$ plotted against the frequency ratio u, and Fig. 5-3b is the phase shift of $C(ju)$ with respect to $R(ju)$ as a function of frequency ratio.

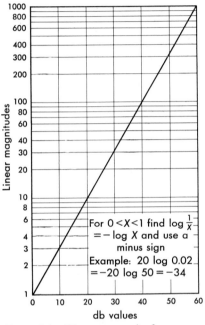

The abbreviation db stands for decibels and is defined as

$$\text{db} = 20 \log_{10} \frac{A_2}{A_1} \quad (5\text{-}21)$$

The decibel was originally defined as a unit of power ratio; however, in servo applications Eq. (5-21) is taken as the definition.   A chart which converts between decibels and voltage ratio is included in Fig. 5-4.

Fig. 5-4.   Linear magnitudes versus decibel values.

The frequency where the peaks of Fig. 5-3a occur versus the damping ratio is calculated and plotted in Fig. 5-5.

It is important to observe the simplicity of obtaining the steady-state component of the solution of differential equations when the driving function is a sinusoid.   It is only necessary to replace d/dt by $j\omega$.   If a transfer function is given in which the Laplace-transform operator p is indicated, replacing p by $j\omega$ will result in the impedance solution.

5-3. Plotting Impedance and Transfer Functions.   The labor required to plot simple impedance and transfer functions point by point for a series of values of frequency is considerable.   A method has been developed for the easy plotting of impedance and transfer functions.   These plots are known as "Bode plots."   This method avoids the difficulty of computing polar plots (i.e., amplitude radial and phase angle clockwise). The method centers about the use of the logarithmic function.   Decibel gain and phase shift are plotted against logarithmic frequency.

To appreciate the advantages of using the logarithm of the transfer function, suppose that the following transfer function

$$KGH(j\omega) = \frac{K(j\omega\tau_1 + 1)(j\omega\tau_3 + 1)}{(j\omega)^n(j\omega\tau_2 + 1)(j\omega\tau_4 + 1)} \tag{5-22}$$

is written in polar form:

$$KGH(j\omega) = \frac{K\sqrt{(\omega\tau_1)^2 + 1}\ \angle\ \tan^{-1}\omega\tau_1\ \sqrt{(\omega\tau_3)^2 + 1}\ \angle\ \tan^{-1}\omega\tau_3}{\omega^n\ \angle\ n90°\ \sqrt{(\omega\tau_2)^2 + 1}\ \angle\ \tan^{-1}\omega\tau_2\ \sqrt{(\omega\tau_4)^2 + 1}\ \angle\ \tan^{-1}\omega\tau_4}$$
$$= A(\omega)e^{j\phi(\omega)} \tag{5-23}$$

$A(\omega)$ is the magnitude of KGH, and $e^{j\phi(\omega)}$ is the corresponding phase

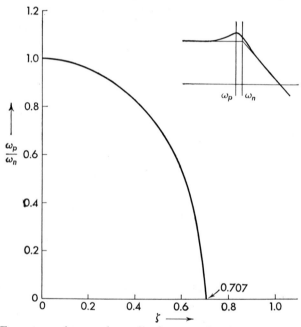

FIG. 5-5. Frequency where peak amplitude occurs for the second-order system.

angle.   The logarithm to the base e of the last part of Eq. (5-23) is

$$\log_e KGH(j\omega) = \log_e A(\omega)e^{j\phi(\omega)} = \log_e A(\omega) + \log_e e^{j\phi(\omega)}$$
$$= \log_e A(\omega) + j\phi(\omega) \tag{5-24}$$

The logarithm of the transfer function has a real part which is the logarithm of the magnitude and an imaginary part which is the phase angle. If Eq. (5-22) is inserted into Eq. (5-24), the magnitude and the phase angle can be written separately in two expressions:

$$\log_e A(\omega) = \log_e \sqrt{(\omega\tau_1)^2 + 1} + \log_e \sqrt{(\omega\tau_3)^2 + 1} - \log_e \omega^n$$
$$- \log_e \sqrt{(\omega\tau_2)^2 + 1} - \log_e \sqrt{(\omega\tau_4)^2 + 1} \tag{5-25}$$

$$\phi(\omega) = \tan^{-1}\omega\tau_1 + \tan^{-1}\omega\tau_3 - n90° - \tan^{-1}\omega\tau_2 - \tan^{-1}\omega\tau_4 \tag{5-25a}$$

Because the logarithm of the product of two quantities is equal to the sum of the logarithms of the quantities, each factored portion of Eq. (5-23) is treated separately. These separate factors are plotted in decibel units, since multiplication of each side of Eq. (5-25) by $20/2.3^*$ converts the units to decibels. The total decibel magnitude is formed simply by summing algebraically each of the individual values. Equation (5-25a) indicates that the phase-angle function is formed in a similar manner by summing the phase-angle function for each of the individual terms in Eq. (5-23).

Since most KGH functions found in servo systems are composed of zeros and poles, the decibel magnitude and phase versus log frequency need be considered for only a few types of singularities. Based upon the knowledge of four simple types, a complete KGH function can be built up simply by appropriately adding the magnitude and phase curves.

5-4. The Asymptotic Approximation. The most commonly encountered functions in servo systems are listed as follows:

Frequency invariant factors.........................	K
Simple* zeros and poles at the origin................	$j\omega$ or $1/j\omega$
Simple zeros......................	$(j\omega\tau_1 + 1)$
Simple poles......................	$(j\omega\tau_2 + 1)^{-1}$
Quadratic zeros and poles..........	$\left[\left(j\dfrac{\omega}{\omega_n}\right)^2 + 2\zeta\dfrac{\omega}{\omega_n}j + 1\right]^{\pm 1}$

*Simple means there is only one zero or pole at a point.

Each of these functions can be plotted point by point. Because of the nature of the plot, however, a linear asymptotic approximation of the decibel magnitude curves permits a rapid method of plotting these factors. In all cases these curves are plotted on semilog paper. The linear scale is the decibel gain plotted against frequency ω, which is plotted on a logarithmic scale. Phase shift is plotted on a linear scale against a logarithmic frequency scale.

Frequency Invariant Factors. The product of the gains which is a constant independent of frequency is plotted from the function

$$20 \log_{10} K \qquad\qquad (5\text{-}26)$$

where K represents the product of all the frequency invariant terms in the KGH function. Equation (5-26) is plotted in Fig. 5-6 as a constant with zero phase shift.

Zeros or Poles at the Origin. For zeros or poles at the origin,

$$(j\omega)^n \qquad \text{or} \qquad \frac{1}{(j\omega)^n} \qquad\qquad (5\text{-}27)$$

---

* Since $\log_e x = (\log_{10} x) \log_e 10 = 2.3 \log_{10} x$, it follows that $20 \log_{10} x = 20/2.3 \log_e x$.

the amplitude and phase curves are found by taking the logarithm of these functions as follows:

$$\log_e (j\omega)^{\pm n} = \pm n \log_e \omega + jn90° \qquad (5\text{-}28)$$

For simple zeros or poles the integer n is unity. The amplitude is $\pm n\ 20 \log_{10} \omega$ db, and the phase shift is $\pm n90°$. The $\pm n$ accounts for either zeros or poles; $+n$ corresponds to zeros, and $-n$ corresponds to poles.

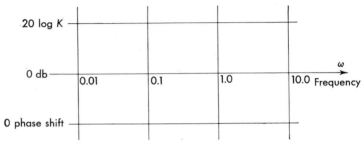

FIG. 5-6. Decibel gain and phase shift for a constant.

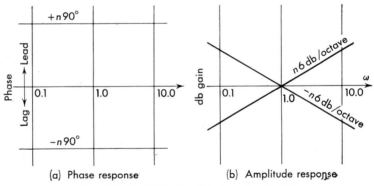

(a) Phase response   (b) Amplitude response

FIG. 5-7. Decibel gain and phase for $(j\omega)^{\pm n}$.

The phase-shift curve for a simple zero or pole is constant at $\pm n90°$. For a single zero at the origin, the phase shift is a constant $+90°$, and for a single pole at the origin, the phase shift is a constant $-90°$ as shown in Fig. 5-7a.

The amplitude is a straight line with a slope approximately equal to $\pm n6$ db/octave, where n is the number of zeros or poles at the origin. An octave is a factor of 2 change in frequency. For a single zero, the straight line is at $+6$ db/octave and intersects the 0-db axis at the point $\omega = 1$. The curve for a single pole, which is shown also in Fig. 5-7b, is a straight line with a slope of -6 db/octave passing through the 0-db axis at the point $\omega = 1$.

These straight lines, which are shown in Fig. 5-7a and b, are not asymptotic approximations but rather the actual curves. When decibel is plotted against the logarithm of the frequency, the amplitude curves are straight lines passing through the 0-db axis at $\omega = 1$.

The $\pm n6$-db/octave slope of the amplitude curves can be verified by considering the change in decibel amplitude for a change in frequency of one octave. This is written

$$\Delta \text{ db} = 20(\log \omega_2 - \log \omega_1) = 20 \log \frac{\omega_2}{\omega_1} \qquad (5\text{-}29)$$

But ω_2 is equal to $2\omega_1$, since an octave corresponds to a factor of 2 change in frequency

$$\Delta \text{ db} = 20 \log_{10} 2 = 20(0.30103) \approx 6 \text{ db/octave} \qquad (5\text{-}30)$$

A straight line with a slope of 6 db/octave on the amplitude curve, which is shown in Fig. 5-7b, intersects the 0-db line at $\omega = 1$.

For ease in plotting, the constant portion of the transfer function K can be combined with the $\pm (j\omega)^n$ term. Usually only a single or double pole exists at the origin. Take as an example a single pole at the origin. The constant and this pole are combined as follows:

$$\frac{K(\omega\tau_1 + 1) \ \cdots}{j\omega(\omega\tau_2 + 1) \ \cdots} = \frac{(\omega\tau_1 + 1) \ \cdots}{[j(\omega/K)](\omega\tau_2 + 1) \ \cdots} \qquad (5\text{-}31)$$

The term to be plotted is

$$\frac{1}{j(\omega/K)} \qquad (5\text{-}32)$$

This term, Eq. (5-32), has the same slope as the single pole at the origin $1/j\omega$, except the amplitude curve intersects the 0-db line at a frequency $\omega = K$. The phase shift remains a constant at $-90°$.

If a double pole is at the origin, the plot is identical except that the amplitude crosses the 0-db line when $\omega = \sqrt{K}$.

It is convenient when working with frequency methods to write the transfer function in the form $\tau p + 1$ so that K includes all the constants factored from the frequency-dependent portion of the transfer function. This is opposite in form to that necessary for a root-locus construction. For root locus the terms should be put in the form $p + (1/\tau)$.

Simple Zeros. For simple zeros of the form

$$j\omega\tau_1 + 1 \qquad (5\text{-}33)$$

a linear asymptotic approximation is used. For $\omega\tau_1 \ll 1$,

$$20 \log_{10} |j\omega\tau_1 + 1| \approx 20 \log_{10} 1 = 0 \text{ db} \qquad (5\text{-}34)$$

For small values of ω the magnitude remains at 0 db. When ω becomes much greater than $1(\omega\tau_1 \gg 1)$,

$$20 \log_{10} |j\omega\tau_1 + 1| \approx 20 \log_{10} \omega\tau_1 \qquad (5\text{-}35)$$

For large values of ω, the amplitude and phase response of a simple zero $(j\omega\tau_1 + 1)$ resemble the response of a simple zero at the origin $j\omega\tau_1$. The slope, for large ω, is $+6$ db/octave. The 6-db/octave straight-line asymptote intersects the 0-db line when $\omega\tau_1 = 1$ or when $\omega = 1/\tau_1$. The point of intersection at $\omega = 1/\tau_1$ is called the "corner frequency." The two straight lines, one along the 0-db axis and the other at $+6$ db/octave intersecting at the point $\omega = 1/\tau_1$, are the asymptotic approximations for a simple zero of the form $j\omega\tau_1 + 1$. This straight-line asymptote is shown in Fig. 5-8a. The procedure to follow when plotting the amplitude curve for $j\omega\tau_1 + 1$ is outlined as follows:

1. Locate the "corner frequency," that is, $\omega = 1/\tau_1$.

2. Plot a 6-db/octave line through this point to the right (increasing frequency) and a straight line along 0 db to the left.

3. If more accuracy is required, the actual curve is found as explained in the next section and as shown on Fig. 5-8a.

The actual curve for the amplitude deviates only slightly from the straight-line asymptotes. As is shown in Fig. 5-8a, the curve rises $+3$ db above the asymptote at the corner frequency and approximately $+1$ db, respectively, at one octave above and one octave below the corner frequency. These deviations from the asymptotic approximation are computed by evaluating the magnitude of the zero $j\omega\tau_1 + 1$ at the corner frequency, at twice, and at one-half the corner frequency, as follows:

At $\omega = 1/\tau_1$

$$20 \log |j1 + 1| = 20 \log \sqrt{2} = 3 \text{ db}$$
$$\text{Deviation from asymptote} = +3 \text{ db}$$

At $\omega = 2/\tau_1$

$$20 \log |j2 + 1| = 20 \log \sqrt{5} = 6.99$$
$$\text{Deviation from asymptote} = 6.99 - 6 \approx +1 \text{ db}$$

At $\omega = 1/2\tau_1$

$$20 \log |j\tfrac{1}{2} + 1| = 20 \log \sqrt{\tfrac{5}{4}} = 0.969$$
$$\text{Deviation from asymptote} \approx +1.0 \text{ db}$$

The phase shift for a simple zero is obtained from the expression

$$\phi = \tan^{-1} \omega\tau_1 \qquad (5\text{-}36)$$

The frequency ω is plotted on a logarithmic scale. The arctangent curve has a value of 45° when $\omega\tau_1 = 1$ which is at the corner frequency. The phase curve starts at 0°, increases to a maximum of 90°, and is symmetric about the 45° point. The complete frequency-response curve for the zero comprises the amplitude curve shown in Fig. 5-8a and the phase-shift curve shown in Fig. 5-8b.

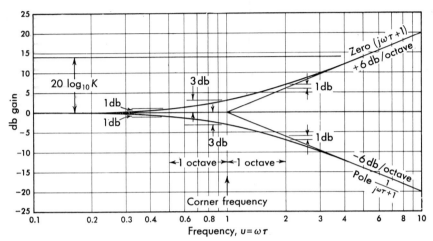

FIG. 5-8a. Amplitude response of K, $j\omega\tau + 1$, and $1/(j\omega\tau + 1)$.

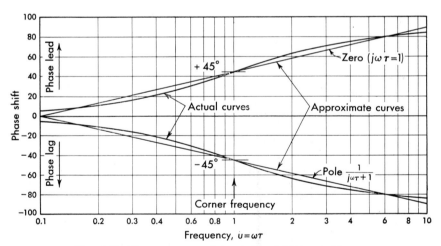

FIG. 5-8b. Phase response of $j\omega\tau + 1$ and $1/(j\omega\tau + 1)$.

Since the phase curve is a familiar arctangent curve, it, too, is often sketched. An approximate straight-line phase curve can be used to aid in sketching the phase response. The straight line passes through 0° at $\frac{1}{10}$ (corner frequency), +45° at the corner frequency and 90° at 10 (corner frequency). If a line is drawn as shown in Fig. 5-9, the maximum deviation from the actual curve is 6°. These straight-line approximations are also included in Fig. 5-8b.

Simple Poles. Simple poles of the form $1/(j\omega\tau_2 + 1)$ can be treated similarly to simple zeros. Since the logarithm of the reciprocal is equal to the negative of the logarithm, or

$$20 \log \frac{1}{(j\omega\tau_2 + 1)} = -20 \log (j\omega\tau_2 + 1) \qquad (5\text{-}37)$$

the curve for a simple pole is similar to that for a simple zero with the exception of a minus sign. For small frequencies, $\omega \ll 1/\tau_2$, the amplitude remains at 0 db. For large frequencies, $\omega \gg 1/\tau_2$, the asymptote

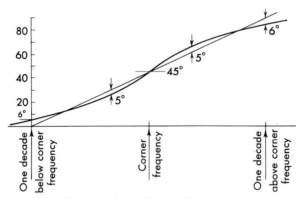

FIG. 5-9. Approximate phase curve.

is a straight line at -6 db/octave. This asymptote, which is shown in Fig. 5-8a, intersects the 0-db axis at $\omega = 1/\tau_2$. $\omega = 1/\tau_2$ is called the corner frequency or the break point for this particular pole. As in the case of the zero, the actual amplitude curve deviates from the straight-line approximation by -3 db at the corner frequency and by -1 db at both $1/2\tau_2$ and $2/\tau_2$.

The phase-shift curve is similar to that for a zero, but since the pole is in the denominator of KGH, the sign is changed when the angle is brought into the numerator

$$\phi = - \tan^{-1} \omega\tau_2 \qquad (5\text{-}38)$$

Equation (5-38) is an arctangent curve which starts from zero phase shift and approaches $-90°$ phase lag for large frequency. The $-45°$ phase-shift point occurs at the corner frequency. The same straight-line approximation that is used for zeros is applicable for poles. The phase curve and the straight-line approximation are included in Fig. 5-8b.

If the transfer function has a repeated zero or pole, for example, if there are two equal poles or two equal zeros, the amplitude curve is similar to that of a single zero or pole.   The slope changes from 6 to 12 db/octave, and the phase shift is at $\pm 90°$ at the corner frequency for a zero or pole, respectively, rather than at $\pm 45°$ for a single zero or pole.   The phase shift varies from zero to $\pm 180°$ rather than zero to $\pm 90°$.   These functions are shown in Fig. 5-10a and b.

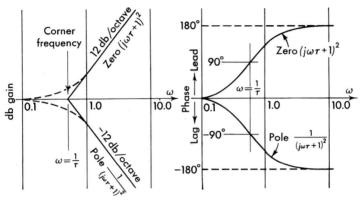

(a) Amplitude response   (b) Phase response

FIG. 5-10. Frequency response of double poles and zeros.

Quadratic Zeros and Poles.   Occasionally, quadratic poles of the form

$$G(j\omega) = \frac{\omega_n^2}{-\omega^2 + j2\zeta\omega_n\omega + \omega_n^2} = \frac{1}{-(\omega/\omega_n)^2 + j2\zeta(\omega/\omega_n) + 1} \quad (5\text{-}39)$$

occur in the KGH function.   Equation (5-39) can be put into dimensionless form by replacing ω/ω_n by the frequency ratio u with the result

$$\frac{1}{(1 - u^2) + j2\zeta u} \quad (5\text{-}40)$$

The magnitude and phase of Eq. (5-40) are plotted in Figs. 5-3a and b. Because the amplitude and phase response for quadratic poles depend not only on the corner frequency but also upon the damping ratio ζ, a dimensionless chart of the form shown in Figs. 5-3a and b is used to make the plot.   The amplitude and phase response are plotted by locating the corner frequency and damping ratio for the particular quadratic factor.   The damping ratio and corner frequency are found by comparison of the given expression with Eq. (5-39).   For example, suppose it is required to plot the function

$$\frac{1}{p^2 + 3p + 10} \quad (5\text{-}41)$$

Equation (5-41) is put into the form of Eq. (5-39) by comparison

$$\frac{\frac{1}{10}}{(p^2/10) + \frac{3}{10}p + 1} = \frac{1}{(p/\omega_n)^2 + 2\zeta(p/\omega_n) + 1} \quad (5\text{-}42)$$

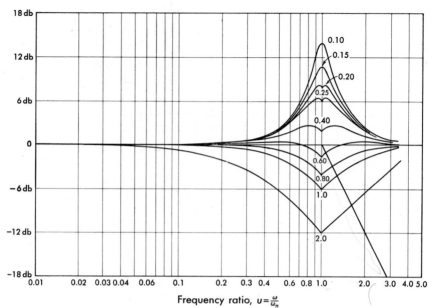

Frequency ratio, $u = \frac{\omega}{\omega_n}$

FIG. 5-11. Amplitude differences for the quadratic function $1/[(1 - u^2) + j2\zeta u]$.

40db / decade

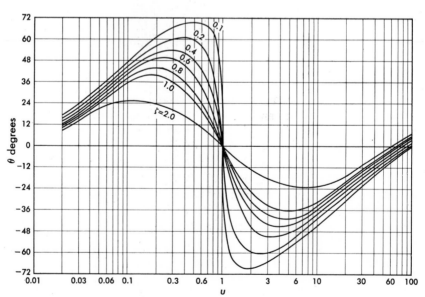

FIG. 5-12. Phase-shift deviation from a straight-line approximation for a second-order system.

Equating like terms,

$$\omega_n = \sqrt{10} \quad \text{and} \quad \zeta = \frac{\omega_n}{2} \frac{3}{10} = \frac{3.0}{2\sqrt{10}} = 0.475 \quad (5\text{-}43)$$

The corner frequency $\omega = \omega_n$ is first located on the Bode plot. The first approximation is drawn in the same manner as a double pole located at the corner frequency ω_n, that is, a -12-db/octave line going to the right and starting from the corner frequency for the amplitude response and an approximation to the arctangent curve extending from 0 to $-180°$ for the phase response. Because the deviation from these asymptotes depends upon the damping ratio, it is necessary to refer to Fig. 5-11 which gives the deviations from the 12-db/octave amplitude for various damping ratios. The deviations from the phase approximation are given in Fig. 5-12. For servo systems which contain not only single-order zeros and poles but also complex poles, use of these charts enables the engineer to make a Bode plot. If a complex zero rather than a complex pole exists in the transfer function, the curves of Figs. 5-3a and b are inverted as is done for simple zeros and poles.

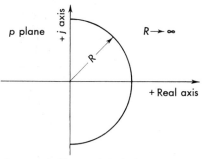

FIG. 5-13. Plot of right half of p plane.

5-5. The p Plane and the KGH Plane. In studying stability from the root-locus point of view, as in Chap. 4, the p plane is drawn. The roots of $1 + KGH$ are located on this p plane. Figure 5-13 shows a p plane for a $1 + KGH$ function. When all the roots are in the left half plane, the transients die out and the system is stable. If the roots should lie in the right half plane, however, the corresponding exponential terms have positive real parts and build up with increasing time. Roots that lie on the imaginary axis produce oscillations which neither build up nor decay. These roots, which are termed marginally stable, are the boundary between stable and unstable systems. The designer is interested in knowing if any roots lie in the right half plane. To discover if any roots of $1 + KGH = 0$ are in the right half plane, a contour, which is shown in Fig. 5-13, is chosen. This contour encircles the entire right half of the p plane. The radius of the contour is made so large that all possible roots in the right half plane are included.

The plot of $KGH(p)$ is called a mapping of a contour located in the p plane into a contour in the KGH plane. When a closed curve C_1, such as shown in the p plane of Fig. 5-14a, is mapped into the KGH plane, another closed curve C_2 is obtained in the KGH plane, as shown in Fig.

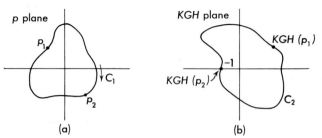

FIG. 5-14. p plane mapped onto $KGH(p)$ plane.

5-14b. For single-valued functions, a correspondence exists between points on C_1, the curve in the p plane, and points on C_2, the mapped curve in the KGH plane. If a point is moved along C_1 in the direction of the arrow (clockwise), the mapped point moves along C_2 in a direc-

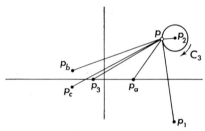

FIG. 5-15. Encirclement of a root in the p plane.

tion depending upon the KGH function. Suppose that p_2 is a root of $1 + KGH = 0$ and that the contour passes through the point p_2 in the p plane, as shown in Fig. 5-14a. If p_2 is a root, then when KGH is evaluated with

$$p = p_2, \quad KGH(p_2) = -1;$$

that is, the contour C_2 in the KGH plane passes through the point -1.

Consider the characteristic equation for a closed-loop system

$$1 + HKGH = \frac{(p - p_1)(p - p_2)(p - p_3)}{(p - p_a)(p - p_b)(p - p_a)} \tag{5-44}$$

where p_1, p_2, . . . are the roots and p_a, p_b, . . . are the poles of $1 + KGH$. Notice that poles of KGH are also poles of $1 + KGH$. Each term in the expression $1 + KGH$ can be considered as a complex vector, as shown in Fig. 5-15. The vector extends from the fixed points, p_1, p_2, p_3

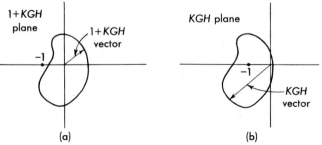

FIG. 5-16. $(1 + KGH)$ plane and KGH plane.

and p_a, p_b, p_c to the variable point p.   Suppose the variable point moves, in a clockwise direction, one complete revolution about p_2, as shown on Fig. 5-15.   The vector $p + p_2$ makes one complete clockwise revolution because the contour encircles this root.   Since all the other roots and poles are external to the contour, the remaining vectors make no net revolutions.   Since the term $p + p_2$ in Eq. (5-44) changes phase by 360° (one complete revolution), the quantity $1 + KGH$ incurs a change of 360°.   Hence, a vector representing $1 + KGH$ (in the $1 + KGH$ plane) would make one clockwise encirclement of the origin.   This is shown in Fig. 5-16.   The remaining roots and poles contribute no net change in phase of $1 + KGH$.

Because the roots are in the numerator of Eq. (5-44), one *clockwise* rotation of p_2 results in one *clockwise* encirclement of the origin for the

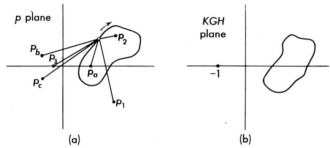

FIG. 5-17. Enclosing a root and a pole in p plane causes no net enclosure of -1 point in KGH plane.

function $1 + KGH$.   The $1 + KGH$ plane is shifted into the KGH plane by shifting the origin, as shown in Fig. 5-16b.   In this plane, one CW (clockwise) encirclement of one root in the p plane produces one CW encirclement of the $-1 + j0$ point in the KGH plane.

Suppose the closed contour in the p plane is made to encircle both a root and a pole, as shown in Fig. 5-17a, in a CW direction.   In this case the vectors from both p_2 and p_a rotate through one complete revolution, or 360°.   The root p_2 contributes $+360°$ to $1 + KGH$, since it is in the numerator of Eq. (5-44).   The pole p_a contributes $-360°$, since it is in the denominator.   Hence the net phase change of $1 + KGH$ is zero, and the contour does not encircle the -1 point in the KGH plane (shown on Fig. 5-17b).

If the closed contour is enlarged to include p_1, p_2, and p_a, the net phase contribution to $1 + KGH$ is $+360°$.   A CW encirclement of a root causes a CW encirclement of the -1 point in the KGH plane.   A CW encirclement of a pole causes a CCW (counterclockwise) encirclement of the -1 point in the KGH plane.

These results can be summarized as follows: A CW encirclement of a region in the p plane causes $\#R - \#P$ clockwise encirclements of the -1 point in the KGH plane. $\#R$ is the number of roots and $\#P$ is the number of poles, both of $1 + KGH$, that are located within the encircled region.

5-6. The Nyquist Stability Criterion. The frequency-analysis method of determining the stability of feedback control systems is based upon the Nyquist criterion. This method provides a simple, graphically obtainable principle that allows the servo engineer to determine the stability of linear systems. A more complete mathematical derivation of the Nyquist criterion is found in Appendix VI.

Roots which lie in the right half of the p plane give rise to an unstable system. Poles of $1 + KGH$ which lie in the right half plane are of concern when the loop is open. Suppose the contour of Fig. 5-13 is made large enough to include the entire right half plane. As this contour is mapped on to the KGH plane, the number of CW encirclements of the -1 point yields stability information.

The Nyquist stability criterion can be stated as follows: Given any open-loop transfer function $KGH(j\omega)$, which is the ratio of two factored polynomials in the variable $j\omega$ and written in the form

$$KGH(j\omega) = \frac{K(j\omega\tau_1 + 1)(j\omega\tau_3 + 1)}{(j\omega)^n(j\omega\tau_2 + 1)(j\omega\tau_4 + 1)} \quad (5\text{-}45)$$

The amplitude and phase polar plot of $KGH(j\omega)$ as the frequency is varied from $-\infty$ to ∞ encircles the $-1 + j0$ point in all N times, where N is given by the following equation:

$$N = \#R - \#P \quad (5\text{-}46)$$

N is the number of clockwise encirclements of the point -1, $\#P$ equals the number of poles of KGH in the right half plane, and $\#R$ is the number of roots of $1 + KGH$ which lie in the right half plane. K is the constant or frequency-invariant portion of the open-loop transfer function, $G(j\omega)$ is the forward-loop transfer function, and $H(j\omega)$ is the feedback transfer function. These functions are indicated in Fig. 5-18

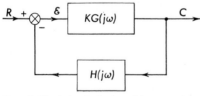

FIG. 5-18. A typical closed-loop system.

and are obtained from the transfer function by substituting $j\omega$ for p. It should be remembered that poles of KGH are also poles of $1 + KGH$, since the unity does not alter the size of an infinite quantity.

In practice, however, the contour shown in Fig. 5-13 can be simplified. Since only systems with constant real coefficients are considered in this text, the roots which appear must be either on the real axis or in complex conjugate pairs.   As a result the map of the $-j\omega$ axis is the mirror image of the $+j\omega$ axis.   Hence it is necessary to plot only the upper portion of the imaginary axis in the p plane.

So that all the right half of the p plane be encircled, the semicircular contour must have a large radius R.   Many physical systems have zero response to an infinite frequency; hence, the large semicircle will usually map into the KGH plane as a point at the origin.   Because the origin of the KGH plane is a considerable distance from the point -1, it is of little concern in the stability investigation.

Practically, only real, positive frequencies from zero to infinity need be mapped, and this plot is obtained by applying sinusoidal inputs and varying the frequency of the signals from zero to infinity.

The Nyquist criterion gives information regarding the number of roots minus the number of poles of $1 + KGH$. KGH is generally the ratio of factored polynomials.   The poles of $1 + KGH$ are identical with the poles of KGH.   The number of poles of KGH in the right half plane can be found from inspection of Eq. (5-45).   Hence, the number of poles with positive real part can easily be determined.   The number of encircle-ments of the point -1 is found from the KGH-plane plot.   Both N and $\#P$ in Eq. (5-46) are known, so that the number of roots of $1 + KGH$ in the right half plane can be found by rearranging Eq. (5-46), with the result

$$\#R = N + \#P \qquad (5\text{-}47)$$

As an example of the application of the Nyquist criterion to a simple case, consider the transfer function

$$KGH = \frac{A}{p(\tau p + 1)} \qquad (5\text{-}48)$$

This is the transfer function for a system which consists of an amplifier driving a motor.   The constant A is the product of the potentiometer constant, the motor constant, and the amplifier gain. τ is the time con-stant of the motor.   When p is replaced by $j\omega$, as discussed in Sec. 5-1, the KGH function is written as a function of frequency

$$KGH(j\omega) = \frac{A}{j\omega(j\omega\tau + 1)} \qquad (5\text{-}49)$$

To apply the Nyquist criterion it is necessary to make a plot of KGH as the frequency is varied from zero to infinity.   For definiteness, let τ be equal to 0.1 sec.

Use is made of the asymptotic approximation (Sec. 5-4) to plot the KGH function as the frequency is varied.   These Bode plots can be used in the following two ways:

1. The polar Nyquist plot can be made from the asymptotic approximation. The stability criterion can be based upon the polar diagram.

2. The stability criterion can be given directly in terms of the Bode diagram, i.e., decibel gain versus log frequency.

The first of the two above-mentioned methods is used to solve the example of Eq. (5-49).

The Bode diagram for the transfer function of Eq. (5-49) is constructed, as indicated in Sec. 5-4, by adding the plots for

$$\frac{A}{j\omega} \quad \text{and} \quad \frac{1}{0.1j\omega + 1} \tag{5-50}$$

This is shown in Fig. 5-19. The plot consists of a straight line with slope -6 db/octave until the frequency $\omega = 10$ is reached. From this corner

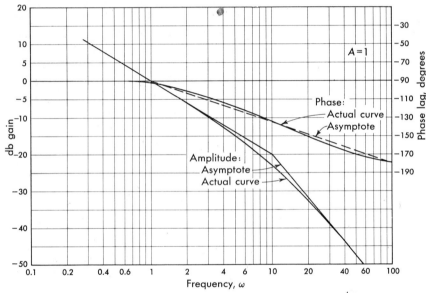

FIG. 5-19. Bode diagram (amplitude and phase) for $\dfrac{A}{(j\omega)(0.1j\omega + 1)}$.

frequency, the curve slopes at -12 db/octave. The curve is plotted for $A = 1$. A change in gain results in a vertical translation of the amplitude curve. The phase curve starts at $-90°$, corresponding to the pole at the origin $1/j\omega$, and continues to $-180°$ along an arctangent curve.

The polar plot is constructed from this Bode plot by plotting corresponding values of amplitude and phase at several frequencies, as shown in Fig. 5-20. Figure 5-20a is a plot of the contour in the p plane, and Fig. 5-20b is the contour mapped into the KGH plane. The arrows on each of these curves indicate the direction of increasing frequency.

Based on the Nyquist criterion, the system of this example (Fig. 5-20b) is stable. Examination of the transfer function of Eq. (5-49) shows that $\#P = 0$; i.e., there are no poles of KGH (and hence $1 + KGH$) in the right half plane. The number of encirclements of the -1 point is zero for any value of amplifier gain A. Hence the system has no roots in the right half plane and is stable for any value of gain.

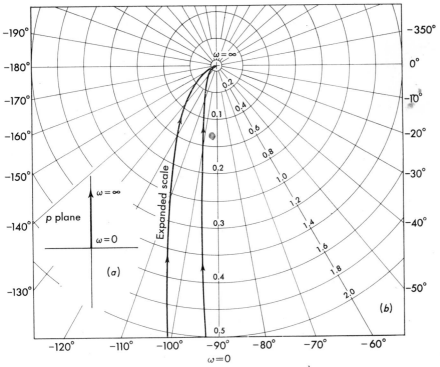

FIG. 5-20. Polar Nyquist diagram of $\dfrac{1}{j\omega(0.1j\omega + 1)}$.

As indicated in Chap. 4, the open-loop response KGH is used to determine the roots of $1 + KGH = 0$. With the frequency-analysis method, the open-loop frequency response KGH is plotted, in magnitude and phase angle, as a Bode plot. The frequency is varied from zero to infinity. When p is replaced by $j\omega$, KGH can be written as follows:

$$KGH(j\omega) = \frac{K_1(j\omega\tau_1 + 1)(j\omega\tau_3 + 1)}{(j\omega)^n(j\omega\tau_2 + 1)(j\omega\tau_4 + 1)} \tag{5-51}$$

It is convenient to put the transfer function in the form shown in Eq. (5-51). If the terms are not in the form $\tau p + 1$, for example

$$KGH = \frac{A(j\omega + 5)(j\omega + 2)}{[(j\omega)^2 + 3j\omega + 18](j\omega + 3)} \tag{5-52}$$

the expression can be divided through to obtain

$$KGH = \frac{A5[(j\omega/5) + 1]2[j(\omega/2) + 1]}{18[(j\omega)^2/18 + (j\omega/6) + 1]3[(j\omega/3) + 1]}$$
$$= \frac{10A}{54}\frac{[(j\omega/5) + 1][(j\omega/2) + 1]}{[(j\omega)^2/18 + (j\omega/6) + 1][(j\omega/3) + 1]} \quad (5\text{-}53)$$

This latter form has the advantage of isolating the factors that multiply

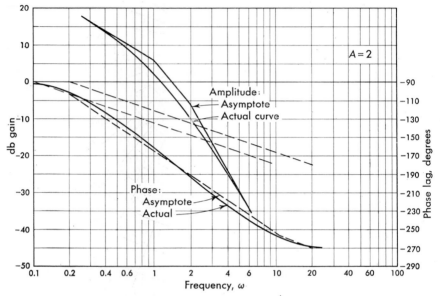

FIG. 5-21. Bode plot for $\dfrac{A}{(j\omega)(j\omega + 1)(\frac{1}{2}j\omega + 1)}$.

the gain. In this case the gain K is related to the amplifier gain as follows:

$$K = {}^{10}\!/_{54}A \quad (5\text{-}54)$$

Consider another example of a servo system which has the following KGH function:

$$KGH(j\omega) = \frac{A}{j\omega(j\omega + 1)(\frac{1}{2}j\omega + 1)} \quad (5\text{-}55)$$

The Bode plot is constructed, with the asymptotic approximation, in Fig. 5-21 for two amplifier gains: $A = 2$ and $A = 10$. The polar plot is constructed by plotting points of corresponding amplitude and phase at several values of frequencies. The plot for the KGH function of Eq. (5-55) is shown in Fig. 5-22. The lower value of gain $A_1 = 2$ results in a KGH plot which does not encircle the point -1 and the system is stable, since $\#P = 0$ by inspection of Eq. (5-55). The higher value gain

$A_2 = 10$ results in a *KGH* function which does encircle the point -1 as the frequency is varied from zero to infinity.   This system is unstable.

Utilizing an amplitude and phase plot of *KGH*, the Nyquist stability criterion enables the engineer to determine if any roots lie in the right half of the *p* plane.

The Nyquist stability criterion and the root-locus method for determining stability are perfect complements to each other.   When the

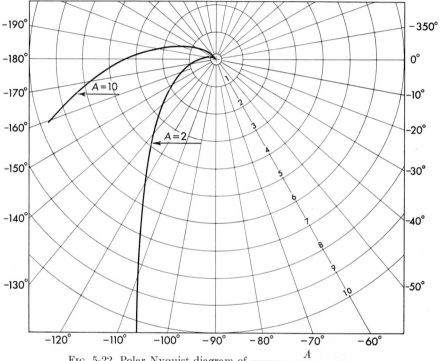

FIG. 5-22. Polar Nyquist diagram of $\dfrac{A}{(j\omega)(j\omega + 1)(\frac{1}{2}j\omega + 1)}$.

designer is in the initial stages of synthesizing a servo system, the root-locus method (based heavily on sketching) is most convenient for rapid analysis.   When the servomechanism is built, however, an amplitude and phase response can usually be run on most physical systems so that system stability can be studied from these experimentally determined curves. If a system is constructed of components whose transfer functions are not known analytically, an amplitude and phase response provides a method of approximating the transfer function experimentally (Sec. 5-14).   It seems, then, that root-locus techniques should be used when analytically designing servo systems.   The frequency-analysis method should be used when experimentally studying systems or when finding experimentally transfer functions which are difficult to derive analytically.

To facilitate the learning of the frequency-analysis method the student should be familiar with the shapes of various transfer functions. For this reason, several simple systems are included in Fig. 5-23 as polar Nyquist diagrams.

5-7. Stability Criterion with the Decibel Gain and Phase versus Frequency Diagrams. The db gain and phase versus logarithmic frequency method of plotting transfer functions of servo systems can be

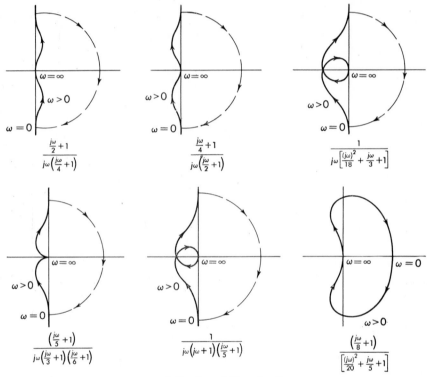

$$\frac{\frac{j\omega}{2}+1}{j\omega\left(\frac{j\omega}{4}+1\right)}$$

$$\frac{\frac{j\omega}{4}+1}{j\omega\left(\frac{j\omega}{2}+1\right)}$$

$$\frac{1}{j\omega\left[\frac{(j\omega)^2}{18}+\frac{j\omega}{3}+1\right]}$$

$$\frac{\left(\frac{j\omega}{5}+1\right)}{j\omega\left(\frac{j\omega}{3}+1\right)\left(\frac{j\omega}{6}+1\right)}$$

$$\frac{1}{j\omega(j\omega+1)\left(\frac{j\omega}{5}+1\right)}$$

$$\frac{\left(\frac{j\omega}{8}+1\right)}{\left[\frac{(j\omega)^2}{20}+\frac{j\omega}{5}+1\right]}$$

FIG. 5-23. Collection of Nyquist diagrams.

used in either of two ways. The amplitude and phase response plotted as a function of frequency (Bode diagram) can be transferred into a polar plot. This is done in the two examples of the previous section. Alternately, the stability criterion can be derived in a form applicable directly to the decibel and phase versus frequency diagram. For certain cases, it may be necessary to make the polar plot for purposes of clarifying the Bode plot. This step is frequently required for conditionally stable systems.

The stability criterion utilizing the polar diagram is based on the critical point -1. If the KGH locus encircles or goes through this point, the system has a root (provided $\#P = 0$, as is often the case) in the right half plane, or on the j axis, and hence is either unstable or marginally stable. The critical -1 point in the KGH plane is located in the Bode diagram by taking the logarithm

$$20 \log_{10} (-1) = 20 \log 1e^{-j180°} = 0 \text{ db} - j180° \qquad (5\text{-}56)$$

The critical point in the Bode diagram is 0 db on the amplitude curve and 180° on the phase curve, both at the same frequency. If the KGH curve encircles the -1 point on a polar plot, the magnitude of KGH will be greater than 1 when the phase shift is 180°. Hence, encirclement of the 0-db and 180° critical point in the Bode diagram means that the amplitude is greater than 0 db when the phase shift is 180°. Under this condition, the system has a root in the right half of the p plane and hence the system is unstable, again provided there are no poles in the right half plane. If the amplitude is exactly 0 db when the phase shift is 180°, then this corresponds to the polar KGH locus passing through the point -1, and the root lies on the j axis. Some examples of both stable and unstable systems are now considered.

5-8. Examples of Bode Construction. Suppose the following transfer function is investigated for its stability:

$$KGH = \frac{K}{p[(p/5) + 1][(p/10) + 1]} \qquad (5\text{-}57)$$

K is the constant gain of the loop, and the GH function is represented by a pole at the origin, at -5, and at -10. The Bode diagram consists of three components: one for the single pole at the origin and one each due to the other two poles. These are shown in Fig. 5-24.

The transfer function is written as a function of ω by replacing p with $j\omega$

$$KGH(j\omega) = \frac{K}{j\omega[(j\omega/5) + 1][(j\omega/10) + 1]} \qquad (5\text{-}58)$$

The corner frequencies at $\omega = +5$ and $\omega = +10$ are first located on the graph of Fig. 5-24. Notice that the frequency scale is logarithmic. Corresponding to the pole at the origin, a straight line, with a slope of -6 db/octave, is first drawn. This line is displaced because of K and goes through the 0-db axis at the point $\omega = 1/K$. In this example, $20 \log K$ is taken as -4 db. Corresponding to the pole at -5, arising from the term $1/[j(\omega/5) + 1]$, a straight line starting at $\omega = +5$ and dropping at -6 db/octave is drawn as shown in Fig. 5-24. The contribution from the term $1/[j(\omega/10) + 1]$ is a line which is asymptotic to 0 db out to the corner frequency, and then it drops off at -6 db/octave. The constant term K in the transfer function of Eq. (5-58) has no phase shift, and the amplitude curve is simply a straight line of magnitude $20 \log K$.

The phase-shift curves corresponding to each of these terms are inserted as shown on the figure. Due to the $1/j\omega$ term the phase is constant at $-90°$. Due to the term $1/[j(\omega/5) + 1]$ the phase proceeds from 0 to $-90°$ and intersects $-45°$ at the corner frequency $\omega = 5$. Corresponding to the term $1/[j(\omega/10) + 1]$ the phase shift changes from zero to $-90°$ and intersects the $-45°$ point at the corner frequency $\omega = 10$.

To obtain the complete frequency response of this system it is only necessary to add the four amplitude curves, obtaining the asymptotic approximation which is shown with a heavy line. The phase-shift curves

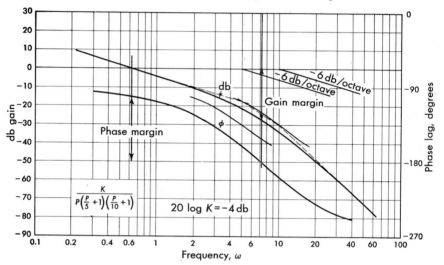

FIG. 5-24. Amplitude and phase response of $\dfrac{K}{j\omega[(j\omega/5) + 1][(j\omega/10) + 1]}$.

for the three terms are also added. This addition results in the composite phase-shift curve shown with the heavy line in Fig. 5-24. Generally, the information obtained from the asymptotes is satisfactory for the determination of stability. For this particular case when the phase shift is at 180°, the amplitude curve is below the 0-db line. If the gain in the example of Fig. 5-24 is greater, the system is closer to instability. In this latter case, the asymptotes would, of necessity, be faired in by noting that the true curve deviates from the asymptote by -3 db at each corner frequency and by -1 db at both half and twice the corner frequency. Another example is given to indicate the nature of the asymptotic approximation when the system is near instability.

Suppose the transfer function

$$KG(p) = \frac{K_1(p + 5)}{p^2(p + 10)} \qquad KG(j\omega) = \frac{\overbrace{\tfrac{1}{2}K_1}^{K}[j(\omega/5) + 1]}{(j\omega)^2[j(\omega/10) + 1]} \qquad (5\text{-}59)$$

be considered for investigation of stability. Note how the terms have been factored into the form $j\omega\tau + 1$. The break points are first located on the Bode diagram. The magnitude curves consist of four parts. The first is a constant, $20 \log_{10} K$. The second curve is contributed by $1/(j\omega)^2$ and is a straight line intersecting the $\omega = 1$ at 0 db with a slope -12 db/octave. The third curve is 0 db to the first break point ($\omega = 5$). From this point the amplitude rises at $+6$ db/octave. Because of the

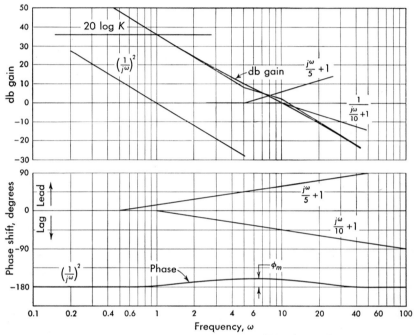

FIG. 5-25. Amplitude and phase of $\dfrac{K[(j\omega/5) + 1]}{(j\omega)^2[(j\omega/10) + 1]}$.

term $1/[j(\omega/10) + 1]$ the amplitude response is zero to the corner frequency $\omega = 10$. From this point the curve drops off at -6 db/octave. These curves are shown in Fig. 5-25.

The phase-shift curve for the constant K is zero and for the $1/(j\omega)^2$ term is a constant $-180°$. A variation from 0 to $+90°$ with the $45°$ point at the corner frequency $\omega = 5$ is contributed by the zero $j(\omega/5) + 1$. A variation from 0 to $-90°$ with the corner frequency phase shift $-45°$ results from the pole at $\omega = 10$. These phase curves are shown in Fig. 5-25. The separate amplitude curves of this system are added together, resulting in the total amplitude response shown by the heavy line on the figure. The phase-shift curves are also added, resulting in the composite system phase shift which is shown with a heavy line.

The actual amplitude curves are found from the asymptotes by raising the amplitude curve at each corner frequency $+3$ db for zeros and lowering at each corner frequency -3 db for poles, also adding (for zeros) or subtracting (for poles) 1 db at one-half and twice the corner frequency. The final amplitude curve is shown in Fig. 5-25 by the heaviest line. Because of the double pole, this system is near instability at the low-frequency end, but the zero produces phase lead which keeps the phase response of the composite system above 180° until the amplitude curve becomes less than 0 db.   To determine the point at which unit amplitude occurs, the smooth curve rather than the asymptote must be used.

5-9. *M* and *N* Contours—Nichols's Charts. The Nyquist stability criterion and the application of this criterion to the stability of servo systems also yield information regarding the degree of stability of a system.

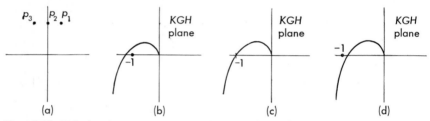

Fig. 5-26. Relation between nearness of approach to the point -1 and the root location.

If a root of $1 + KGH = 0$ exists on the j axis in the p plane, the plot of KGH goes through the point -1; see, for example, Fig. 5-14a and b of this section.   If the root is in the right half plane the plot of KGH would encircle the point -1.   The correspondence between the plot in the p plane and the map in the KGH plane can be further extended as in Fig. 5-26.

Figure 5-26b, c, and d indicates the mapping of the p plane onto the KGH plane for three locations of the root p_i.   If one of a pair of roots is located at the point p_1 on Fig. 5-26a, a plot somewhat as shown in Fig. 5-26b results as the frequency is varied from zero to infinity.   The KGH map encircles the point -1, which indicates that the transient component has two roots in the right half plane.   The system oscillates with increasing amplitude.   If, however, one of a pair of roots is located at the point p_2, the plot in the KGH plane resembles that of Fig. 5-26c, in which the curve goes through the point -1.   This system exhibits oscillations which neither build up nor die out.   If one of the roots is located at the point p_3, the corresponding plot of KGH neither encircles nor goes through the point -1 but misses the point, as shown in Fig. 5-26d.

The closer the root p_3 is to the axis, the closer the curve KGH is to the -1 point. On the basis of this, a relation exists between the nearness of approach to the point -1 in the KGH plane and the nearness to the j axis in the p plane. Since the distance from the j axis is the constant in the exponential term $\zeta \omega_n$, the damping ratio which exists in the system is related to the nearness of approach to the point -1. The nearness of approach of the KGH plot to the point -1 can be related exactly to the system damping ratio for a second-order differential equation. For higher-order systems, the relative stability can be approximated.

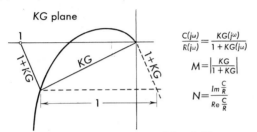

FIG. 5-27. Definition of M and N.

The M and N contours are based upon the closed-loop transfer function

$$\frac{C(j\omega)}{R(j\omega)} = \frac{KG(j\omega)}{1 + KG(j\omega)} \qquad (5\text{-}60)$$

for systems with unity feedback, $H = 1$. The open-loop transfer function $KG(j\omega)$ and the denominator $1 + KG(j\omega)$ are vectors. Both of these vectors are shown on Fig. 5-27. Equation (5-60) can be written in an alternate form (polar form):

$$\frac{C(j\omega)}{R(j\omega)} = \left| \frac{KG(j\omega)}{1 + KG(j\omega)} \right| \angle \tan^{-1} \frac{\text{Im } (C/R)(j\omega)}{\text{Re } (C/R)(j\omega)} \qquad (5\text{-}61)$$

where Im means "imaginary part of" and Re means "real part of." The M and N functions are defined in terms of the amplitude and phase of Eq. (5-61):

$$\frac{C(j\omega)}{R(j\omega)} = M \angle \tan^{-1} N \qquad (5\text{-}62)$$

Hence these functions are defined as follows:

$$M = \left| \frac{KG}{1 + KG} \right| \quad \text{and} \quad N = \frac{\text{Im } C(j\omega)/R(j\omega)}{\text{Re } C(j\omega)/R(j\omega)} \qquad (5\text{-}63)$$

The M and N curves are lines along which the magnitude is constant ($M = $ constant) and lines along which the phase angle is constant ($N = $ constant). On polar paper, these M and N curves are easily shown to be circles.

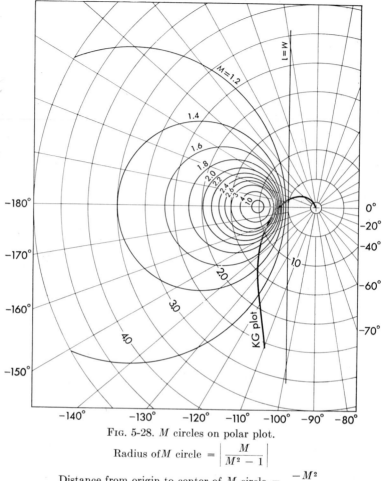

FIG. 5-28. M circles on polar plot.

$$\text{Radius of } M \text{ circle} = \left| \frac{M}{M^2 - 1} \right|$$

$$\text{Distance from origin to center of } M \text{ circle} = \frac{-M^2}{M^2 - 1}$$

The M circles are shown on Fig. 5-28. The larger the value of M, the smaller the circle about the point -1. These circles are not concentric about the point -1 but are located according to the expression

$$\text{Radius of } M \text{ circle} = \left| \frac{M}{M^2 - 1} \right|$$

$$\text{Distance from origin to center of } M \text{ circle} = \frac{-M^2}{M^2 - 1} \qquad (5\text{-}64)$$

The derivation of these expressions is included in Appendix VII. The smaller the value of M, the farther is the center of the circle from the point -1. A series of M circles is plotted on the polar plot for the particular function.   The KG function is tangent to some particular M circle, which corresponds to the maximum value of M (called M_p) for that particular KG.   From a knowledge of the value of M_p, an estimate of the damping ratio can be obtained.

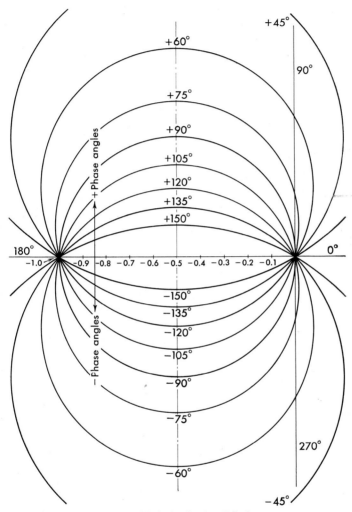

Fig. 5-29. N circles in the KG plane.

For example, in Fig. 5-28 the polar plot of $KG(j\omega)$ is shown as the frequency is varied from zero to infinity.   On this plot the curve is tangent to the $M = 3$ curve. M_p for this system is equal to 3.

The N circles are shown on Fig. 5-29.   The center of all circles lies along the line Re $KG = -\frac{1}{2}$.   The circles are located along this line according to the equations

$$\text{Radius of } N \text{ circle} = \sqrt{\frac{1}{4} + \left(\frac{1}{2N}\right)^2} \qquad (5\text{-}65a)$$

$$\text{Distance from negative real axis} = +\frac{1}{2N} \qquad (5\text{-}65b)$$

The N circles, which are also derived in Appendix VII, are significant in determining closed-loop phase shift. For systems whose feedback function is unity ($H = 1$), the phase shift between input and output is a constant if the KG locus runs along one of the N circles.

5-10. Nichols's Charts. Before the development of the root-locus techniques and the design of servo systems from their pole-zero configurations, the Nyquist, or frequency-analysis, technique was highly refined. As a result, a great number of extensions of Nyquist theory exist in this field today. The inverse KG locus, the magnitude and phase for inverse KG, M and N contours, and Nichols's charts are only a few. Reference to many of the texts cited in the bibliography[5,7,38,52] will yield a considerable amount of information about these other techniques.

In Sec. 5-3, the Bode diagram is constructed using decibel gain and the phase lag in degrees as vertical coordinates with frequency plotted horizontally against a logarithmic scale. The two plots are combined into one if the gain in decibels is plotted against the phase shift of KG. Used in this fashion the point -1 of the polar diagram maps into the 0-db and $-180°$ point on this rectangular diagram. The encirclements of this critical point are determined in the same way as for the standard polar plot.

Passing from the polar system to the rectangular is essentially a transformation. The M and N circles on the polar plot are transformed into M and N contours in the rectangular system. The plot of these contours for various values of M and N is known as a "Nichols chart," and one form of this chart is shown in Fig. 5-30. The use of the Nichols chart is similar to that described under the M and N circles using polar Nyquist diagrams except that a different set of coordinates is used. The rectangular system of coordinates is generally used in conjunction with the decibel gain and phase versus log frequency diagrams (Bode plots), since the same coordinates are plotted.

The Nyquist diagrams, however plotted, are all equivalent diagrams, and no further information can be inferred from one which cannot be similarly obtained from the other. The principal advantage of the Bode diagram choice of coordinates lies in the ease with which system modifications are translated into changes in the Nyquist diagram.

As an example of the use of the Nichols chart solution consider a

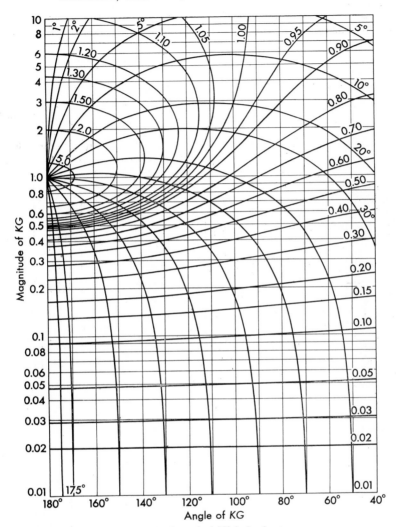

FIG. 5-30. A typical Nichols chart.

system that is represented by an open-loop transfer function of the following form:

$$KG = \frac{K_1}{p[p^2 + 60p + 10^4]} \qquad (5\text{-}66)$$

Suppose it is desired to find the value of K_v such that $M_p = 1.50$. The transfer function is rewritten

$$KG = \frac{K_1 \omega_n^{-2}}{p[(p/\omega_n)^2 + (2\zeta p/\omega_n) + 1]} \qquad (5\text{-}67)$$

where $\omega_n = 100$ radians/sec and $\zeta = 0.3$. When p is set equal to $j\omega$ and the substitution

$$u = \frac{\omega}{\omega_n} = \omega 10^{-2} \tag{5-68}$$

is made in Eq. (5-67), the transfer function becomes

$$KG(ju) = \frac{K_1 \omega_n^{-3}}{ju(1 - u^2 + 2j\zeta u)} \tag{5-69}$$

The magnitude of $KG(ju)/K_1\omega_n^{-3}$ is plotted by adding the plot of $|1/1 - u^2 + 2j\zeta u|$ to the straight line, which is the amplitude of $|1/ju|$,

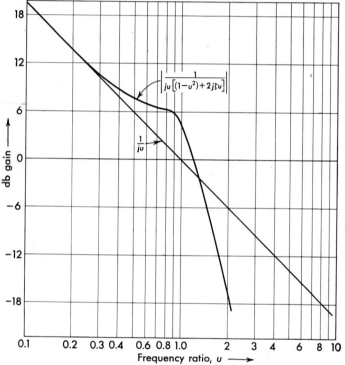

FIG. 5-31. Plot of $|G(ju)/K_1\omega_n^{-3}|$ versus u.

at -6-db/octave slope. This latter curve passes through the 0-db axis at $u = 1$. The amplitude curve is shown on Fig. 5-31.

The phase curve for $KG(ju)/K_1\omega_n^{-3}$ is plotted in Fig. 5-32 by adding $1/1 - u^2 + 2j\zeta u$ found in Fig. 5-4 to $-90°$.

The rectangular diagram, shown in Fig. 5-33, is constructed in a point-by-point fashion from Figs. 5-31 and 5-32. The Nichols chart in the form of a transparent template (Fig. 5-30) is superposed on top of Fig. 5-33 and shifted vertically until the locus of $KG(ju)/K_1\omega_n^{-3}$ is tangent to the $M = 1.5$ curve. To do this, the gain must be reduced by a factor of 3 (shown in Fig. 5-33). The $M = 1.5$ curve is drawn in Fig. 5-33 in the correct position. The resonant frequency found at the

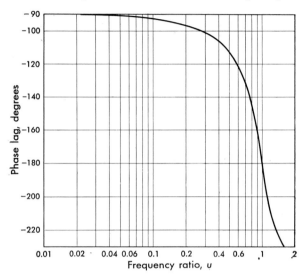

FIG. 5-32. Plot of the phase of $G(ju)/K_1\omega_n{}^{-3}$.

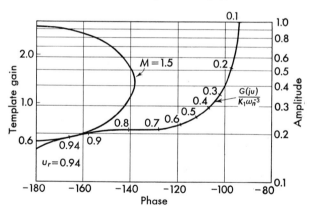

FIG. 5-33. Locus of $G(ju)/K_1\omega_n{}^{-3}$ plus $M = 1.5$ contour superimposed (gain factor $= \frac{1}{3}$)

point of tangency is $u_r = 0.94$ or

$$\omega_r = u_r\omega_n = 94 \text{ radians/sec} \qquad (5\text{-}70)$$

The velocity constant is given by

$$K_v = \frac{K_1}{\omega_n{}^2} = 33.3 \qquad (5\text{-}71)$$

5-11. Determining How Stable a System Is from the Frequency Method. Besides answering the question as to whether a system is or is not stable, the frequency-analysis method gives other information with respect to how stable the system is. That is, an approximation to the damping ratio ζ of the transient component of the closed-loop system can be obtained. For small values of damping ratio the KGH locus passes closer to the point -1 without enclosing it, as contrasted to large values of ζ which yield KGH plots that pass at some distance from the

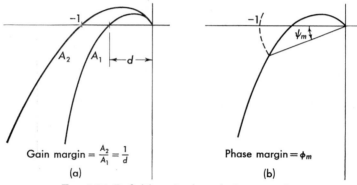

$$\text{Gain margin} = \frac{A_2}{A_1} = \frac{1}{d}$$

(a)

$$\text{Phase margin} = \phi_m$$

(b)

Fig. 5-34. Definition of gain and phase margin.

point -1. Two quantities which give damping-ratio information are known as the phase and gain margin and are defined as follows:

The *gain margin*, which is defined in Fig. 5-34a, is the factor by which the servo gain must be multiplied when the phase is 180° to produce marginal stability. Hence, if the system is stable with a gain A_1, the gain can increase or can be multiplied by the gain margin before marginal stability occurs. Marginal stability will result for a loop gain A_2 that causes the locus to pass through the -1 point. The gain A_2 is found as follows:

$$A_2 = \text{gain margin} \cdot A_1 = \frac{1}{d} A_1 \qquad (5\text{-}72)$$

where d is shown on Fig. 5-34a and is measured along the $-180°$ axis. Hence when the phase shift of KGH is 180°, the gain margin is the factor by which the gain can be multiplied to produce marginal stability.

The *phase margin* ϕ_m is 180° minus the phase lag that occurs at unity gain and is defined in Fig. 5-34b. The phase lag is read from the $KGH(j\omega)$ plot at the point where the magnitude of $KGH(j\omega)$ is unity. On a polar plot this angle is easily found with a compass. Place the point of the compass at the origin with the opposite end at the -1 point. Rotate the compass down, as shown on Fig. 5-34b, until it intersects the $KGH(j\omega)$ contour. The included angle is the phase margin ϕ_m.

The closeness of approach to the point -1 can be interpreted in terms of the damping ratio. In particular, the relationship between the damping ratio ζ and the phase margin ϕ_m can be calculated analytically for a second-order system. The curve relating the phase margin to the damping ratio is shown in Fig. 5-35. The equation for this curve is derived in Appendix VIII. It is not possible to obtain the curve relating the damping ratio to the gain margin, since, for a second-order system, only for infinite frequency does the system have a phase shift of 180°. Hence no value of gain will cause instability. It is shown in Chap. 4 that a second-order system is stable for any value of gain.

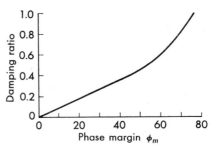

FIG. 5-35. Damping ratio ζ versus phase margin ϕ_m.

A good approximation to the ζ versus ϕ_m curve is found from the linear portion of Fig. 5-35. Reference to Appendix VIII, where the curve is derived, indicates that in the region

$$0 < \phi_m < 40° \tag{5-73}$$

the damping ratio is given approximately by

$$\zeta = \frac{\pi}{360} \phi_m \tag{5-74}$$

As an example of the use of phase and gain margin, consider again the example of Eq. (5-57). The phase and gain margin are read directly from Fig. 5-24. At the frequency where the amplitude characteristic crosses the 0-db line, the phase shift ϕ_0 is read as $-126°$. The phase margin is 54°. The system of Fig. 5-24, however, has no gain margin, since the phase shift is 180° only for a very large frequency, at which any multiplication of the gain has no effect. Often only one of the two margins (either gain or phase) yields useful information; as in this case, the meaningful one is used.

The *M criterion* is discussed in Sec. 5-9. The relative stability of a system can be ascertained from the nearness of approach of the KG locus to the -1 point. The problem of estimating the damping ratio from the Nyquist diagram is, however, only approximate. In many cases the nearness of approach to the point -1 is used to estimate the damping. Considering more quantitatively, the ratio of the distance from the origin to the distance from the point $p = -1$ is taken as a measure of the nearness to the point -1. This definition is arbitrary and is of value only if its use gives satisfactory results. The usefulness of this definition can be evaluated by comparison with other methods, for example, the root-locus technique of Chap. 4.

The maximum value of M, denoted by the symbol M_p, can be related to the closed-loop damping ratio. Large values of M_p, which refer to a large resonant rise in the closed-loop frequency response, correspond to small damping ratio. A small resonant rise, small M_p, corresponds to larger values of damping ratio.

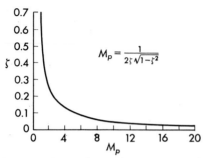

$$M_p = \frac{1}{2\zeta\sqrt{1-\zeta^2}}$$

Fig. 5-36. Damping ratio ζ versus maximum M (M_p).

The exact relationship between the damping ratio and M_p is determined for a second-order system. Only for this system,

$$G(p) = K/p(\tau p + 1)$$

and $H(p) = 1$, does a unique analytical relationship exist between M_p and ζ. This relationship, which is derived in Appendix VIII, is shown plotted in Fig. 5-36. The assumption is usually made that this same relationship is approximately correct for higher-order systems. Use of Fig. 5-36 will be found to be quite misleading if the system has several complex roots near the j axis. It is unfortunate, in fact, that this

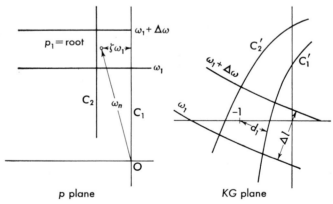

Fig. 5-37. Frequency-gradient method of approximating damping ratio.

relationship is least accurate for unusual systems where the engineer's experience and intuition are least reliable.

The most important use of M_p, phase margin, and gain margin is in determining the "relative stability" of a system. Even though these methods yield only approximate results in finding the absolute value of ζ, they are valuable in determining whether a change in a particular system has resulted in a greater or lesser degree of stability.

The *frequency gradient method* of estimating ζ is often more significant than the phase or gain margin or the M criterion in estimating the damping of the least stable roots. An approximate expression for the damping ratio can be obtained from the distance of nearest approach and the frequency gradient along the KG locus. The equation is derived from a consideration of Fig. 5-37 in which all the terms are defined. The ratio of distances in the p plane are approximately equal, for small distances, to the ratio of distances in the KG plane. For small ζ the distance $\zeta\omega_n$ is approximately $\zeta\omega_1$. The distance $\zeta\omega_1$ is related to d_1, the distance from the -1 point to the curve c_1', in the same manner in which the distance $\Delta\omega$ in the p plane is related to the distance Δl in the KG plane. Written in mathematical form,

$$\frac{\zeta\omega_1}{d_1} \approx \frac{\Delta\omega}{\Delta l} \qquad (5\text{-}75)$$

Equation (5-75) is rearranged

$$\zeta \approx \frac{d_1(\Delta\omega/\Delta l)}{\omega_1} \qquad (5\text{-}76)$$

This equation is often more reliable in the unusual cases where the damping is low. Since the M criterion often gives poorer results in these cases, it is a good complement. The degree of approximation becomes poorer, of course, as the distance of nearest approach becomes larger.

5-12. Comparison of Various Methods of Finding ζ. As an example of finding ζ for the least damped roots, the system of Fig. 5-38 is considered.

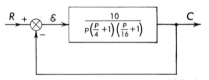

Fig. 5-38. Example system which is solved by several methods.

In this example it is necessary to determine: "How stable is this particular system?" The damping ratio ζ is computed by the following methods:

1. Root locus
2. M criteria
3. Phase margin
4. Frequency gradient

The root-locus plot for the system under consideration is shown on Fig. 5-39. The transfer function is written in the correct form for root-locus analysis as

$$KGH(p) = \frac{640}{p(p+4)(p+16)} \qquad (5\text{-}77)$$

Three trials are sufficient to locate the point on the locus where $K = 640$. From Fig. 5-39 the damping ratio is found to be $\zeta = 0.139$.

The polar Nyquist plot for the system of Fig. 5-38 is plotted in Fig. 5-40 from the expression

$$KG(j\omega) = \frac{10}{j\omega[(j\omega/4) + 1][(j\omega/16) + 1]} \qquad (5\text{-}78)$$

Several M circles are shown on this plot. The peak value of M, M_p, which corresponds to the circle that is tangent to the KG plot is 3.80. Reference to Fig. 5-36 indicates that an $M_p = 3.80$ corresponds to a damping ratio of $\zeta = 0.141$.

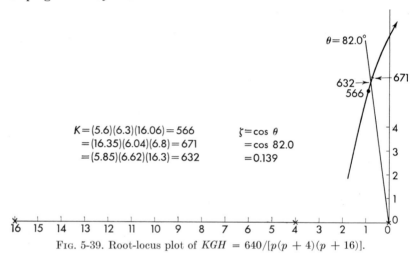

FIG. 5-39. Root-locus plot of $KGH = 640/[p(p + 4)(p + 16)]$.

The phase margin for this system is found from Fig. 5-40 to be $\phi_m = 16.7°$. From Fig. 5-35 the damping ratio is found to be $\zeta = 0.145$.

The damping ratio is estimated with the frequency gradient method by measuring the lengths and frequencies from Fig. 5-40. For this example,

$$d_1 = 0.60 \text{ in.} \qquad \omega_1 = 6 \text{ cps}$$
$$\Delta l = 0.42 \text{ in.} \qquad \Delta\omega = 0.6 \text{ cps}$$

These values are combined as follows:

$$\frac{d_1 \, \Delta\omega}{\omega_1 \, \Delta l} = \frac{(0.60 \text{ in.})(0.6 \text{ cps})}{(6 \text{ cps})(0.42 \text{ in.})} = 0.143 \qquad (5\text{-}79)$$

Table 5-1 shows the comparison of ζ found by the four methods. Comparison of the various methods of obtaining the damping ratio in

TABLE 5-1. COMPARISON OF METHODS OF COMPUTING DAMPING RATIO

Method used   Damping ratio

Root locus = 0.139
M criterion = 0.141
Phase margin = 0.145
Frequency gradient = 0.143

this particular example indicates a greater degree of agreement than can normally be expected. Since the system is only third order and since one of the poles, $p + 16$, is so far to the left the agreement is quite close.

In general, the more complex the system, the more the results obtained from the frequency-analysis methods deviate. In addition, the performance of a complex system cannot be described by a single quantity ζ but

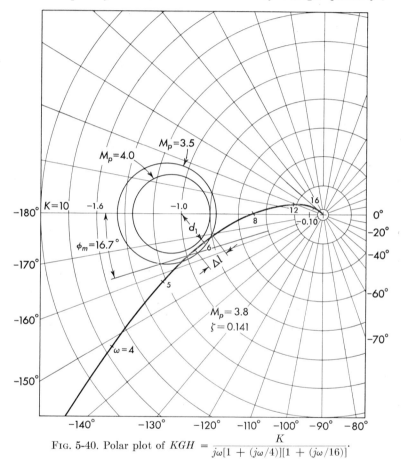

FIG. 5-40. Polar plot of $KGH = \dfrac{K}{j\omega[1 + (j\omega/4)][1 + (j\omega/16)]}$.

requires an understanding of where the roots are located and how changes in the system affect these locations. The root-locus method provides such information.

5-13. Closed-loop Frequency Response. In feedback-control-system design, the transfer function for which the Nyquist diagram is plotted is not the transfer function of the complete system with the feedback loop closed. Nor is it the transfer function of the open loop taken from input to output. It is the transfer function of the entire open loop taken from the point where it is open, around the loop, and back to that point again. It is, however, possible to obtain the transfer function and, hence, the frequency response of the closed loop. This transfer function for a single-loop system is given by

$$\frac{C(j\omega)}{R(j\omega)} = \frac{KG(j\omega)}{1 + KG(j\omega)\, H(j\omega)} = \frac{1}{H(j\omega)} \frac{KG(j\omega)\, H(j\omega)}{1 + KG(j\omega)\, H(j\omega)} \qquad (5\text{-}80)$$

The frequency response of the entire system can be determined by manipulating the KGH function into the form given in the last part of Eq. (5-80). Frequently this may be required, for a closed-loop servo, to ensure that the system satisfies the specifications.

The M contours represent the magnitude of $KG/(1 + KG)$ [or, alternately, $KGH/(1 + KGH)$]. When the values of M are read at points along the KG plot, a closed-loop amplitude-frequency plot is formed. The closed-loop phase response is available by reading points from the N contours. The Nichols chart of Fig. 5-30 is useful in obtaining the closed-loop frequency response. The KG locus is plotted on the Nichols chart similar to that which is done in Fig. 5-33. The closed-loop magnitude is read from the intersection of the KG locus with the M contour. The closed-loop phase response is read from the intersection with the N contour. By reading M and N at several values of frequency, the closed-loop frequency response is obtained.

If the transfer function has a feedback function $H(j\omega) \neq 1$, the result read from the Nichols chart must be divided, usually graphically,* by $H(j\omega)$ as indicated by Eq. (5-63).

These plots, however, represent one of the last stages of the problem and come only after questions of gain, stability, and steady-state errors have been answered. Any frequency-response specifications such as bandwidths can be determined from this over-all plot.

5-14. Experimental Data. One of the most important uses of the frequency method of servo analysis lies in the area of determining the transfer functions for certain components. Because of difficulty in analysis of pneumatic and hydrodynamic systems, magnetic amplifiers, rotating components, and the like, an analytic expression for the transfer function may be difficult to obtain. Pneumatic valves, for example, do not readily lend themselves to analytic determination. Very often, however, a frequency plot is obtained on these systems and the decibel gain and phase shift versus logarithmic frequency is plotted. The design can be constructed on the basis of an approximate transfer function determined from the experimentally derived frequency plots. Although the approximation problem in network synthesis and other fields of electrical engineering has been considered in great detail,[2,11] the asymptotic approxi-

* Reference 5, pp. 266–274, outlines such a procedure.

mations afforded by the Bode plots are most helpful in practical servo design.

Consider the example shown on Table 5-2 in which the experimental amplitude and phase characteristics of a system are tabulated. It is desired to obtain a transfer function which approximates these characteristics. If the characteristics are plotted, as in Fig. 5-41, against the logarithmic frequency, a series of straight lines can be fitted to these data.

TABLE 5-2. EXPERIMENTAL FREQUENCY DATA

f	ω	Decibel gain
60	377	−7.75
50	314	−4.3
40	251	−0.2
35	219	0.75
25	157	5.16
20	126	7.97
16	100	10.53
10	63	15.03
7	44	16.90
2.5	16	20.43
1.3	8	21.6
0.22	1.2	24.0
0	0	24.1

By noting the corresponding corner frequencies, a transfer function is obtained. For the example given in Fig. 5-41, an approximate transfer function is calculated from the amplitude curve

$$KGH = \frac{15.9}{(0.049p + 1)(0.0067p + 1)} \tag{5-81}$$

Often the phase response for the approximate transfer function will not completely agree with the experimental curve. The problem of obtaining the best match for both amplitude and phase curves is simplified if linear asymptotes are used for both amplitude and phase curves and the two curves are utilized simultaneously. The phase-shift curve can be approximated by the straight line of Fig. 5-8b.

Use of this approximate transfer function, Eq. (5-81), in conjunction with the remaining analytically obtainable transfer functions permits the servo engineer to analyze the system. A more accurate study may require that the actual element be used with a computer. An analogue computer can simulate all of the system except the actual element. Very often, however, such a computer or simulator is difficult to locate and expensive to use. Careful application of an experimentally determined

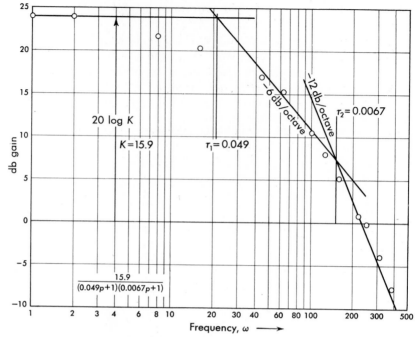

FIG. 5-41. Approximate transfer function for experimental data.

transfer function yields useful, although approximate, information in quite a short time.

Having once obtained a transfer function from this frequency analysis, the engineer continues the synthesis of the servo by means of the root-locus techniques described in Chap. 4.

PROBLEMS

5-1. Derive the sinusoidal steady-state transfer functions for the systems of Fig. 5P-1.

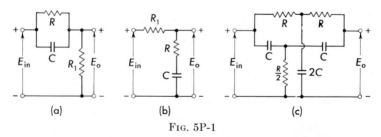

FIG. 5P-1

5-2. Plot the amplitude and phase response of the transfer function of Prob. 5-1 for $R_1 = 0.5R = 100K$ and $C = 1uf$.

5-3. Find the sinusoidal steady-state transfer functions for the systems of Prob. 2-2, Chap. 2.

5-4. Show that the substitution $p = j\omega$ is applicable to find the steady-state solution for any linear differential equation (system) with constant coefficients when the driving function is sinusoidal and the initial conditions are zero.

5-5. Plot the rise in the amplitude-frequency response versus the damping ratio ζ for the function

$$y = \frac{e_o}{e_{in}} = \frac{1}{(1 - u^2) + j2\zeta u}$$

where

$$u = \frac{\omega}{\omega_n}$$

5-6. Use the asymptotic approximation to construct amplitude and phase diagrams versus log frequency for the following transfer functions:

(a) $\dfrac{1}{p}$

(b) $\dfrac{1}{(p + 5)(p + 10)}$

(c) $\dfrac{1}{p(p + 5)}$

(d) $\dfrac{5p + 1}{20p + 1}$

(e) $\dfrac{1}{p(4p^2 + 3p + 2)}$

(f) $\dfrac{9(p^3 + 2p + 1)}{3p^3 + 4p^2 + 7p + 2}$

5-7. Sketch polar diagrams for the following transfer function:

(a) $\dfrac{1}{\tau_1 p + 1}$

(b) $\dfrac{\tau_1 p + 1}{\tau_2 p + 1}$

(c) $\dfrac{1}{(\tau_1 p + 1)(\tau_2 p + 1)}$

where $\tau_1 = 5$, $\tau_2 = 20$.

5-8. From the curves of Prob. 5-6, plot polar Nyquist plots for the given transfer functions, and from the polar diagrams determine the stability of each system.

5-9. Construct amplitude and phase versus log frequency diagrams for the transfer functions of Prob. 4-7 of Chap. 4. Estimate the gain that will result in a damping ratio of 0.2.

5-10. Plot a Bode plot for

$$\frac{10K(p + 1)}{p^2(p + 10)}$$

and discuss stability for various values of K.

5-11. Obtain the transfer function for the amplitude curve shown on Fig. 5P-11.

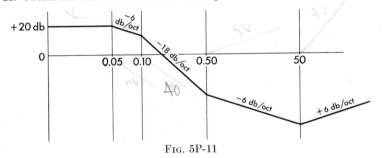

Fig. 5P-11

5-12. Plot a polar Nyquist diagram for the function

$$KGH = \frac{K}{p(p/4 + 1)(p/16 + 1)(4p + 1)}$$

for $K = 1$ and $K = 4$. Which is stable?

5-13. For the system of Prob. 5-12 with $K = 1$, obtain an approximation to the damping ratio by each of the following four methods:

> (a) M criterion   (b) Root locus
> (c) Phase margin   (d) Frequency gradient

Compare results.

5-14. The open-loop response of a control system is given by

$$y = \frac{K}{p(p + 1)(p/5 + 1)}$$

Find K such that the closed loop response has a damping ratio equal to 0.20, which corresponds to an $M_p = 2.54$.

5-15. Use the M criterion to determine the gain K that corresponds to a $\zeta = 0.2(M_p = 2.54)$ for the systems of Prob. 4-9, Chap. 4.

5-16. A position servo consists of an electronic amplifier (which has a transfer function of A), a magnetic power amplifier, and a motor. The motor transfer function

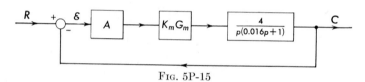

FIG. 5P-15

is $4.0/p(0.016p + 1)$, and the transfer function of the magnetic amplifier is $K_M G_M$. The block diagram for the system is shown in Fig. 5P-15. The experimental frequency data on the magnetic amplifier was taken and is shown in the table. Determine the gain A so that the system has a damping ratio of 0.20.

Frequency f	Decibel gain	Phase shift, deg
120	−7.8	−165
100	−4.3	−160
80	−0.2	−159
70	0.75	−151
50	5.16	−139
40	7.97	−128
32	10.53	−126
20	15.03	−90
14	16.90	−55
5	20.43	−37
2.5	21.6	−27
0.5	24.0	−10
0	24.0	0

5-17. Use the Nichols chart to plot the closed-loop frequency response $KG/(1 + KG)$ for Prob. 5-14 with each of the following values of M_p: 1.3, 2.0, and 5.0.

5-18. Three identical amplifiers with the individual characteristics shown on Fig. 5P-18 are ganged together.   The 3-db points are as shown.

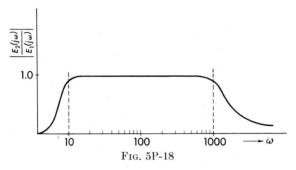

Fig. 5P-18

(a) What is the transfer function of the ganged amplifiers, that is, what is the open-loop transfer function?

(b) Show in a polar plot the combined characteristic of the ganged amplifiers. Can the closed-loop system utilizing the ganged amplifiers in the open loop be unstable?   Why?

CHAPTER 6

SERVOMECHANISM EQUALIZATION

6-1. Introduction. The design of a feedback control system involves a compromise between the magnitude of the steady-state error and the degree of stability. After the first analysis of the system it may be found that the system has too great a steady-state error (possibly K_v is too small). Alternatively, the steady-state errors may be within specification, but the system is too close to instability (i.e., the damping ratio is too small). In either case the system must be "equalized." In general terms, servo equalization consists of changing the loop gain, adding zeros and poles, or making any change that will bring the steady-state error and the degree of stability within the desired specification.

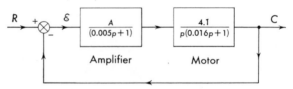

FIG. 6-1. Position servo system.

6-2. Equalization by Gain Adjustment. As an example, consider the system of Fig. 6-1 which has an open-loop transfer function

$$KG = \frac{4.1A}{p(0.005p + 1)(0.016p + 1)} \tag{6-1}$$

Suppose that the steady-state error requirement is met by this system but that the damping is too low. The reduction in gain necessary to increase the damping ratio from 0.1 to 0.2 is obtained from the root-locus plot of Fig. 6-2 as

$$K_{(\zeta=0.2)} = 0.64K_{(\zeta=0.1)} \tag{6-2}$$

The error coefficient K_v, however, is reduced by the same factor as the gain. Although the stability is improved, the velocity error is increased. If the system is simple, it may be expedient to equalize by gain reduc-

172

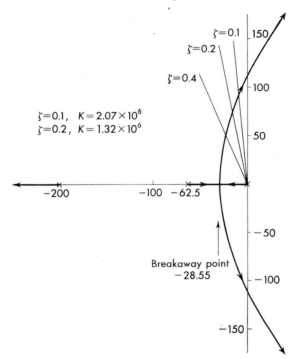

FIG. 6-2. Root-locus plot for the system with transfer function

$$\frac{4.1A}{(0.016)(0.005)} \; \frac{1}{p(p + 200)(p + 62.5)}$$

tion.   In general an optimum system does not result, and in more complex cases gain variation alone is not sufficient.

6-3. Equalization by Inserting a Network.   When the system requires an improvement in the steady-state error or the degree of stability which is greater than that which can be obtained by gain variation, the insertion of a network in the loop may be required.   Consider, for example, the system of Fig. 6-1 with a network, of transfer function G_N, inserted in the forward loop, shown in Fig. 6-3.   It is again desired to raise ζ to 0.2 but without sacrificing the magnitude of gain.

The amplifier time constant is 0.005 and the amplifier gain is A.   The network, which is shown in Fig. 6-4, is inserted in the loop at a point

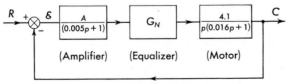

FIG. 6-3. Equalized position servo.

where the impedance which is seen by the network is low (ideally zero) and the impedance which loads the output of the network is high (ideally infinite). The transfer function of the network chosen for this example is

$$G_N(p) = \frac{p + (1/\tau_1)}{p + (1/\tau_2)} \qquad (6\text{-}3)$$

where $\qquad \tau_1 = R_1 C \qquad$ and $\qquad \tau_2 = \dfrac{R_1 R_2 C}{R_1 + R_2} \qquad (6\text{-}4)$

As a first case, suppose $R_1 = R_2$ and it is required to determine the value of the RC product that will yield the maximum velocity-error

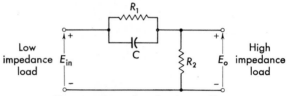

FIG. 6-4. A passive circuit equalizer.

coefficient K_v, which corresponds to the minimum error for $\zeta = 0.2$. If RC is represented by τ, the open-loop transfer function is

$$KG(p) = \frac{A (5.13 \times 10^4)[p + (1/\tau)]}{p(p + 200)(p + 62.5)[p + (2/\tau)]} \qquad (6\text{-}5)$$

The transfer function of Eq. (6-5) is written in standard form for root-locus solution. The velocity coefficient is

$$\begin{aligned}
K_v &= \lim_{p \to 0} \frac{A (5.13 \times 10^4)(p + 1/\tau)}{(p + 200)(p : 62.5)(p + 2\tau)} \\
&= \frac{A (5.13 \times 10^4)(1/\tau)}{(200)(62.5)(2/\tau)} \cong 2A
\end{aligned} \qquad (6\text{-}6)$$

It is to be noticed that the network changes K_v by a factor of 2 because $R_1 = R_2 = R$ acts as a voltage divider. The method of optimizing this system is outlined as follows:

1. The poles and zeros are located on the p plane.

2. The $\zeta = 0.2$ line is drawn from the origin ($\theta = \cos^{-1} \zeta$, where θ is measured from the negative real axis).

3. The one variable pole and one variable zero are moved along the negative real axis. For the different positions of the pole and zero, the point is found on the $\zeta = 0.2$ line where the sum of the angles equals 180°.

4. The gain is determined at this point $KG(p) = 1$, which yields a closed-loop damping ratio of $\zeta = 0.20$ for the specific value of τ.

A typical root-locus sketch is shown on Fig. 6-5 for one location of the equalizer zero and pole ($1/\tau = 120$). This zero and pole are moved along the real axis until an optimum K_v is obtained for a specific damping ratio of $\zeta = 0.20$.   Included in Fig. 6-6 is a plot of K_v versus the time constant $1/RC = 1/\tau$.   A maximum K_v $(= 168)$ occurs for a $\tau = RC = 8.33$ msec. An improvement in K_v of approximately a factor of 3 results by inserting the network of Fig. 6-4 with $R_1 = R_2$, since the velocity constant is approximately 50 for $1/RC = 0$.

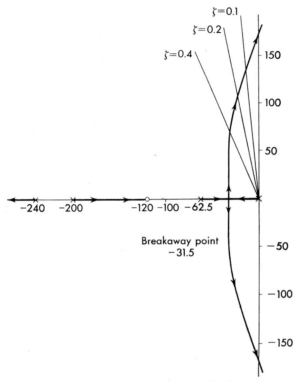

FIG. 6-5. A typical root-locus plot for

$$\frac{4.1A}{(0.016)(0.005)} \frac{p + 120}{p(p + 200)(p + 62.5)(p + 240)}$$

As the final step, suppose that R_1 is not held equal to R_2 but that in optimizing this system the amplifier gain is limited to 1,000.   Since the zero and the pole now bear no specific relation (τ_2/τ_1 not necessarily equal to $\frac{1}{2}$), more freedom is available and a larger K_v is possible.   The problem now becomes somewhat complicated because an optimum must be found when two quantities are varying simultaneously.   The problem is attack by holding the ratio of τ_2/τ_1 fixed and plotting a curve of K_v versus $1/\tau_1$.   By taking several τ_2/τ_1 ratios, an optimum solution is approached.   To determine the values of R_1, R_2, and C that give a maximum K_v

it is necessary to use a technique of successive approximations. The velocity constant K_v is given by

$$K_v = \lim_{p \to 0} pKG(p) = \lim_{p \to 0} \frac{A5.13 \times 10^4[p + (1/\tau_1)]}{(p + 200)(p + 62.5)[p + (1/\tau_2)]}$$

$$K_v = A \frac{5.13 \times 10^4}{1.25 \times 10^4} \frac{\tau_2}{\tau_1} = 4.1A \frac{\tau_2}{\tau_1} \tag{6-7}$$

where $\tau_2 = [R_1R_2/(R_1 + R_2)]C$ and $\tau_1 = R_1C$. The method of solution consists of plotting a family of K_v versus $1/\tau_1$ curves for several specific

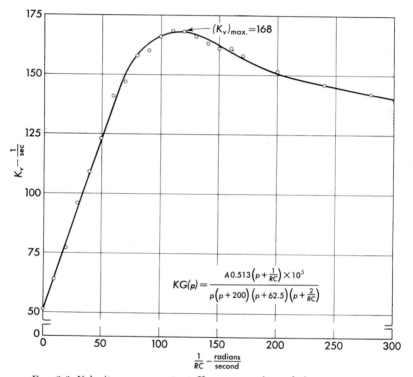

FIG. 6-6. Velocity-error constant K_v versus reciprocal time constant.

ratios of τ_2/τ_1. Examination of these curves indicates how K_v depends upon the parameter τ_2/τ_1. Interpolation between the curves results in the maximum K_v possible with a fixed value of $A = 1,000$.

The method of optimizing this system is outlined in the following step-by-step procedure:

1. Obtain curves of K_v versus $1/\tau_1$ for the specific parameter values of $\tau_2/\tau_1 = 0.1, 0.2, 0.3, 0.4, 0.6, 0.7, 0.8,$ and 0.9. The method used to obtain the curves is the same as the previous case. The curves for these ratios are shown in Fig. 6-7. The maximum value of K_v increases with-

out limit as τ_2/τ_1 approaches zero. Each curve has only one maximum which is located near the point $1/\tau_1 = 120$. As K_v increases, A increases. This indicates that K_v is limited only by the maximum value of amplifier gain A available. In this problem A is limited to 1,000.

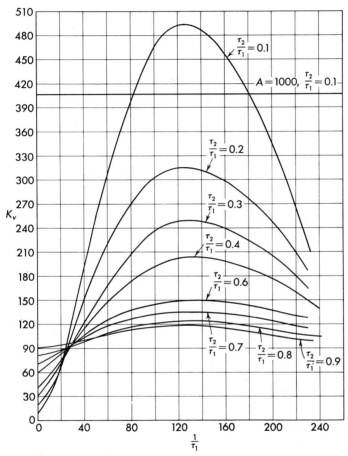

FIG. 6-7. Velocity-error constant K_v versus $1/\tau_1$ for different ratios of τ_2/τ_1.

2. Calculate the velocity constant K_v for $\tau_2/\tau_1 = 0.1$ and 0.2 with $A = 1,000$. With $\tau_2/\tau_1 = 0.2$ the maximum K_v results for a gain of less than 1,000. The maximum K_v, which is obtained when $\tau_2/\tau_1 = 0.1$, occurs when the gain is in excess of 1,000. The ratio of τ_2/τ_1 necessary to obtain a maximum K_v with the gain A limited to 1,000 lies between $\tau_2/\tau_1 = 0.1$ and $\tau_2/\tau_1 = 0.2$.

3. Interpolate between $\tau_2/\tau_1 = 0.1$ and $\tau_2/\tau_1 = 0.2$ to determine the accurate value of τ_2/τ_1 for $A = 1,000$. Various values of τ_2/τ_1 are chosen between 0.1 and 0.2 for two values of $1/\tau_1$ (= 120 and 128). The two

corresponding curves, which are included in Fig. 6-8, are plotted for K_v versus τ_2/τ_1. A line which satisfies the equation

$$K_v = 4,100 \, \frac{\tau_2}{\tau_1}$$

is drawn through these curves. Where this line intersects the curve, a ratio of τ_2/τ_1 is obtained which provides a maximum K_v for each value of $1/\tau_1$.

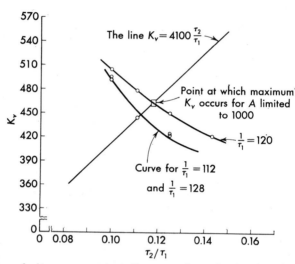

FIG. 6-8. The velocity-error constant K_v versus the ratio of τ_2/τ_1 for three different values of $1/\tau_1$, also the line $K_v = 4,100 \, \tau_2/\tau_1$.

4. Plot the maximum K_v values versus $1/\tau_1$, which are found in step 3, for $A = 1,000$. Figure 6-9 shows the plot of this example. The maximum occurs for $\tau_2/\tau_1 = 0.118$ and $1/\tau_1 = 120$. A maximum K_v of 463 is obtained. This is an improvement by a factor of nearly 10.

5. Calculate the component values from the optimum conditions of step 4. From the values $1/\tau_1 = 120$ and $\tau_2/\tau_1 = 0.118$ the component values are specified as follows:

$$\frac{R_2}{R_1 + R_2} = 0.118 \quad \text{and} \quad C = \frac{1.112 \times 10^{-3}}{R_2} \quad (6\text{-}8)$$

R_1, R_2, and C cannot be found in absolute value unless some other condition, such as input or output impedance, is specified. In a practical circuit the impedance level at the point where the network is to be inserted must be considered.

6-4. Method of Servomechanism Equalization. The example of the previous section indicates the method of equalizing a system with a passive circuit.   Although a procedure requiring a trial-and-error approach is presented, each trial is rapidly analyzed and a solution is obtained. The procedure can be generalized with the following outline:

1. Determine the constants and transfer functions of all the "unalterable" components.   For example, a position servo requires a motor to drive the output shaft.   This is an unalterable component, since without the motor there would be no servo and most motor transfer functions

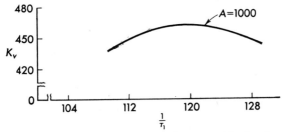

FIG. 6-9. The velocity-error constant K_v versus $1/\tau_1$ for $A = 1,000$.

are identical in form.   Use frequency techniques to determine the transfer functions of difficult components.

2. Determine the steady-state errors.   Add any necessary poles at the origin to reduce this error (in many systems this is not necessary, since the unalterable components contain poles at the origin).

3. Determine the degree of stability of the basic system.   If this is not satisfactory (that is, ζ too small), choose a network.

4. Move the zeros and poles of the network until a suitable degree of stability is obtained.

Since the first choice of a network requires some experience, the next sections consider some common networks that can be used to equalize simple servo systems.

A myriad of electric networks exists for servo compensation.   These networks consist of zeros and poles which are introduced either to shift the unstable branches of the locus back into the left half plane or to alter the gain gradient (variation of a point on the locus with a change in gain) along the locus.   It is often impossible to accomplish both of these

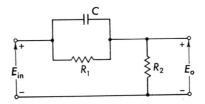

FIG. 6-10a. Passive circuit lead network.

effects with one network.   Certain networks have a greater effect than others.

6-5. Passive Circuit Lead Network.   The circuit of a lead network, sometimes referred to as a passive circuit differentiator, is shown in Fig. 6-10a.   The transfer function for this network, with zero source and infinite load impedance, is

$$\frac{E_o}{E_{in}} = G(p) = \frac{p + (1/a\tau)}{p + (1/\tau)} \qquad (6\text{-}9)$$

where $a = 1 + (R_1/R_2)$ and $\tau = R_1 R_2 C/(R_1 + R_2)$. The network is represented on the p plane of Fig. 6-10b by a pole at $p = -1/\tau$ and a zero at $p = -1/a\tau$. The zero is closer to the origin than the pole, and the ratio of the two distances is a. The example of the previous section indicates that an improvement of about a factor of 10 in K_v is possible by appropriately choosing the component values for the lead network. If τ is small, both the pole and the zero are remote and effectively cancel each other. As τ is made larger, the zero enters the region where the locus is affected. For very large τ, the pole also becomes significant.

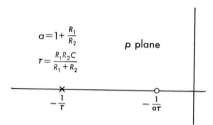

FIG. 6-10b. Zero-pole configuration for a lead network.

As another example, consider the effect of inserting a passive circuit lead network into a third-order system. The open-loop transfer function

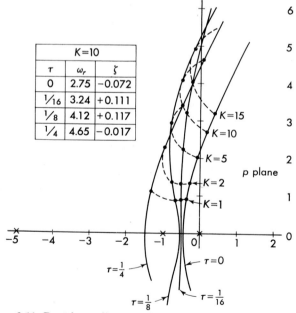

K=10		
τ	ω_r	ζ
0	2.75	−0.072
$\frac{1}{16}$	3.24	+0.111
$\frac{1}{8}$	4.12	+0.117
$\frac{1}{4}$	4.65	−0.017

FIG. 6-11. Root-locus diagrams for the system transfer function

$$G(p)H(p) = \frac{20K}{p(p + 1)(p + 5)} \frac{p + (1/4\tau)}{p + (1/\tau)}$$

for the system and equalizer is

$$KGH = \underbrace{\frac{20K}{p(p+1)(p+5)}}_{\text{system}} \underbrace{\frac{p+(1/4\tau)}{p+(1/\tau)}}_{\text{equalizer}} \qquad (6\text{-}10)$$

This is plotted on Fig. 6-11 for several values of τ. Points are connected on each locus for gains of 1, 2, 5, 10, and 15. The lead network, as can be seen from Fig. 6-11, produces a different effect depending upon both τ and K. Generally, the lead network increases the damping ratio ζ and also increases the frequency of oscillation.

6-6. Passive Lag Network. A passive circuit lag network, which is often termed an integrator, is shown in Fig. 6-12a. For zero source and infinite load impedance the transfer function is

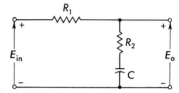

FIG. 6-12a. Passive circuit lag network.

$$\frac{E_o}{E_{in}} = G(p) = \frac{1}{a}\frac{p+(1/\tau)}{p+(1/a\tau)} \qquad (6\text{-}11)$$

where $a = 1 + (R_1/R_2)$
$\qquad \tau = R_2C$

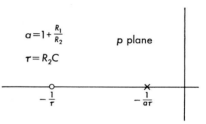

FIG. 6-12b. Zero-pole configuration for a lag network.

Insertion of a lag network in a system produces a zero and pole in the p plane. The zero is located at $-1/\tau$, and the pole at $-1/a\tau$. As can be seen from Fig. 6-12b, the pole is closer to the origin. If τ is large, both zero and pole are near the origin and show no stabilizing effect except to introduce another root which is near the zero (located at $1/\tau$) for all values of gain. Such a root gives rise to a response with a long time constant (approximately equal to τ). As τ is decreased, the zero approaches the other roots and has a stabilizing effect. For still smaller τ, the pole becomes effective and exerts a destabilizing effect.

The system of Fig. 6-11 is again stabilized but with a lag network instead of a lead network. The transfer function for the system containing the lag network can be written

$$KGH = \frac{5K/4}{p(p+1)(p+5)}\frac{p+(1/\tau)}{p+(1/4\tau)} \qquad (6\text{-}12)$$

The root-locus plot for several values of τ is shown in Fig. 6-13. Points of constant K (5 and 10) are connected on each locus. Inspection of these loci indicates that with a careful choice of τ the system can be made more stable.   It should be noticed, however, that with an improper choice of τ the system can be made less stable.

Lag networks possess certain disadvantages.   If the time constant τ is too large, a long exponential root occurs in the system.   The effect of this root can be minimized by keeping the zero close to the pole.   The root-locus diagrams of Fig. 6-13 show the location of the root with the

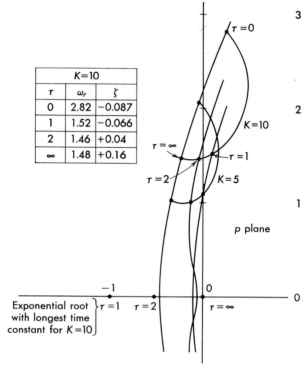

K=10		
τ	ω_r	ζ
0	2.82	−0.087
1	1.52	−0.066
2	1.46	+0.04
∞	1.48	+0.16

Fig. 6-13. Root-locus diagrams for the system transfer function

$$G(p)H(p) = \frac{5K/4}{p(p+1)(p+5)} \frac{p+(1/\tau)}{p+(1/4\tau)}$$

longest time constant for $K = 10$.   The choice of a value of τ which will provide effective stabilization with a satisfactory exponential time constant is often impossible.

6-7. Summary of Various Equalizer Networks.   In an effort to present some of the possibilities available with passive circuit networks, Table 6-1 is included.   The circuit for the network, the transfer function, and the zero-pole configuration are given for each case.

Only simpler networks are included in the table.   The positions of the zeros and poles are given on the p plane or can be discerned from the transfer function.   As an example, suppose it is desired to locate the poles of network $-d$ given in Table 6-1.   The poles are found by factor-

TABLE 6-1. COMMON PASSIVE CIRCUIT EQUALIZER NETWORKS

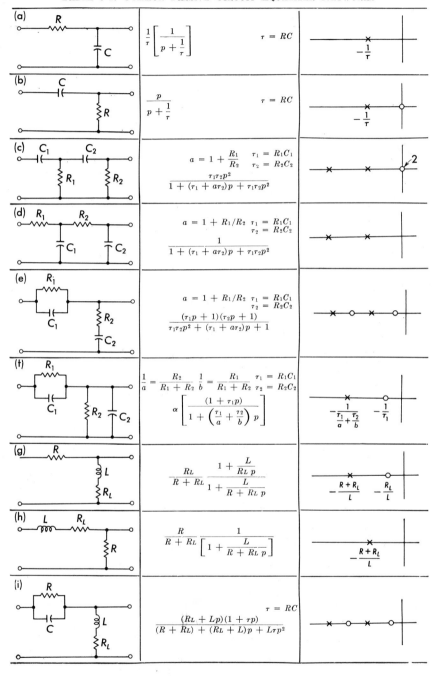

ing the denominator with the binomial expression

$$\frac{1}{\tau_1\tau_2}\left[-\frac{(\tau_1+a\tau_2)}{2}\pm\sqrt{\frac{(\tau_1+a\tau_2)^2}{4}-\tau_1\tau_2}\right] \tag{6-13}$$

The locations of these poles are found by substituting numerical values into Eq. (6-13). This same denominator is common to several of the networks on Table 6-1.

TABLE 6-2. SEVERAL ADJUSTABLE NETWORKS

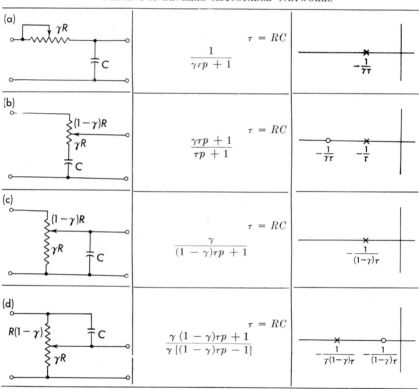

The transfer functions for the networks of both Tables 6-1 and 6-2 are derived for zero source and infinite load impedance. When the network is used in an application where these impedance conditions are not fulfilled, the transfer functions deviate from the ideal.

6-8. Adjustable Networks. The ability to adjust experimentally a single potentiometer and hence alter the zero-pole configuration of an equalizer is often most valuable in servo design. Besides reshaping the root-locus plots, an adjustable network is often necessary for setting the phase shift in an a-c servo (cf. Chap. 7). Table 6-2 includes the circuits, transfer functions, and zero-pole configurations for several adjustable networks. The time constant τ for all networks is RC. The fraction of total rotation of the potentiometer is represented by γ.

Figure 6-14a presents an adjustable network which is shown in Chap. 7 to be valuable for phase shifting a-c control systems. The transformer has a center-tapped secondary. The transfer function, for the conditions of small source and large load impedance, is

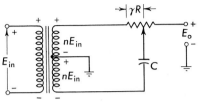

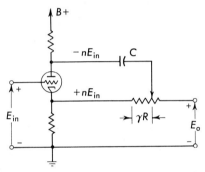

Fig. 6-14a. Adjustable phase-shift network (passive).

$$\frac{E_o}{E_{in}} = n \frac{1 - p\tau\gamma}{1 + p\tau\gamma} = n \frac{1 - j\omega\tau\gamma}{1 + j\omega\tau\gamma}$$
$$= n\angle -2\tan^{-1}\omega\tau\gamma \quad (6\text{-}14)$$

Since the voltages nE_{in} applied to this network are derived from a transformer, the transfer function of Eq. (6-14) is not applicable at zero frequency. If the voltages are derived at the output of a d-c phase inverter, as shown in Fig. 6-14b, Eq. (6-14) is applicable at zero frequency. Equation (6-14) represents a so-called "allpass network"; that is, as γ is varied

Fig. 6-14b. Adjustable phase-shift network (active).

there results essentially no amplitude change, while the phase lag is variable from 0 to -180 for a fixed frequency. The zero-pole configuration for this phase shifter is shown in Fig. 6-15 for two specific values of γ.

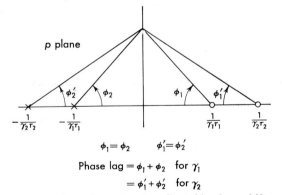

$\phi_1 = \phi_2 \qquad \phi_1' = \phi_2'$

Phase lag $= \phi_1 + \phi_2$ for γ_1
$= \phi_1' + \phi_2'$ for γ_2

Fig. 6-15. Zero-pole configuration for adjustable phase-shift network.

6-9. Parallel Equalization. Previous methods of equalization are termed "series equalization" because networks with the appropriate zero-pole configuration are inserted in the forward (or series) loop. With

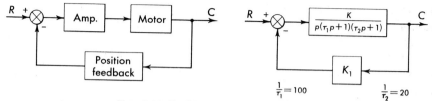

FIG. 6-16. Position servo block diagram.

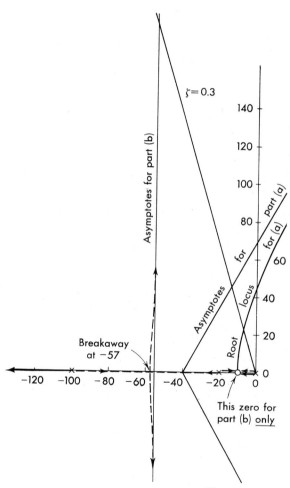

FIG. 6-17. a. Root locus for $\dfrac{K}{p(p+20)(p+100)}$.

b. Root locus for $\dfrac{K(p+10)}{p(p+20)(p+100)}$.

"parallel equalization" the equalizing network is inserted in the feedback path of the control system. Use of this form of equalization usually leads to multiple-loop* systems. Since there exists a large number of a-c transducers, this method provides an especially good means for stabilizing servos where the signal is all alternating current.†

Consider the example of Fig. 6-16 where the simple position servo of Chap. 1 is shown. The amplifier time constant is τ_1, and τ_2 is the motor time constant. For a gain K of 24×10^4 the system roots, shown on

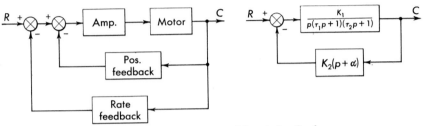

Fig. 6-18. Position servo with rate feedback.

the root-locus sketch of Fig. 6-17a, cross the j axis and the system becomes unstable. Suppose that an output-shaft rate signal is added to the position signal and fed back to the input, as in Fig. 6-18. In this figure α is the ratio of the position feedback voltage to the rate feedback voltage. The same numerical values as used in Fig. 6-16 are inserted into the system of Fig. 6-18. When α is taken equal to 10, the following open-loop transfer function results:

$$KGH = \frac{K_1 K_2(p + 10)}{p(p + 20)(p + 200)} \qquad (6\text{-}15)$$

The root-locus sketch for this function is included on Fig. 6-17b. The insertion of the equalizer in the feedback loop adds a zero on the p plane. The system is now stable with the same value of gain ($K = 24 \times 10^4$) at which it was previously unstable.

In general, rate generators provide signals proportional to shaft velocity. These components are discussed in Chap. 8. When rate generator signals are added to the position signals, a zero of the following form is inserted into the p plane:

$$K(p + \alpha) \qquad (6\text{-}16)$$

where α is the ratio of position to rate signal. When a rigid reference frame is not available, for example in an airborne or shipboard appli-

---

* See Sec. 4-14 for a discussion of the root-locus analysis of multiple-loop servos. Section 6-10 presents an example of a multiple-loop system.

† Alternating-current systems are discussed in Chap. 7.

cation, a gyroscope* is customarily used to measure simultaneously the position and rate of the object being controlled. Rate feedback provides an effective stabilization method when an output motion is available. In many cases, for example an all-pneumatic or an all-electric system, the servo output is not mechanical, and hence a rate generator cannot be used.

In general, however, stabilizing networks other than rate generators can be used in the feedback loop. First derivative of the output, second derivative, or a combination of these can be used to achieve the desired equalization. The type and amount of feedback depend upon the particular system.

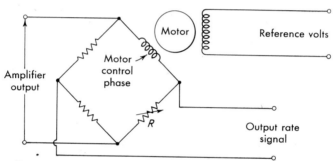

FIG. 6-19. Rate signal taken from the back emf of a-c motor.

Although many motor manufacturers build a-c and d-c rate generators, these are often expensive. Use of the back emf of the motor, which is developed by either a-c or d-c motors when rotating, may be a convenient expedient to obtain the rate signal. The back emf, which corresponds to the generator action of a rotating machine, is proportional to velocity and can be utilized to stabilize servo systems in the same manner as a rate generator signal. The output of the power device (possibly an amplifier) is applied across a bridge circuit on Fig. 6-19.

The bridge is balanced to yield zero output with full-load voltage across the motor windings and with the motor stalled. The resistance R is varied to balance the bridge when the motor is stalled. As the motor is allowed to rotate, the back emf unbalances the bridge and an output rate signal results. This signal is fed back to the input in the same manner as the signal from a rate generator would be utilized.

6-10. Multiple-loop Servos. Parallel equalization often leads to systems which comprise more than one feedback loop. In some cases multiple-loop servos are inherent in the system; in others they are intentionally introduced to modify the undesirable transfer function of certain components.

* See Chap. 9 for a discussion of both position and rate gyroscopes.

Block diagrams of some common types of multiple-loop systems are shown in Fig. 6-20.   Figure 6-20a is typical of systems in which a minor loop is established to modify the transfer function G_2; an example is the use of position feedback around an electric or pneumatic control motor to convert it from an integrating device to a positioning device.   Figure 6-20b is typical of the cross-coupling problems encountered in aircraft-engine controls and guided-missile control systems.

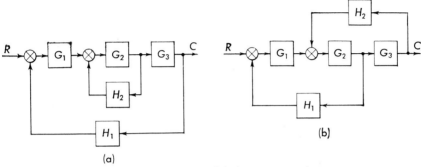

(a)

(b)

FIG. 6-20. Typical multiple-loop servo systems.

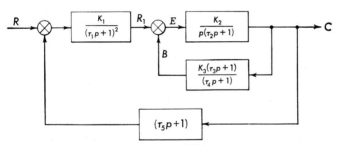

FIG. 6-21. An example of a multiple-loop control system.

Use of the block-diagram identities of Chap. 1 usually permits the reduction of the block diagrams and transfer functions.   The root-locus method, as discussed in Sec. 4-14, is a convenient method of analysis of multiple-loop systems.

To illustrate the use of a second loop to stabilize a system, the example of Fig. 6-21 is considered.   This example is not necessarily a practical problem but has been selected to demonstrate how an unstable system can be stabilized with a second loop.   The transfer functions of the individual blocks are given on the figure.   The numerical values for the constants are taken as follows:

$$\begin{array}{ll} K_2 = 300 \text{ sec}^{-1} & \tau_2 = 1.0 \text{ sec} \\ K_3 = 0.1 & \tau_3 = 0.1 \text{ sec} \\ \tau_1 = 0.1 \text{ sec} & \tau_4 = 0.3 \text{ sec} \end{array} \qquad (6\text{-}17)$$

The problem is to determine whether rate feedback (represented by τ_5) can stabilize the system when K_1 is adjusted to give a natural frequency of 1.5 cps for the closed-loop system.

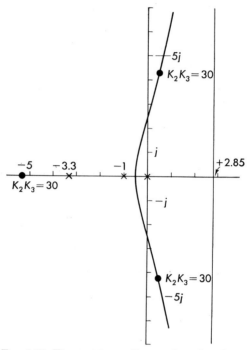

FIG. 6-22. The root-locus diagram for minor loop.

The root-locus diagram which is shown in Fig. 6-22 for the minor loop is first plotted. For $K_2K_3 = 30$, the roots of the system are located as follows:

$$p = -5.35 \qquad p = +0.5 + j4.25 \qquad p = +0.5 - j4.25 \qquad (6\text{-}18)$$

The inner loop can now be replaced by a single transfer function in which the roots of Eq. (6-18) become the poles of the new transfer function. Care must be exercised, however, in writing this transfer function. The roots of the characteristic equation are found from a solution of

$$\frac{K_2K_3(\tau_3 p + 1)}{p(\tau_2 p + 1)(\tau_4 p + 1)} = -1 \qquad (6\text{-}19)$$

The roots p_1, p_2, and p_3 are found from this equation without making a distinction between the forward and feedback transfer functions. In writing the over-all transfer function C/R_1, however, a distinction does arise. The correct form is found from an examination of the over-all transfer function:

$$\frac{C}{R_1} = \frac{\dfrac{K_2}{p(\tau_2 p + 1)}}{1 + \dfrac{K_2 K_3(\tau_3 p + 1)}{p(\tau_2 p + 1)(\tau_4 p + 1)}}$$

$$= \frac{K_2(\tau_4 p + 1)}{K_2 K_3 \left[\dfrac{p(\tau_2 p + 1)(\tau_4 p + 1)}{K_2 K_3} + (\tau_3 p + 1) \right]} \qquad (6\text{-}20)$$

$K_2 K_3$ is factored from the denominator of Eq. (6-20) so that the dimensions are correct when substituting the roots

$$\left(1 + \frac{p}{p_1}\right)\left(1 + \frac{p}{p_2}\right)\left(1 + \frac{p}{p_3}\right) = \frac{p(\tau_2 p + 1)(\tau_4 p + 1)}{K_2 K_3} + \tau_3 p + 1 \quad (6\text{-}21)$$

As a check on the constants $K_2 K_3$, set $p = 0$ in Eq. (6-21) with the result that both sides of the equation reduce to unity. Hence the inner-loop transfer function must be written as follows:

$$\frac{C}{R_1} = \frac{(1/K_3)(\tau_4 p + 1)}{[1 + (p/p_1)][1 + (p/p_2)][1 + (p/p_3)]} \qquad (6\text{-}22)$$

The roots of the inner loop become the poles in the outer-loop root locus. Generally the zeroes of the over-all transfer function are the zeroes of the forward transfer function and the poles of the feedback function. The constant is readily found by a limiting process (that is, set $p = 0$). For this example, the poles are located at the points indicated in Eq. (6-18).

In addition the two remaining poles exist at $p = -10$. A zero is located at $p = -1/\tau_5$ and at $p = -3.33$ for the minor loop function.

Root-locus diagrams for the complete system are shown in Fig. 6-23 for $\tau_5 = 0.5$, 1.0, and 2.0 sec as well as the limiting curve for $\tau_5 \to \infty$. This series of loci show that for $\omega_n = 9.4$ a value of $\tau_5 = 1.0$ gives a marginal stability. As τ_5 increases, the degree of stability improves. The limiting value of $\tau_5 = \infty$ gives a $\zeta = +0.044$. Although the system is made stable, further equalization is required since this system cannot be considered satisfactory.

6-11. Comparison of Various Equalizers. In an attempt to indicate a comparison of several types of equalizers, the following system is studied:

$$KG(p) = \frac{K}{p(1 + 0.5p)(1 + 0.2p)} \qquad (6\text{-}23)$$

Although this system is only third order, the wide variety of results indicate the degree of freedom afforded the servo engineer in synthesizing a

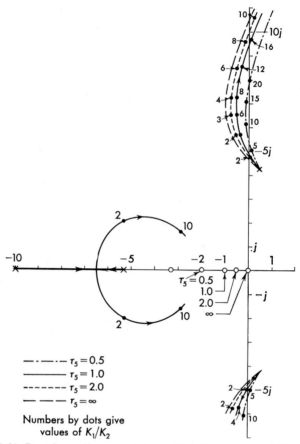

Fig. 6-23. Root-locus diagram of the multiple-loop system of Fig. 6-21.

particular system. The results are not general; they apply only to this particular system, which is equalized by the following methods:

1. No compensation
2. Series lead network of the form

$$G_1(p) = \frac{0.25(1 + 0.3p)}{(1 + 0.075p)} \tag{6-24}$$

3. Tachometer plus unity feedback of the form

$$H(p) = 1 + 0.3p \tag{6-25}$$

4. Series-parallel lead network of the form

$$G_1 = \frac{(1 + 1/6p)}{(1 + 1/60p)} \qquad H = \frac{(1 + 1/6p)}{(1 + 1/60p)} \tag{6-26}$$

For each equalizer, the system is analyzed by both Bode and root-locus methods. A typical root-locus diagram is included in Fig. 6-24. All the intermediate Bode and root-locus diagrams are not included; however, the results are summarized in Table 6-3. All systems are designed for $\zeta = 0.4$.

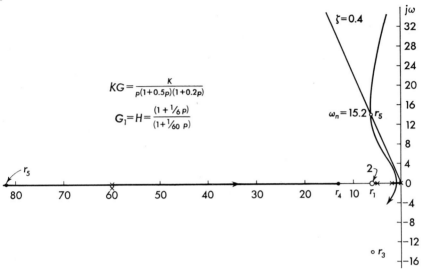

$$KG = \frac{K}{p(1+0.5p)(1+0.2p)}$$

$$G_1 = H = \frac{(1+\tfrac{1}{6}p)}{(1+\tfrac{1}{60}p)}$$

Fig. 6-24. Root-locus diagram for a system with series-parallel compensation.

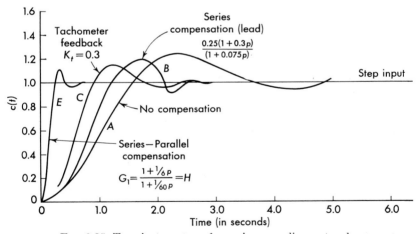

Fig. 6-25. Transient response for various equalizer networks.

The results tabulated in Table 6-3 are further compared in Fig. 6-25, where the response to a step function is plotted for each system. The time base for all cases is the same. In this particular comparison the last equalizer yields the most desirable solution.

TABLE 6-3. COMPARISON OF VARIOUS EQUALIZER NETWORKS

Summary of results: All designs except "D" have $M_p = 3$ db or $\zeta = 0.4$	A — No compensation $G = \dfrac{K}{p(1+0.5p)(1+0.2p)}$		B — Series lead network $\dfrac{0.25(1+0.3p)}{(1+0.075p)}$		C — Tachometer plus unity feedback $H(p) = 1 + 0.3p$ $K_t = 0.3$		D — Same as C except that $M_p = 6$ db	E — Series-parallel lead networks $G_1 = \dfrac{(1+1/6p)}{(1+1/60p)}$ $H = \dfrac{(1+1/6p)}{(1+1/60p)}$
	Bode	Root locus	Bode	Root locus	Bode	Root locus	Bode	Root locus
Performance characteristics:								
Velocity constant K_v	1.59	1.0	3.16	2.9	2.14	2.1	2.9	5.4
ω_R, radian/sec	1.26	1.25	2.4	2.4	2.55	2.43	4.1	10
ω cutoff (down 3 db)	2.16	2.15	3.8	3.9	4.3	4.2	7.0	16.2
Transient rise time	......	1.6	......	1.2	......	0.91	......	0.24
Transient overshoot, %	......	24	......	20	......	14	......	12
Resonant peak, db	+3	+3	+3	+2.7	+0.5	+0.35	+0.2	+0.2

194

PROBLEMS

6-1. For each of the following loop transfer functions choose the gain necessary to obtain $\zeta = 0.2$ and $\zeta = 0.4$.

(a) $\dfrac{K}{p(0.005p + 1)(0.016p + 1)}$

(b) $\dfrac{K(p + 10)}{p(0.005p + 1)(0.016p + 1)}$

(c) $\dfrac{K}{p(0.005p + 1)^2(0.016p + 1)}$

6-2. Determine the transfer function of a network that will stabilize the system of Fig. 6P-2. G_e is the transfer function of the network. The input and output impedances that the network sees are, respectively, zero and infinite.

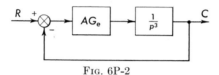

Fɪɢ. 6P-2

6-3. It is desired to support a body electrostatically. The block diagram of a servo to accomplish this is shown in Fig. 6P-3.

$\dfrac{1/M}{p^2 - (K_2/M)}$ = transfer function of body supported with an electrostatic field

F_s = force supplied by servo

K_b = transfer function of position pickoff

$AG(p)$ = amplifier and equalizer transfer function

K_e = transfer function of force field

The values are

$$K_b = 1.1 \times 10^2 \text{ volts/in.}$$
$$K_e = 2.5 \times 10^{-5} \text{ lb/volt}$$
$$M = 10^{-3} \text{ lb-sec}^2/\text{ft}$$
$$\sqrt{\frac{K_2}{M}} = 315 \text{ radians/sec}$$
$$A = \text{amplifier gain}$$

(a) Take $G(p) = \alpha p + 1$, and choose α and A for the optimum system. Compute the steady-state error to a step function input.

(b) Take $G(p) = \alpha p + 1 + \gamma/p$, and choose α, γ, and A for an optimum system.

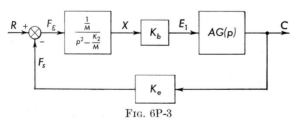

Fɪɢ. 6P-3

6-4. The system of Fig. 6P-4 represents the basic form of a strip chart recorder. An unknown d-c voltage $e_x(t)$ is to be dynamically recorded. A reference voltage E_R is accurately maintained across the slide-wire potentiometer. In most commercial systems, E_R is automatically compared with the voltage of a *standard cell* and the same servo that is shown in Fig. 6P-4 serves as the self-correcting feedback system.

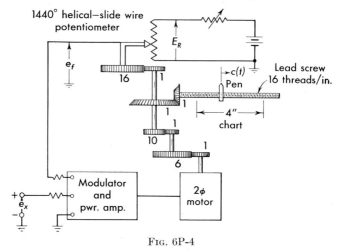

FIG. 6P-4

The operation entails a comparison of $e_x(t)$ and $e_f(t)$. The difference voltage $e_x(t) - e_f(t)$ is converted into an a-c error voltage through the use of a chopper modulator. The a-c error voltage drives a power amplifier which excites the control phase of a two-phase servomotor. The servomotor jointly drives the lead screw mechanism and the helical potentiometer in the proper direction to reduce the error signal.

Motor data:
Stall torque................ 3.84 in.-oz with 74 volts applied to the control winding
No-load speed.............. 3,600 rpm
Rotor inertia.............. 0.96×10^{-3} oz-in.-sec^2

The gear train moment of inertia referred to the motor shaft is found to be 1.63×10^{-3} oz-in.-sec^2. Neglect friction and backlash in this study. The transfer function of the modulator-amplifier combination is found to be A. Let $c(t)$ be the linear displacement in inches of the pen on the strip chart.

(a) Formulate a block diagram for the system using $e_x(t)$ as the input and $c(t)$ as the controlled output.

(b) What is the necessary value of gain A for a damping ratio of 0.7, and what is the corresponding undamped angular frequency? *Note:* this information can be obtained directly from the equations.

(c) With the gain set as in (b), what is the steady-state error (in inches) for a step input of 100 mv?

(d) If you were to use this recorder, to what value would you set the damping and why?

6-5. The system of Fig. 6P-5 is a speed regulator in which the speed depends upon a potentiometer setting e_r. Tachometric feedback is employed to compare a voltage e_b, which is proportional to the angular velocity of the output shaft, with the reference voltage e_r. The error voltage $e_r - e_b$ is amplified and used to excite the generator field.   The generator then drives the motor and load.   Assume no back emf induced in the field of the alternator and assume zero output impedance for the amplifier. The back emf of the motor is $K\omega$.

$$e_g = K_f i_f = R_a i_a$$

Motor torque $L_m = K_a i_a$

$$e_b = K_b \omega$$
$$K_f = 50 \text{ volts/amp}$$
$$A = 50$$
$$L_f = 1.2 \text{ henrys}$$

$$K_b = 0.1 \text{ volt/(radian)(sec)}^{-1}$$
$$K_a = 0.5 \text{ lb-ft/amp}$$
$$J = 0.25 \text{ slug-ft}^2$$
$$K = 0.3 \text{ volt/(radian)(sec)}^{-1}$$
$$R_f = 25 \text{ ohms}$$
$$R_a = 1.5 \text{ ohms}$$

(a) Form the block diagram for the system.   Express individual transfer functions in terms of the system parameters, that is, K_a, K_b, J, A, etc.

(b) Write the closed-loop transfer function $\bar{\omega}/E_r$.

(c) Determine the stability of the system.

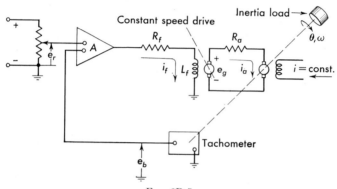

FIG. 6P-5

6-6. A servo is described by the transfer function

$$G(p) = \frac{K}{p^2(p + 1)}$$

(a) For what values of K is the system stable?

(b) Insert a series equalizer $G_e(p) = (1/a)[(a\tau p + 1)/(\tau p + 1)]$, and choose the best values of a and τ.

(c) Is there any other equalizer that may be superior?

6-7. For the multiple-loop servo shown on Fig. 6P-7, $G_1 = 8/p^3$ and $G_2 = p^n$.   For what values of n is the system stable?

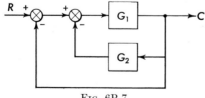

FIG. 6P-7

6-8. It is desired to select a lead network of the form

$$G_N = \frac{1 + 4\tau p}{1 + \tau p}$$

and to insert this in the servo of Fig. 6P-8.   Obtain a plot of ζ, the damping ratio, and ω_n, the undamped natural resonant frequency, as a function of τ for $0 \leq \tau \leq 0.75$. What is the optimum setting for τ?

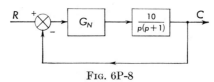

FIG. 6P-8

CHAPTER 7

DESIGN OF D-C AND A-C EQUALIZERS

7-1. Introduction. In the previous chapter the various methods of equalizing feedback control systems are discussed. Both series and parallel equalization are employed in the examples of Chap. 6. The problem of equalizing a servo system is at least twofold:

1. Locate the zeros and poles required for stability.
2. Design a network that satisfies the desired zero-pole configuration.

This present chapter treats the second part of the equalizer problem— the design or synthesis of the network that will satisfy the zero-pole configuration found necessary in the theoretical discussion of Chap. 6.

The first part of this chapter deals with the problems of network synthesis* and the equalization of d-c control systems. Procedures for the design of simple networks and examples of the use of these procedures are discussed.

Because of the following reasons, it may be advantageous to use an a-c system.

1. Drift (random fluctuations of d-c level) in d-c amplifiers.
2. Difficulty of design of the d-c amplifier. Alternating-current amplifiers can be coupled using transformers or capacitors with no problem of drift.
3. Simplicity of components.

The analysis of a-c systems, which is discussed in Chap. 6, is similar to that of d-c systems. It is not necessary to take notice of the presence of the carrier or a-c signal during the initial phases. For example, to a first approximation transfer functions of both a-c and d-c servomotors are the same. The practical method of mechanizing the required zero-pole configuration, however, is different from the d-c case. The latter portion of this chapter considers the special techniques which can be used for the design of a-c equalizers.

* The author is indebted to Dr. Louis Weinberg for much of the material in this chapter. Most of the material in the sections on synthesis was obtained from his excellent summary "Network Synthesis," a section of the book "Servomechanisms and Feedback Control Handbook," edited by J. G. Truxal and published by McGraw-Hill Book Company, Inc.

7-2. The Network Synthesis Problem. The design or synthesis of an equalizer network comprises the following items:

1. A transfer function, which is specified by a particular zero-pole configuration, is given, and a network with these given characteristics is to be found. A solution may not exist; however, if it does exist, it is generally not unique. Thus, the most practical network can be chosen from a large number of equivalent possibilities.

2. As a first step, a check is made (often by inspection) to determine if the given function satisfies the necessary and sufficient conditions for physical realizability. Only finite passive lumped-parameter networks that obey the reciprocity theorem are considered. A function is said to be physically realizable if a network representation of that function can be devised, the network containing only a finite number of mutual inductances, ideal transformers, and positive resistances, capacitances, and inductances.

3. The design procedure is generally carried out step by step, each step reducing the degree of the given transfer function. Both the network configuration and the element values are found with the procedure.

The system function of a network is defined as a function of the complex variable p, representing the ratio of a response variable to an excitation variable. More precisely, a system function is equal to the ratio of the Laplace transform of the response, or output variable, to the Laplace transform of the driving function, or input variable. It is also the transform of the impulse response of the network. There are two types of system functions of interest: the driving-point function and the transfer function. For a driving-point function (or, as it is often called, a two-terminal function) the input and output are measured at the same pair of terminals. Hence, any input or output impedance or admittance is a driving-point function. For a transfer function, on the other hand, the input and output are measured at two different pairs of terminals. For example, in the general four-terminal network, shown in Fig. 7-1, with the input applied at terminal pair 1-1', $Y_{11} = I_1/E_1$ is a driving-point admittance, E_2/E_1 the transfer voltage ratio, I_2/I_1 the transfer current ratio, E_2/I_1 the transfer impedance, and I_2/E_1 the transfer admittance.

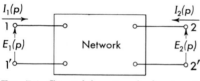

FIG. 7-1. General four-terminal network.

The most general type of system function for a finite lumped-parameter network is a real rational function, which is given by a quotient of polynomials of the form

$$G(p) = \frac{N(p)}{D(p)} = \frac{a_m p^m + \cdots + a_1 p + a_0}{b_n p^n + \cdots + b_1 p + b_0} = K\frac{(p + p_1) \cdots (p + p_m)}{(p + p_1') \cdots (p + p_n')}$$

$$(7\text{-}1)$$

where $K = a_m/b_n$ is a constant multiplier and the as and bs are real constants.

For stability it is necessary that $D(p)$ have no zeros in the right half plane, thus $D(p)$ must be a Hurwitz polynomial, where a Hurwitz polynomial is defined as one having zeros only in the left half plane. For certain restricted networks, $D(p)$ may have zeros on the imaginary axis.

7-3. Realizability Conditions for Two-terminal Networks. The necessary and sufficient conditions for the physical realizability of two-terminal, two-element kind networks are presented without proof in this section. Numerous references, which include the proofs, are cited in the bibliography. A network possessing only two types of elements is called a two-element kind network; for example, an RC network is made up of resistances and capacitances only.

a. RC (and RL) Driving-point Functions.* A system function may be realized as the driving-point impedance of an RC network if it satisfies all the following conditions:

1. The zeros and poles are all simple and lie on the negative real axis or at the origin of the complex plane.

2. The zeros and poles alternate along the negative real axis.

3. The critical frequency of smallest magnitude (i.e., the one at or nearest the origin) is a pole.

4. The constant multiplier K is positive.

A function with these characteristics is given by the factored form

$$Z = K \frac{(p + p_2)(p + p_4) \ldots (p + p_m)}{(p + p_1)(p + p_3) \ldots (p + p_n)} \tag{7-2}$$

where all the critical frequencies p_j are positive real numbers and

$$0 \leqslant p_1 < p_2 < p_3 \ldots \tag{7-3}$$

Since $Y = 1/Z$, an RC admittance must possess the characteristics (1), (2), and (4), but its critical frequency of smallest magnitude must be a zero. Since the critical frequencies of an RC function are all on the negative real axis, its characteristics may be shown completely by a plot as a function of the real variable $\sigma(p = \sigma + j\omega)$. Because of the alternation of the simple poles and zeros the derivative will possess one sign throughout: negative for impedances and positive for admittances. Several typical plots are shown in Fig. 7-2.

The discussion is confined to RC networks; however, if the word impedance is substituted for admittance and vice versa, all the statements apply to RL networks.

a. LC Driving-point Functions.[17,25] Foster's reactance theorem states that a system function may be realized as the driving-point impedance

* See Ref. 22, pp. 208–216.

or admittance of an LC network (without mutual inductance or ideal transformers) if it satisfies all the following conditions:

1. The zeros and poles are all simple and occur on the imaginary axis as conjugate pairs.

2. The zeros and poles alternate (this is termed the separation property of the zeros and poles).

3. The constant multiplier K is positive.

An LC driving-point function is called a reactance function if it is an impedance, a susceptance function if an admittance.

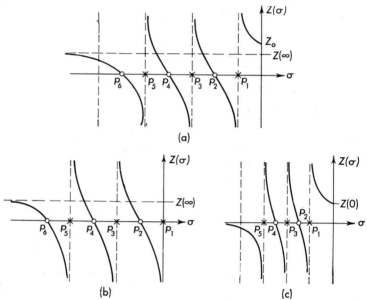

Fig. 7-2. Variation of RC impedance functions with σ.

An example of a reactance function is

$$Z = \frac{N(p)}{D(p)} = \frac{(p^2 + \omega_1{}^2)(p^2 + \omega_3{}^2) \cdots}{p(p^2 + \omega_2{}^2)(p^2 + \omega_4{}^2) \cdots} \qquad (7\text{-}4)$$

in which $0 < \omega_1 < \omega_2 < \omega_3$.

c. RLC Driving-point Functions.[6]   The conditions for realizability of a rational function as a general driving-point impedance (or admittance) are that it be a positive real function.   A rational function Z is defined as positive real if it satisfies the following two conditions:

1. Z is real for p real.

2. Re $Z(p) \geqslant 0$ for Re $p \geqslant 0$.

The above two conditions may be stated in an equivalent form that is more suitable for testing purposes as follows:

1. Z is real for p real.

2. The denominator polynomial of Z is a Hurwitz polynomial, or may have zeros on the j axis. If Z has poles on the j axis, these poles must be simple and have real and positive residues.

3. Re $Z(j\omega) \geqslant 0$ for all real values of ω.

7-4. Two-terminal Network Synthesis.[25,54] The synthesis of two-element kind driving-point functions is considered in this section. Two methods of synthesis for the driving-point functions are presented, one employing a partial-fraction and the other a continued-fraction expansion.

a. Foster Synthesis. The Foster form of an RC network is obtained by a partial-fraction expansion of the impedance function. Each term may be realized by recognition, the first term corresponding to a resistance and each of the other terms to the impedance of an RC parallel combination. A series connection of all these basic structures yields the total impedance. Since $Z(p)$ satisfies the conditions for realizability as an RC network, all residues are positive.

Since the expansion of an admittance Y may yield negative terms (or residues), Y/p is expanded and then multiplication of both sides of p yields an expansion for Y with all positive coefficients. The over-all admittance is then given by a parallel connection of R, C, or RC series combinations.

One expansion procedure is based on a partial-fraction development of $Y(p)$ as follows:

$$\frac{Y}{p} = \frac{k_0}{p} + \sum_{i=1}^{n} \frac{k_i}{p + \alpha_i} \tag{7-5}$$

where all k_i are zero or real and positive, and all α_i are real and positive.

As an example of such a partial-fraction expansion, consider the following admittance function:

$$Y = \frac{(p + 2)(p + 6)}{(p + 4)(p + 10)} \tag{7-6}$$

Examination of the physical realizability conditions of Sec. 7-3 indicates that Eq. (7-6) can be synthesized as an RC network.

To obtain one expansion with only positive coefficients, Y/p is expanded as follows:

$$\frac{Y}{p} = \frac{(p + 2)(p + 6)}{p(p + 4)(p + 10)} = \frac{K_0}{p} + \frac{K_1}{(p + 4)} + \frac{K_2}{(p + 10)} \tag{7-7}$$

Based upon the partial-fraction expansion technique, as discussed in Appendix I (Sec. I-5), the constants in Eq. (7-7) are found as follows:

1. Multiply both sides of Eq. (7-7) by p, set $p = 0$, and solve for K_0:

$$\frac{p(p + 2)(p + 6)}{p(p + 4)(p + 10)} = K_0 + \frac{K_1 p}{p + 4} + \frac{K_2 p}{p + 10} \tag{7-8}$$

$$K_0 = \frac{(2)(6)}{(4)(10)} = \frac{3}{10}$$

2. Multiply both sides of Eq. (7-7) by $p + 4$, set $p = -4$, and solve for K_1:

$$K_1 = \frac{(-4 + 2)(-4 + 6)}{(-4)(-4 + 10)} = \frac{(-2)(+2)}{(-4)(+6)} = \frac{1}{6} \tag{7-9}$$

3. Multiply both sides of Eq. (7-7) by $p + 10$, set $p = -10$, and solve for K_2:

$$K_2 = \frac{(-10 + 2)(-10 + 6)}{(-10)(-10 + 4)} = \frac{(-8)(-4)}{(-10)(-6)} = \frac{8}{15} \tag{7-10}$$

In general the constants are found by multiplying the equation by each of the poles. When p is set equal to the value of the pole, the constant is found. Hence for Eq. (7-7) the expansion for Y is found by multiplying both sides of the equation by p as follows:

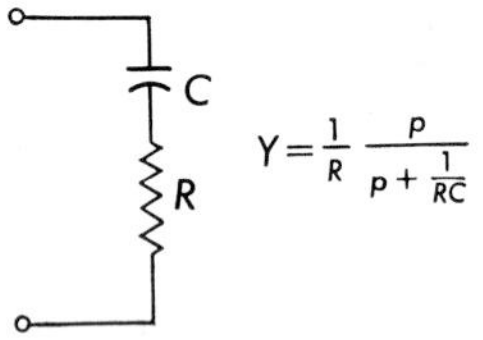

$$Y = \frac{3}{10} + \frac{\frac{1}{6} p}{p + 4} \frac{\frac{8}{15} p}{p + 10} \tag{7-11}$$

$Y = \frac{1}{R} \dfrac{p}{p + \frac{1}{RC}}$

FIG. 7-3. Admittance of a series RC network.   The admittance of a series combination of a capacitor and a resistor is shown in Fig. 7-3. Hence, the circuit for the admittance of Eq. (7-11) is given in Fig. 7-4.

The partial-fraction expansion of an impedance $Z(p)$, which is realizable as an RC network, is expanded as follows:

$$Z(p) = k_\infty + \frac{k_0}{p} + \frac{k_1}{p + p_1}$$
$$+ \cdots + \frac{k_n}{p + p_n} \tag{7-12}$$

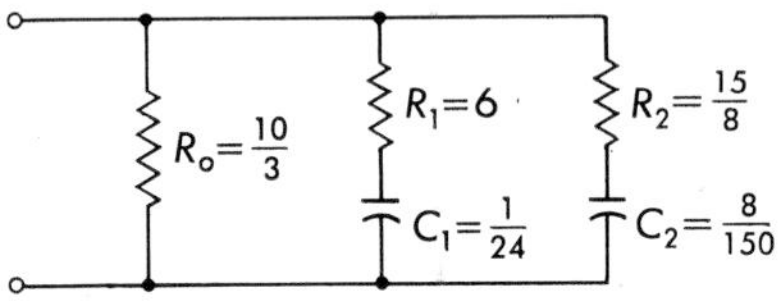

where all k_i are zero or real and positive quantities and all p_i are real and positive. As an example of such a partial-fraction expansion, consider the function given in Eq. (7-6) which is written as an impedance

$R_0 = \frac{10}{3}$ $R_1 = 6$ $R_2 = \frac{15}{8}$ $C_1 = \frac{1}{24}$ $C_2 = \frac{8}{150}$

FIG. 7-4. Partial-fraction synthesis of

$$Y(p) = \frac{(p + 2)(p + 6)}{(p + 4)(p + 10)}$$

$$Z = \frac{(p + 4)(p + 10)}{(p + 2)(p + 6)} \tag{7-13}$$

The second form of partial-fraction expansion is as follows:

$$Z = k_\infty + \frac{k_1}{p + 2} + \frac{k_2}{p + 6} \tag{7-14}$$

The constants are found, as discussed in Appendix I and as indicated in the above example [Eq. (7-7)], as follows:

$$k_\infty = \lim_{p \to \infty} \frac{(p+4)(p+10)}{(p+2)(p+6)} = 1 \tag{7-15}$$

$$k_1 = \frac{(p+4)(p+10)}{p+6}\bigg|_{p=-2} = 4 \tag{7-16}$$

$$k_2 = \frac{(p+4)(p+10)}{p+2}\bigg|_{p=-6} = 2 \tag{7-17}$$

The expansion is written as follows:

$$Z = 1 + \frac{4}{p+2} + \frac{2}{p+6} \tag{7-18}$$

and the network is included in Fig. 7-5.

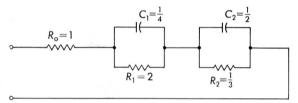

FIG. 7-5. Partial-fraction synthesis of $Z(p) = \dfrac{(p+4)(p+10)}{(p+2)(p+6)}$

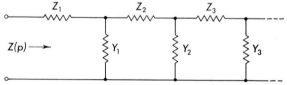

FIG. 7-6. Continued-fraction expansion results in a ladder network.

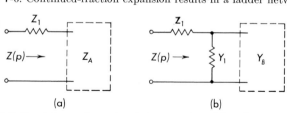

FIG. 7-7. Breakdown of a network in a continued-fraction expansion.

b. *Cauer Synthesis.* The continued-fraction or Cauer synthesis yields a two-terminal ladder-type network. The impedance of the network of Fig. 7-6 can be written as a series of terms, the first of which is Z_1:

$$Z(p) = Z_1 + Z_A \tag{7-19}$$

and is shown in Fig. 7-7a. The impedance Z_A can be written as an admittance

$$Y_A = \frac{1}{Z_A} = Y_1 + Y_B \tag{7-20}$$

which is shown in Fig. 7-7b. This process is continued with the result

$$Z(p) = Z_1 + \cfrac{1}{Y_1 + \cfrac{1}{Z_2 + \cfrac{1}{Y_2 + \cfrac{1}{Z_3 + \cdots}}}} \tag{7-21}$$

Any expression

$$Z(p) = \frac{N(p)}{D(p)} \tag{7-22}$$

is easily written in the form of a continued fraction by a process of repeated division

$$Z(p) = a(p) + \frac{N_1(p)}{D(p)} = a(p) + \frac{1}{D(p)/N_1(p)}$$

$$= a(p) + \cfrac{1}{b(p) + \cfrac{1}{N_1(p)/D_1(p)}} = \text{etc.} \tag{7-23}$$

Since the order of $N(p)$ and $D(p)$ does not differ by more than unity, each of the quotients $a(p)$, $b(p)$, etc., are simple circuits. The process is carried out until a recognizable circuit is obtained for one of the remaining fractions.

The expansion may be made about infinity or zero; in each case the partial quotients all have positive coefficients. In the expansion about infinity the general form is as follows:

$$Z = d_1 + \cfrac{1}{c_1 p + \cfrac{1}{d_2 + \cfrac{1}{c_2 p + \cfrac{1}{d_3 + \cdots}}}} \tag{7-24}$$

The first term corresponds to a resistance in the series arm of value d_1 ohms; the second term to a shunt capacitance of value c_1 farads.

In the expansion about the origin, the general form can be written as follows:

$$Z = \frac{c_1}{p} + \cfrac{1}{d_1 + \cfrac{1}{\cfrac{c_2}{p} + \cfrac{1}{d_2 + \cfrac{1}{\cfrac{c_3}{p} + \cdots}}}} \tag{7-25}$$

The poles at the origin and the constants are alternately removed from the function. The first term corresponds to a capacitance of c_1 farads in the series arm; the second term to a conductance of d_1 ohms in the shunt arm; etc.

For the expansion about infinity, the polynomials are written in the normal order in descending powers of p, whereas for the expansion about zero, the polynomials are written in ascending powers of p.

As an example of the continued-fraction expansion of a two-terminal admittance function, consider the function of Eq. (7-6)

$$Y = \frac{(p+2)(p+6)}{(p+4)(p+10)} = \frac{p^2 + 8p + 12}{p^2 + 14p + 40} \tag{7-26}$$

The expansion about infinity is first found. Since Y has no pole at infinity, no operation is performed in the first cycle. In the second cycle, the function is divided as follows:

$$
\begin{array}{r}
1 \\
p^2 + 8p + 12 \,\overline{\smash{\big)}\, p^2 + 14p + 40} \\
\underline{p^2 + 8p + 12} \quad \dfrac{1}{6}p \\
+ 6p + 28
\end{array}
$$

$$
\begin{array}{r}
\overline{\smash{\big)}\, p^2 + 8p + 12} \\
p^2 + \dfrac{14}{3}p \qquad \dfrac{9}{5} \\
\underline{\phantom{p^2 + \dfrac{14}{3}p}} \\
\dfrac{10}{3}p + 12 \,\overline{\smash{\big)}\, 6p + 28}
\end{array}
\tag{7-27}
$$

$$
\begin{array}{r}
6p + \dfrac{108}{5} \qquad \dfrac{25}{48}p \\
\underline{\phantom{6p + \dfrac{108}{5}}} \\
\dfrac{32}{5} \,\overline{\smash{\big)}\, \dfrac{10}{3}p + 12} \\
\dfrac{10}{3}p \qquad \dfrac{8}{15} \\
\underline{\phantom{\dfrac{10}{3}p}} \\
12 \,\overline{\smash{\big)}\, \dfrac{32}{5}} \\
\dfrac{32}{5} \\
\underline{\phantom{\dfrac{32}{5}}}
\end{array}
$$

The expression is rewritten as follows:

$$Y = \cfrac{1}{1 + \cfrac{1}{\frac{1}{6}p + \cfrac{1}{\frac{9}{5} + \cfrac{1}{\frac{25}{48}p + \frac{1}{\frac{8}{15}}}}}} \tag{7-28}$$

and the RC network is shown on Fig. 7-8.

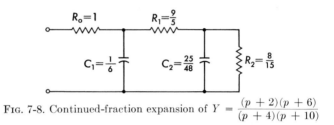

FIG. 7-8. Continued-fraction expansion of $Y = \dfrac{(p + 2)(p + 6)}{(p + 4)(p + 10)}$

The continued-fraction expansion about the origin is found by dividing the polynomials which are written in descending order. The resulting continued fraction is written as follows:

$$Y = \frac{3}{10} + \cfrac{1}{\frac{200}{19p} + \cfrac{1}{\frac{361}{630} + \cfrac{1}{\frac{3,969}{76p} + \frac{1}{\frac{8}{63}}}}} \tag{7-29}$$

The corresponding RC network is shown in Fig. 7-9. The values of the components are made reasonable with an impedance-level change. To raise the impedance level by a factor b the impedance of each type of element is multiplied by b. Hence, multiply every R and L by b, and divide every C by b.

7-5. Realizability Conditions for Four-terminal-network Synthesis. A rational function is realizable as a transfer impedance (or transfer admittance) of an RLC network if it satisfies the following necessary and sufficient conditions:

1. The function is real for p real.

2. The denominator has zeros in the left half plane or on the j axis.   If zeros are present on the j axis, these zeros must be simple and the function must have real (positive or negative) residues in these poles.

3. The degree of the numerator may be at most one greater than the degree of the denominator.

To be realizable as a transfer voltage ratio, a rational function must also have real coefficients but it cannot have a pole at the origin or at infinity.   It must be analytic in the right half plane; if poles occur on the j axis, they must be simple and have pure imaginary residues.

The above conditions place no explicit restrictions on the zeros of the transfer function; they may lie anywhere in the plane.   However, the transfer function of a grounded network without mutual inductance cannot possess zeros on the positive real axis.   Finally, restricting the network to have a resistance termination requires that no poles occur on the j axis in any of the transfer functions.

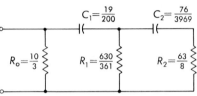

FIG. 7-9. Continued-fraction expansion of
$$Y = \frac{(p + 2)(p + 6)}{(p + 4)(p + 10)}$$

It is possible to establish restrictions on the magnitude of the gain of RLC and RC networks.   Most procedures are concerned with synthesis within a constant multiplier, since an amplifier easily compensates any loss of gain through the network.   For this reason, such conditions are not discussed in this book.

7-6. Four-terminal-network Synthesis.   Two linear equations completely describe the behavior of a four-terminal (two-terminal-pair) network; an n-terminal-pair network requires n equations for its complete description.   Of the many different sets of equations that may be used, two convenient sets are

$$\begin{aligned}E_1 &= Z_{11}I_1 + Z_{12}I_2 \\ E_2 &= Z_{21}I_1 + Z_{22}I_2\end{aligned} \qquad (7\text{-}30)$$

and the inverse set of equations

$$\begin{aligned}I_1 &= Y_{11}E_1 + Y_{12}E_2 \\ I_2 &= Y_{21}E_1 + Y_{22}E_2\end{aligned} \qquad (7\text{-}31)$$

where $Z_{12} = Z_{21}$ and $Y_{12} = Y_{21}$ by the reciprocity theorem.

The Zs are called the open-circuit impedances; the Ys, the short-circuit admittances.   The definitions of these system functions are contained in the equations

$$\begin{aligned}Z_{11} &= \left.\frac{E_1}{I_1}\right|_{I_2=0} & Z_{21} &= \left.\frac{E_2}{I_1}\right|_{I_2=0} \\[2mm] Z_{12} &= \left.\frac{E_1}{I_2}\right|_{I_1=0} & Z_{22} &= \left.\frac{E_2}{I_2}\right|_{I_1=0}\end{aligned} \qquad (7\text{-}32)$$

and
$$Y_{11} = \frac{I_1}{E_1}\bigg|_{E_2=0} \qquad Y_{21} = \frac{I_2}{E_1}\bigg|_{E_2=0}$$
$$Y_{12} = \frac{I_1}{E_2}\bigg|_{E_1=0} \qquad Y_{22} = \frac{I_2}{E_2}\bigg|_{E_1=0}$$
(7-33)

The Zs are evaluated (or measured in the laboratory) with all terminal pairs open-circuited (a current source having an infinite internal impedance); the Ys with short-circuit constraints at the terminals (a voltage source having zero internal impedance).

In many synthesis procedures an identification of the appropriate Zs (or Ys) is made with the given system function, and then these Zs are realized by a network of the desired form. Both ungrounded networks (lattice) and grounded networks (ladders) are discussed in the next section.

7-7. Elementary Lattice and Ladder Synthesis. Any realizable RC transfer function can be realized by a lattice network, which is shown in

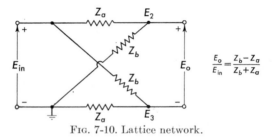

FIG. 7-10. Lattice network.

Fig. 7-10. The transfer function for this network is found for the condition of zero source and infinite load impedance. The equations about the two nodes E_2 and E_3 with the lower input node taken as ground are written

$$E_2 \left(\frac{1}{Z_a} + \frac{1}{Z_b} \right) = E_{in} \frac{1}{Z_a}$$
$$E_3 \left(\frac{1}{Z_a} + \frac{1}{Z_b} \right) = E_{in} \frac{1}{Z_b}$$
(7-34)

Solution of these equations yields

$$E_o = E_2 - E_3 = \frac{E_{in}[(1/Z_a) - (1/Z_b)]}{[(1/Z_a) + (1/Z_b)]} = E_{in}\left(\frac{Z_b - Z_a}{Z_b + Z_a} \right) \quad (7\text{-}35)$$

The two-terminal impedance functions Z_a and Z_b are found by identifying numerator and denominator with the desired transfer function.

Either the impedance, Eqs. (7-30), or admittance equations, Eqs. (7-31), can be used to determine the transfer voltage ratio. The impedance form is found by setting the output current I_2 equal to zero, since the load impedance is assumed to be infinite. The transfer voltage ratio, or transfer function, is written

$$\frac{E_o}{E_{in}} = \frac{Z_{12}}{Z_{11}} \tag{7-36}$$

If the transfer function is denoted as $E_o/E_{in} = Z_{12}(p)/Z_{11}(p)$, the two-terminal impedances are found as follows:

$$Z_b - Z_a = Z_{12}(p)$$
$$Z_b + Z_a = Z_{11}(p) \tag{7-37}$$

Adding and subtracting Eqs. (7-37),

$$Z_b = \tfrac{1}{2}[Z_{11}(p) + Z_{12}(p)]$$
$$Z_a = \tfrac{1}{2}[Z_{11}(p) - Z_{12}(p)] \tag{7-38}$$

Each of the functions Z_a and Z_b can be divided by $Kq(p)$, where $q(p)$ is any desired polynomial in the operator p. Since a ratio of impedances is taken in Eq. (7-36), the $Kq(p)$ cancels out of the fraction. $q(p)$ is inserted to aid in realizing the two-terminal impedance functions that result. Division of Eqs. (7-38) by $Kq(p)$ yields the equations

$$Z_b = \frac{1}{2}\frac{Z_{11}(p) + Z_{12}(p)}{Kq(p)} \qquad Z_a = \frac{1}{2}\frac{Z_{11}(p) - Z_{12}(p)}{Kq(p)} \tag{7-39}$$

Consider, as an example, the following transfer function:

$$\frac{E_o}{E_{in}} = \frac{(p + 30)^2}{(p + 50)(p + 100)} = \frac{p^2 + 60p + 900}{p^2 + 150p + 5,000} \tag{7-40}$$

The quantities Z_a and Z_b are found from Eqs. (7-38) as follows:

$$Z_b = \tfrac{1}{2}(p^2 + 150p + 5,000 + p^2 + 60p + 900)$$
$$Z_a = \tfrac{1}{2}(p^2 + 150p + 5,000 - p^2 - 60p - 900)$$

These quantities are divided by $q(p)$:

$$Z_a = \frac{90p + 4,100}{Kq(p)} = \frac{90}{K} + \frac{4,100}{Kp}$$
$$Z_b = \frac{2p^2 + 240p + 5,900}{Kq(p)} = \frac{2p}{K} + \frac{240}{K} + \frac{5,900}{Kp}$$

In this case it is convenient to take $Kq(p) = Kp$. The two-terminal impedances Z_a and Z_b are shown in Fig. 7-11. The numerical values become reasonable in size when K is taken equal to 10^{-2}.

In general, Z_a and Z_b can be built with passive elements if the subtraction necessary in Eq. (7-39) results in all positive components. Practically, the lattice network has the disadvantage of possessing no com-

mon ground between input and output.   To overcome this problem it is
necessary to drive the input with a balanced signal, for example, from a
transformer or difference amplifier.   Alternatively, the load may be
driven in push-pull so that the common ground problem can be obviated.
Another difficulty with the lattice network is the number of elements
necessary.   For the example taken here, ten elements are necessary to
achieve the desired transfer function.

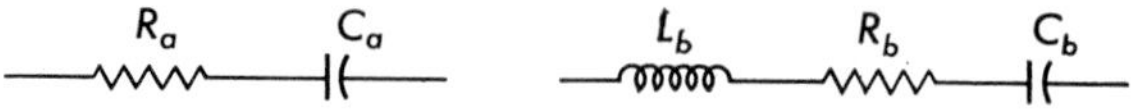

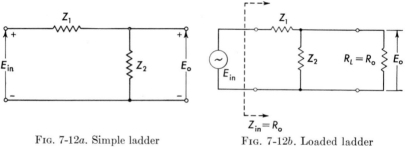

$$R_a = \frac{90}{K} = 9000 \ \Omega$$

$$C_a = \frac{K}{4100} = 2.44 \ \mu\text{f}$$

$$Z_a = \frac{90}{K} + \frac{4100}{Kp}$$

$$L_b = \frac{2}{K} = 200h$$

$$R_b = \frac{240}{K} = 24{,}000 \ \Omega$$

$$C_b = \frac{K}{5900} = 1.69 \ \mu\text{f}$$

$$Z_b = \frac{2p}{K} + \frac{240}{K} + \frac{5900}{Kp}$$

Fig. 7-11. Lattice elements.

Fig. 7-12a. Simple ladder
network.

Fig. 7-12b. Loaded ladder
network.

Synthesis of the necessary two-terminal impedances Z_a and Z_b is accomplished by reference to Table 7-1 or use of any of the two-terminal synthesis procedures of Sec. 7-4.   It is important to maintain a low source
and high load impedance.

Because of the disadvantage of an ungrounded network, considerable
emphasis has been placed on three-terminal networks.   One terminal is
common to the input and the output and hence can be grounded.   A
ladder network[24] is an example of such a grounded network.   Since many
synthesis procedures have been developed* (and are being developed),
only a very simple and limited example is considered in this text.   The
ladder synthesis is based upon the circuit of Fig. 7-12a.   When this network is operated from zero or low source impedance and infinite or large

* See Ref. 54, pp. 190–220.

TABLE 7-1. PASSIVE CIRCUIT IMPEDENCE FORMS

(a) L C / R	$R\dfrac{\left[p^2 + \frac{1}{LC}\right]}{p^2 + \frac{R}{L}p + \frac{1}{LC}}$	(j) L / C R	$R\dfrac{p^2 + \frac{1}{RC}p + \frac{1}{LC}}{p^2 + \frac{1}{LC}}$
(b) R C / L	$R_p\dfrac{\left[p + \frac{1}{RC}\right]}{p^2 + \frac{R}{L}p + \frac{1}{LC}}$	(k) R / L C	$R\dfrac{p^2 + \frac{1}{RC}p + \frac{1}{LC}}{p\left(p + \frac{R}{L}\right)}$
(c) R L / C	$\dfrac{p + \frac{R}{L}}{C\left[p^2 + \frac{R}{L}p + \frac{1}{LC}\right]}$	(l) C / R L	$\dfrac{L\left[p^2 + \frac{1}{RC}p + \frac{1}{LC}\right]}{p + \frac{1}{RC}}$
(d) C L / C_1	$\dfrac{p^2 + \frac{1}{LC}}{C_1 p\left[p^2 + \frac{1}{L}\frac{C_1 + C}{C_1 C}\right]}$	(m) R / C C_1	$\dfrac{(C + C_1)\left[p + \frac{1}{R(C + C_1)}\right]}{CC_1 p\left(p + \frac{1}{RC}\right)}$
(e) C R / C_1	$\dfrac{p + \frac{1}{RC}}{C_1 p\left[p + \frac{1}{R}\frac{C_1 + C}{C_1 C}\right]}$	(n) L / C L_1	$L\dfrac{p\left[p^2 + \frac{1}{C}\left(\frac{L + L}{LL_1}\right)\right]}{p^2 + \frac{1}{LC}}$
(f) C L / L_1	$\dfrac{LL_1 p\left(p^2 + \frac{1}{LC}\right)}{(L + L_1)p^2 + \frac{1}{C(L + L_1)}}$	(o) L / R L_1	$L_1\dfrac{p\left[p + R\frac{L + L_1}{LL_1}\right]}{p + R/L}$
(g) R L / L_1	$\dfrac{LL_1 p\left(p + \frac{R}{L}\right)}{(L + L_1)p + \frac{R}{(L + L_1)}}$	(p) L / C C_1	$\dfrac{(C + C_1)\left[p^2 + \frac{1}{L(C + C_1)}\right]}{CC_1 p\left[p^2 + \frac{1}{LC}\right]}$
(h) R L / R_1	$\dfrac{R_1(p + R/L)}{p + \frac{(R + R_1)}{L}}$	(q) L / R R_1	$\dfrac{(R + R_1)\left[p + \frac{1}{L}\frac{RR_1}{R + R_1}\right]}{p + R/L}$
(i) R C / R_1	$\dfrac{RR_1\left(p + \frac{1}{RC}\right)}{(R + R_1)\left[p + \frac{1}{C(R + R_1)}\right]}$	(r) C / R R_1	$\dfrac{R_1\left[p + \frac{1}{C}\frac{R + R_1}{RR_1}\right]}{p + \frac{1}{RC}}$

load impedance, the transfer function can be written

$$\frac{E_o}{E_{in}} = \frac{Z_2}{Z_1 + Z_2} = \frac{1}{1 + (Z_1/Z_2)} \qquad (7\text{-}41)$$

When Eq. (7-41) is rearranged and the open-circuit impedances of Eq. (7-36) utilized, the following equation results:

$$\frac{E_{in}}{E_o} - 1 = \frac{Z_{11}}{Z_{12}} - 1 = \frac{Z_{11} - Z_{12}}{Z_{12}} = \frac{Z_1}{Z_2} \qquad (7\text{-}42)$$

As an example of this procedure, consider the problem: After the design of a control system, it is found that an equalizer is required which has the following transfer function:

$$\frac{E_o}{E_{in}} = \frac{(p + 30)^2}{(p + 50)(p + 100)} = \frac{Z_{12}}{Z_{11}} \qquad (7\text{-}43)$$

Find a network that yields this transfer function. Substituting Eq. (7-43) into Eq. (7-42), the ratio of Z_1/Z_2 is found:

$$\frac{Z_1}{Z_2} = \frac{p^2 + 150p + 5,000}{p^2 + 60p + 900} - 1 = \frac{90p + 4,100}{p^2 + 60p + 900}$$

To find Z_1 and Z_2 identify numerators and denominators as follows:

$$Z_1 = \frac{90p + 4,100}{Kq(p)} \qquad Z_2 = \frac{p^2 + 60p + 900}{Kq(p)}$$

where, as in the lattice synthesis, $q(p)$ is any desired polynomial in the operator p which is inserted to aid in realizing the two-terminal imped-

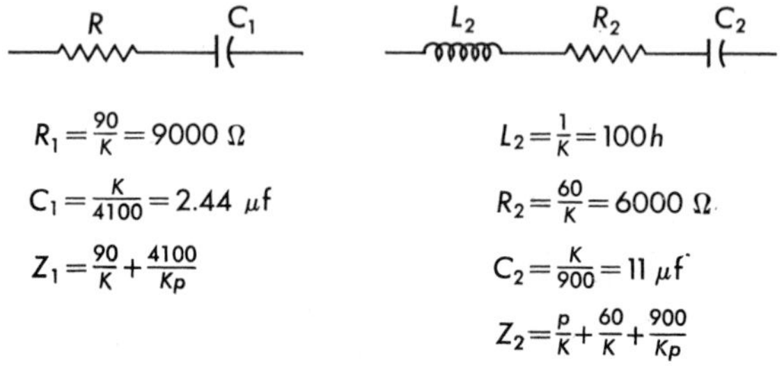

$$R_1 = \frac{90}{K} = 9000 \ \Omega$$

$$C_1 = \frac{K}{4100} = 2.44 \ \mu f$$

$$Z_1 = \frac{90}{K} + \frac{4100}{Kp}$$

$$L_2 = \frac{1}{K} = 100h$$

$$R_2 = \frac{60}{K} = 6000 \ \Omega$$

$$C_2 = \frac{K}{900} = 11 \ \mu f$$

$$Z_2 = \frac{p}{K} + \frac{60}{K} + \frac{900}{Kp}$$

FIG. 7-13. Example of ladder network synthesis.

ance functions. Since the ratio of Z_1 to Z_2 is taken, $q(p)$ cancels out of the fraction. In this example take $Kq(p) = Kp$ and

$$Z_1 = \frac{90}{K} + \frac{4,100}{Kp} \qquad Z_2 = \frac{p}{K} + \frac{60}{K} + \frac{900}{Kp}$$

In this case the two-terminal networks are easily identified by inspection. The networks, which are shown in Fig. 7-13, consist of a resistor and capacitor in series for Z_1 and a series R, L, C combination for Z_2. Reasonable component sizes are obtained when K is taken equal to 10^{-2}

If the subtraction $(E_{in}/E_o) - 1$ performed in Eq. (7-42) results in all positive signs, the Z_1 and Z_2 impedances can be found. A series of two-terminal impedance networks and their corresponding impedance functions are included in Table 7-1.

Practically it is not possible to obtain a zero source and infinite load impedance. Usually a 10:1 impedance ratio is sufficient to yield the desired transfer function. That is, the source impedance should be $\frac{1}{10}$ the magnitude of the network input impedance at the frequencies of operation. The load impedance should be 10 times the magnitude of the network output impedance at the operating frequencies. When a 10:1 impedance change is not possible, a constant resistance ladder network may prove useful. The equations for such a network are obtained from the circuit shown in Fig. 7-12b. The transfer function is written as follows:

$$\frac{E_o}{E_{in}} = \frac{R_o Z_2}{R_o Z_1 + R_o Z_2 + Z_1 Z_2} = \frac{Z_2/R_o}{Z_1/R_o + Z_2/R_o + (Z_1/R_o)(Z_2/R_o)} \quad (7\text{-}44)$$

and the input impedance is given by

$$Z_{in} = \frac{Z_1 R_o + Z_2 R_o + Z_1 Z_2}{R_o + Z_2}$$

$$= \left[\frac{Z_1/R_o + Z_2/R_o + (Z_1/R_o)(Z_2/R_o)}{1 + Z_2/R_o} \right] R_o \quad (7\text{-}45)$$

For the condition that the input impedance is equal to the load impedance, i.e., $Z_{in} = R_o$, Eq. (7-45) is equaled to R_o with the result,

$$\frac{Z_1}{R_o} + \frac{Z_2}{R_o} + \frac{Z_1}{R_o}\frac{Z_2}{R_o} = 1 + \frac{Z_2}{R_o} \quad (7\text{-}46)$$

When Eq. (7-46) is substituted into Eq. (7-44), the following design expression results:

$$\frac{E_o}{E_{in}} = \frac{Z_2/R_o}{1 + Z_2/R_o} \quad \text{or} \quad \frac{Z_2}{R_o} = \frac{1}{E_{in}/E_o - 1} \quad (7\text{-}47)$$

Similarly, the design equation for Z_1 is written from Eq. (7-46) as follows:

$$\frac{Z_1}{R_o} = \frac{1}{1 + Z_2/R_o} = + \frac{E_o}{E_{in}} \quad (7\text{-}48)$$

Application of Eqs. (7-47) and (7-48) for the constant resistance ladder is similar to that for the simple ladder network.

A full treatment of network synthesis would require a volume in itself. The references[6,24,25,54] included at the conclusion of this book provide considerable additional material on network synthesis.

7-8. Active Network Synthesis. Much is known about the characteristics and synthesis of two-terminal networks. The synthesis of four-terminal active networks can be based upon passive two-terminal networks. The use of an amplifier, however, does not result in a transfer function which differs from a ratio of two polynomials. The constant multiplier may be changed, but the form of the transfer function remains the same.

One of the most direct methods of active network synthesis lies in the operational amplifier approach. Consider the network shown in Fig.

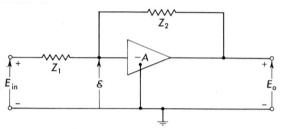

FIG. 7-14. Operational amplifier used for active network synthesis.

7-14. The transfer function is found by summing the currents flowing into node a as follows:

$$\frac{E_{in} - \varepsilon}{Z_1} + \frac{E_o - \varepsilon}{Z_2} = 0 \qquad (7\text{-}49)$$

The sum is equal to zero, since no current flows into the amplifier input. If the gain of the amplifier $-A$ is large, the error ε is negligible and the transfer function takes the form

$$\frac{E_o}{E_{in}} = -\frac{Z_2}{Z_1} \qquad (7\text{-}50)$$

The transfer function is simply the ratio of two-terminal impedance functions, the synthesis of which is given in previous sections.

As an example, if $Z_1 = R_1$ and $Z_2 = 1/pC_2$, the transfer function becomes

$$\frac{E_o}{E_{in}} = -\frac{1}{R_1 C_1 p} \qquad (7\text{-}51)$$

which is an integrator (pole at the origin). If $Z_1 = 1/pC$ and $Z_2 = R_2$, the transfer function is

$$\frac{E_o}{E_{in}} = -R_2 C_1 p \qquad (7\text{-}52)$$

which is a differentiator (zero at the origin).

Consider again the example of Eq. (7-43) with a negative sign inserted:

$$\frac{E_o}{E_{in}} = \frac{-(p + 30)^2}{(p + 50)(p + 100)} = \frac{-(p + 30)}{p + 50} \frac{p + 30}{p + 100} \qquad (7\text{-}53)$$

Equating Eqs. (7-50) and (7-53) and solving for the two-terminal impedance functions,

$$Z_2 = \frac{p + 30}{p + 50} \quad \text{and} \quad Z_1 = \frac{p + 100}{p + 30} \tag{7-54}$$

Reference to Table 7-1 indicates several two-terminal networks that will
satisfy Eq. (7-54) (cf. g, h, i, q, r).

This active network synthesis requires no subtraction, as do both the
ladder and lattice synthesis procedures.   The two-terminal impedances
are positive and can be synthesized easily.   If the network is to be used
at zero frequency, however, the high-gain amplifier must operate at direct
current.   A d-c amplifier is difficult to design and operate.   If the low-
frequency response is not required because of the form of the network
(a differentiator, for example, has zero output for direct current), an a-c
amplifier can be used.   However, when the network requires d-c response,
the need for a d-c amplifier limits the use of this method of equalization.

7-9. Suppressed-carrier Modulation.   The form of the signal that is
present in a-c servos is shown in Fig. 7-15 for a sinusoidal modulating sig-

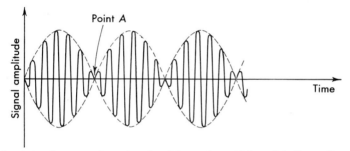

Fig. 7-15. Suppressed-carrier signal for a sinusoidal modulating voltage.

nal.   This signal is termed "double sideband suppressed carrier."   The
equation for this signal is given as follows:

$$e = \sin \omega_s t \sin \omega_c t = \cos (\omega_c - \omega_s)t - \cos (\omega_c + \omega_s)t \tag{7-55}$$

where ω_s is the signal frequency and ω_c is the carrier or modulating frequency.   Typical carrier frequencies are 60, 400, 1,000 cps, etc.   Signal
frequencies are usually small—0 to 10 cps.   The name for this type of
modulation arises from the second part of Eq. (7-55).   Notice that only
the frequencies $\omega_c + \omega_s$ and $\omega_c - \omega_s$ exist in this expression.   Since there
is no component at the carrier frequency, this type of modulation is
termed "suppressed carrier."   A frequency spectrum* (i.e., a plot of
harmonic magnitudes plotted against frequency) is plotted in Fig. 7-16
to a log scale.

* See Ref. 20, p. 143.

Of more importance than the name of the signal is how it arises in servo systems. The special transformer, which is shown in Fig. 7-17, has a secondary that can be rotated mechanically with respect to the primary. When the mechanical angle θ between the windings is 90°, full voltage e_1 is developed across the secondary. As θ is varied, a voltage is developed

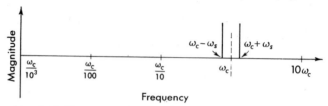

Fig. 7-16. Frequency spectrum for suppressed-carrier signal.

across the output. For small θ, this voltage can be written as

$$e_o = e_1 \sin \omega_c t \sin \theta \approx (e_1 \sin \omega_c t)\theta \qquad (7\text{-}56)$$

It is this type of signal which is developed at the output of a-c position pickoffs. (Chapter 8 considers several types of a-c transducers.) A pickoff, which is described by Eq. (7-56), produces a linear voltage with respect to shaft position for small angular rotations.

The sign of the signal is contained in the phase of the carrier signal. In the region where the signal amplitude approaches the origin (point A on Fig. 7-15), the carrier signal shifts phase by 180°. This is also shown

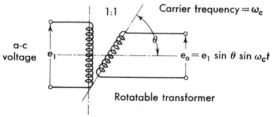

Fig. 7-17. Rotatable transformer produces a suppressed carrier signal.

in Eq. (7-56). The carrier signal changes sign as θ changes sign. If an all-a-c system is employed, the torque output from the motor is proportional to the magnitude of the signal. The direction of the torque applied depends upon the phase of the carrier. If a low-frequency signal is required, a phase-sensitive demodulator* must be used to restore correct polarity information to the output.

7-10. Alternating-current Servo Equalization. Many types of a-c servos exist. In some, a-c signals exist throughout the loop; in others,

---

* In theory such a demodulator adds in a carrier or reference signal. The sum is then rectified and filtered to yield the low-frequency signal. See Ref. 1, chaps. 9 and 5, for demodulator circuits.

at least a part of the servo employs d-c components.   This latter variety normally requires a modulator and demodulator to transform from direct to alternating current and vice versa.   A modulated carrier servo usually employs envelope feedback (i.e., the feedback signal is also suppressed carrier.   An a-c rate generator would provide such a signal).   Although various types of a-c servos are in use, the method of analysis of such systems is essentially the same as in the d-c servo case.

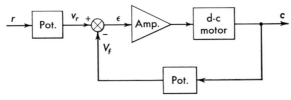

Fig. 7-18. An all-d-c servo system.

Consider the simple d-c position servo which is shown in Fig. 7-18.   In this system a potentiometer, excited with a d-c voltage, is used to transduce the input and output shaft position into voltage.   A d-c amplifier and d-c motor complete the system.

A hybrid a-c–d-c system is shown in Fig. 7-19.   The potentiometers are excited by a d-c voltage.   The error voltage is amplified in a d-c preamplifier.   The d-c signal is now suppressed-carrier-modulated.   This can be accomplished with an electromechanical chopper or with electronic circuits.   The a-c signal is amplified and used to drive the a-c motor.

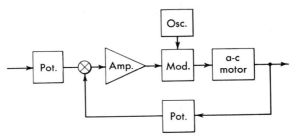

Fig. 7-19. Hybrid a-c–d-c servo system.

An all-a-c system is shown in Fig. 7-20.   In this system all components are alternating current; the amplifier is transformer or resistance-capacitance coupled, the subtraction is performed with transformers, and the position pickoffs are induction type.

If equalization is necessary in the servo, special techniques must be employed so that the equalizer operates only on the signal and not on the carrier.   Any of the d-c equalizers of the previous section operate only on a low-frequency signal.   If the signal of Eq. (7-55) were inserted into one of these "d-c equalizers," the output would not have the correct form. For example, if the signal of Eq. (7-55) were inserted into the lead network of Fig. 6-10a, the only result, with $\omega_c \gg 1/RC$, would be attenuation of the output by a constant amount

$$\frac{R_2}{R_1 + R_2} \tag{7-57}$$

The network has no equalizing effect upon the suppressed-carrier signal. Since the zeros and poles of the network are located in the low frequencies, 0 to 10 cps in most servo applications, the normal d-c network has no effect in the region of the carrier (ω_c) frequency, 400 cps.

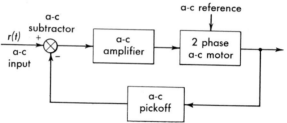

FIG. 7-20. An all-a-c servo system.

Figure 7-21 represents the block diagram of a common method of equalizing a-c servos—demodulation-modulation technique. All the advantages of a-c pickoffs and a-c amplifiers are maintained. The a-c signal is reduced to direct current (low frequency) with the phase-sensitive demodulator. The equalization is accomplished with the networks, discussed previously, and the signal is again returned to alternating current with a modulator. Practically, the system of Fig. 7-21 is mechanized in a num-

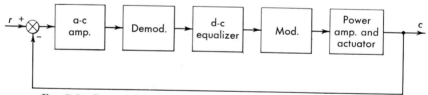

FIG. 7-21. Demodulation-modulation method of equalizing a-c servos.

ber of ways. For example, the equalized d-c signal can be used to drive a magnetic amplifier* whose output is alternating current. Alternatively, the equalized d-c signal might be used directly to drive a d-c actuator through a d-c power stage.

Phase-sensitive demodulators and modulators necessary for the equalization of a-c servos act essentially as switches, which are controlled by a reference signal of the same frequency as the modulating frequency. Actual circuits for both demodulators and modulators are discussed in

---

* Magnetic amplifiers are discussed in Chap. 9.

Chap. 9.   It is sufficient to consider a demodulator as a unit that reduces the suppressed-carrier a-c signal to direct current (or low frequency) and a modulator, a unit that modulates the signal on a carrier.   This is shown in the block diagram of Fig. 7-22.   A hybrid a-c–d-c system, in which the suppressed carrier is demodulated to a low-frequency signal, can be equalized with the d-c networks of this chapter.

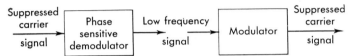

FIG. 7-22. Block diagram for a demodulator and modulator.

7-11. All a-c Servos—Carrier Networks.   It is possible to stabilize a-c servos with passive circuits in the forward loop without reducing the a-c signal to direct current.   The networks that accomplish this are called "carrier networks."   Bridged- and parallel-T networks* are two such carrier networks.   A resistor-shunt bridged-T is shown in Fig. 7-23.   When the network is inserted at a point where the input impedance is low and the output impedance is high, the transfer function is

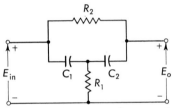

Fig. 7-23. Resistor-shunt bridged-T.

$$\frac{E_2(ju)}{E_1(ju)} = \frac{(1 - u^2) + jurn}{(1 - u^2) + jun} \quad (7\text{-}58)$$

The following dimensionless quantities are defined

$$u = \frac{\omega}{\omega_o} \qquad \omega_o = \frac{1}{\sqrt{R_1 C_1 R_2 C_2}} \qquad (7\text{-}59)$$

$$r = \frac{R_1(C_1 + C_2)}{R_1(C_1 + C_2) + C_2 R_2}$$

$$n = \omega_o[R_1(C_1 + C_2) + R_2 C_2]$$

The amplitude (in decibels) and phase versus logarithmic frequency is shown on Fig. 7-24.

The ability of a bridged-T network to stabilize an all-a-c servo can be understood by reference to Fig. 7-25.   Equation (7-55) and Fig. 7-16 show that a suppressed-carrier signal contains two components—one at $\omega_c - \omega_s$ and the other at $\omega_c + \omega_s$.   The signal varies about the carrier at ω_c exactly as the d-c signal varies about zero frequency.

In Fig. 7-25 are shown the amplitude and phase of a lead network.   In the same figure are shown the amplitude and phase of a bridged-T network

---

* A design procedure for these bridged- and parallel-T networks is included in Appendix IX.   See also pages 117–123 of Ref. 29.

with the carrier frequency reduced to zero ($\omega_c = 0$). The similarity between these two networks is seen from this comparison. When the suppressed-carrier signal is passed through a bridged-T network, the sidebands (at $\omega_c \pm \omega_s$) respond in an analogous fashion to direct current through a lead network. Hence a bridged-T network equalizes a-c suppressed-carrier systems in a similar manner as a passive circuit differentiator stabilizes a d-c servo. Except for low-frequency (60 cps) systems,

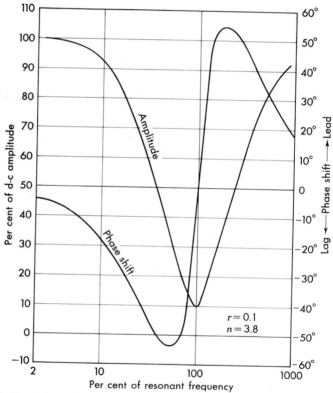

FIG. 7-24. Typical amplitude and phase response of a bridged-T notch network.

carrier networks usually find little use. Reasons for this are summarized as follows:

1. Networks with a small Q, for a fixed time constant, attenuate the sidebands at $\omega_c \pm \omega_s$ so that the signal to noise ratio is lowered. This effect is less at the lower frequencies (60 cps).

2. Shift of the reference frequency causes the sidebands to receive nonsymmetrical amplitude and phase response, and hence distortion results. Although these networks are not recommended for most a-c

servo equalization, they do find other application in servo work (cf. Sec. 7-14).

The general procedure for synthesizing an a-c equalizer is summarized as follows:

1. Determine the correct d-c network from the stability analysis.

2. Find the network with approximately the same gain and phase characteristics about ω_c (carrier frequency) as the d-c network has about zero frequency.

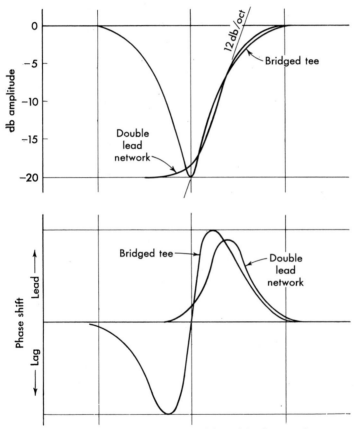

FIG. 7-25. Comparison of bridged-T and lead network.

This latter problem is solved, when $\omega_c \gg \omega_s$, by a transformation of frequency.* The $j\omega$ in the transfer function of the network,

$$\frac{E_o}{E_{in}} = G(j\omega) \qquad (7\text{-}60)$$

is replaced by a function of frequency $p(j\omega)$. Provided the maximum

* See Ref. 54, pp. 401–409, for a more extensive treatment of this subject.

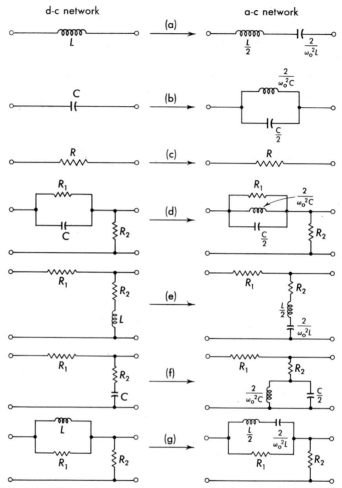

FIG. 7-26. Alternating-current network equivalents for d-c networks.

signal frequency is less than the carrier frequency, it can be shown* that a frequency transformation of the form

$$p(j\omega) = j\frac{\omega}{2}\left(1 - \frac{\omega_c^2}{2\omega^2}\right) \tag{7-61}$$

transforms the d-c network into the desired a-c equivalent. An inductance L in the original d-c network is replaced by an impedance

$$j\omega\frac{L}{2} + \frac{\omega_o^2 L}{j2\omega} \tag{7-62}$$

* See Ref. 54.

which is an inductance in series with a capacitance, as shown in Fig. 7-26a. A capacitance C is replaced by a network with an admittance

$$j\frac{\omega C}{2} + \frac{\omega_o{}^2 C}{j2\omega} \tag{7-63}$$

which is a capacitance in parallel with an inductance, as shown in Fig. 7-26b. Resistances remain unchanged. Figure 7-26 includes the a-c equivalents for several d-c lead and lag networks.

As an example, suppose the network shown in Fig. 7-27a was required to stabilize the d-c servo. The transformation of this d-c network to operate with a 400-cps carrier system results in the network which is shown in Fig. 7-27b.

Practical application of these networks requires

1. High-Q inductors to prevent sideband attenuation

2. Closely controlled carrier frequency to prevent frequency shift

The values of either L or C require adjustment so that the resonant circuit can be accurately tuned to the carrier frequency.

7-12. Electromechanical Networks. Because of the analogy (cf. Chap. 2) between electrical and mechanical networks, it is reasonable to expect that mechanical components can be utilized for stabilizing servos.

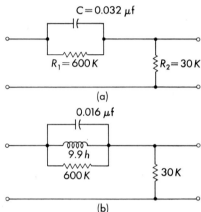

FIG. 7-27. (a) Direct-current network equalizer. (b) Alternating-current equivalent network for d-c equalizer.

Since a two-phase motor* converts the suppressed-carrier-voltage input into a low-frequency shaft position, the motor functions as a demodulator. This section treats the electromechanical integrator and differentiator.

An electromechanical integrator is shown in the block diagram of Fig. 7-28. The transfer function E_o/E_{in} is given by

$$\frac{E_o}{E_{in}} = \frac{E_1 A K_m/N}{p(\tau p + 1)} \tag{7-64}$$

where the quantities are defined in Fig. 7-28. For low frequencies, the motor time constant is neglected and the system is described by the equation

$$\frac{E_o}{E_{in}} = \frac{E_1 A K_m}{N}\frac{1}{p} \tag{7-65}$$

* See chap. 9 for a more detailed discussion of two-phase motors.

This equation represents an integration

$$e_o = \frac{E_1 A K_m}{N} \int_0^t e_{in}\, dt \qquad (7\text{-}66)$$

An integrator is used in a system to reduce the steady-state error to zero. For a small constant input the motor will continue to turn at constant velocity. The integrator output is taken from a potentiometer which can be excited with either alternating or direct current.

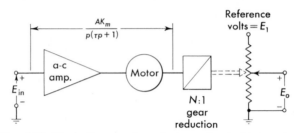

FIG. 7-28. Block diagram of an electromechanical integrator.

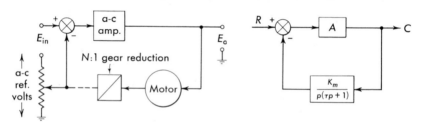

FIG. 7-29. Block diagram of electromechanical differentiator.

Figure 7-29 shows the block diagram of an electromechanical lead network. The transfer function of the closed loop is

$$\frac{E_o}{E_{in}} = \frac{A}{1 + \dfrac{A K_m/N}{p(\tau p + 1)}} = \frac{A p(\tau p + 1)}{p(\tau p + 1) + A\,\dfrac{K_m}{N}} \qquad (7\text{-}67)$$

For large forward loop gain A and for small values of motor time constant τ, the transfer function is

$$\frac{E_o}{E_{in}} = \frac{N}{K_m}\, p \qquad (7\text{-}68)$$

This equation represents a differentiation

$$e_o = \frac{N}{K_m} \frac{de_{in}}{dt} \qquad (7\text{-}69)$$

Hence the network of Fig. 7-29 is a suppressed-carrier differentiator. In both Figs. 7-28 and 7-29 the amplifiers are tuned so that a high gain is obtained with a narrow bandwidth and noise is kept to a minimum.

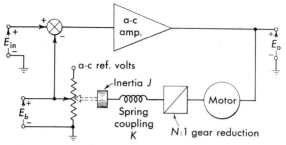

FIG. 7-30. An electromechanical network equalizer.

A variety of transfer functions are obtained if other mechanical components, such as damping or spring rate, are added to the motor shaft. For example, consider the transfer function for the electromechanical system of Fig. 7-30.   The following equation can be written:

$$NL = K_1 E_a - K_2 p \frac{\bar{\theta}_1}{N} \tag{7-70}$$

where K_1 and K_2 are defined in Sec. 1-3.

$$NL = N^2 J_m p^2 \frac{\bar{\theta}_1}{N} + K \left(\frac{\bar{\theta}_1}{N} - \bar{\theta}_2 \right) \tag{7-71}$$

and

$$J p^2 \bar{\theta}_2 + K \left(\bar{\theta}_2 - \frac{\bar{\theta}_1}{N} \right) = 0 \tag{7-72}$$

When these equations are solved, the feedback transfer function H becomes

$$H = \frac{E_b}{E_o} = \frac{K_s}{[N^2(JJ_m/K)p^3 + (JK_2/K)p^2 + (N^2 J_m + J)p + K_2]} \tag{7-73}$$

With a high-gain amplifier in the forward loop, Eq. (7-73) reduces to

$$\frac{E_o}{E_{in}} = \frac{A}{1 + AH} \approx \frac{1}{H} \tag{7-74}$$

The over-all transfer function is approximated:

$$\frac{E_o}{E_{in}} = p \left[N^2 \frac{JJ_m}{K} p^3 + \frac{JK_2}{K} p^2 + (N^2 J_m + J)p + K_2 \right] \tag{7-75}$$

This system produces a zero at the origin plus three other zeros, whose locations depend upon the mechanical constants.

7-13. Various Methods of Stabilizing A-C Servos.   Because of the widespread use of a-c servos, especially 400 and some 60 cps, many schemes have been advanced for stabilizing these systems.   These methods primarily deal with changes in the load that result in output-shaft damping. The application of these devices is generally limited to small instrument-type a-c servos whose output is mechanical motion. Although these methods are fairly inexpensive, usually the damping is improved at the expense of the steady-state error. Although the units

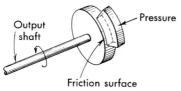

shown in the figures are for rotational motion systems, the extension to linear motion outputs is clear.

a. Coulomb Friction. Friction surfaces rubbing on the output shaft, as shown in Fig. 7-31, produce output-shaft damping. For systems where accuracy requirements are not severe, the friction opposes shaft

Fig. 7-31. A coulomb friction damper.

motion and creates an inexpensive and simple damper. Since this damper is nonlinear,* care must be exercised when using such dampers. The disadvantages of coulomb-friction damping are summarized:

1. Life is limited by wear.
2. As the unit wears the degree of damping changes.
3. Output power is wasted.
4. Static and velocity errors are introduced in shaft position.

b. Viscous Friction. This damping can be obtained, as shown schematically in Fig. 7-32, by mounting paddles on a shaft. The paddles are caused to move through grease or oil, depending upon the motion and the amount of damping required. The rotating paddle disk exerts a restraining torque proportional

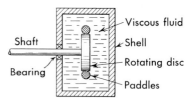

Fig. 7-32. A viscous friction damper.

to velocity. This damping unit is simple and rugged and has long life. The disadvantages of viscous damping are summarized:

1. The viscosity and hence the degree of damping are temperature sensitive.
2. Some inertia is added to output shaft.

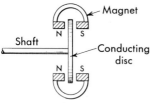

Fig. 7-33. An eddy-current damper.

c. Eddy-current or Foucault Damping. This type of damping, which is shown in the sketch of Fig. 7-33, produces an approximate viscous damping by means of a magnetic field. A conducting (copper or aluminum) cup is attached to the output shaft and is rotated through a magnetic field. The eddy currents induced in the cup set up a magnetic field which reacts with the original field in such a manner that a retarding torque is produced on the output

* See Sec. 10-3 for a discussion of coulomb friction. Chapter 10 considers the analysis of systems containing such nonlinearities.

shaft. This unit is easily constructed, is highly reliable, and has no fluid to leak out. Disadvantages of eddy-current damping are summarized:

1. The maximum damping available is small.

2. The resistance of the disk and hence the degree of damping are temperature sensitive.

d. Damping Proportional to Acceleration. Both viscous- and magnetic-acceleration dampers are utilized in position systems. The viscous-acceleration damper is shown on Fig. 7-34. The unit is similar to the viscous velocity damper of Fig. 7-32, except that the shell is fixed to the shaft and the disk is free to rotate. When the velocity suddenly changes, the moment of inertia of the disk produces a restraining torque on the shaft. The unit dissipates energy only when the velocity changes— an acceleration damper. The unit produces no additional velocity error. The disadvantages are summarized:

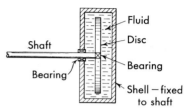

FIG. 7-34. Viscous-acceleration damping.

1. Shaft moment of inertia is greatly increased.

2. The mechanical construction is more complex.

3. The unit requires a special bearing.

e. Direct Current through Motor Windings. When the torque output of instrument servos is sufficient, a certain degree of damping can be obtained simply by running a small amount of direct current through the a-c windings. An example of this technique is shown in Fig. 7-35. A diode in a parallel resistance network permits a controllable amount of direct current through the motor reference phase. The disadvantages of this type of damping are

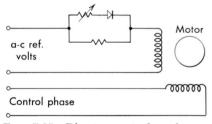

FIG. 7-35. Direct-current through a-c motor results in motor damping.

1. Only a small amount of damping is possible.

2. Motor torque is reduced.

7-14. Practical Considerations in A-C Servo Design. In Sec. 6-11 a comparison of several methods of equalizing a servo system is considered. This comparison does not consider that the system may utilize alternating current. This problem should be considered after the equalizer transfer function is found. The series lead network, system B, can be inserted into the a-c system in several ways:

1. Use of a demodulator and modulator (see Fig. 7-21)

2. Frequency transform the network as shown in Sec. 7-11

An a-c rate generator geared to the output shaft easily produces the $H(p) = 1 + 0.3p$ for system C.

System E is least suitable for an a-c system, since two d-c networks, which would require two sets of demodulators and modulators, would be required.

In the design of an a-c system, the methods of servo analysis (cf. Chaps. 3, 4, and 5) are used, in the same manner as in the design of d-c systems. The main difference between the d-c and a-c servo design problem lies in the practical area of mechanizing the network.

Of utmost importance in the design is the carrier phase shift. For full torque on the two-phase servo motor, the control and reference phase must be 90° apart in phase. If the phase is 60°, the power is 70 per

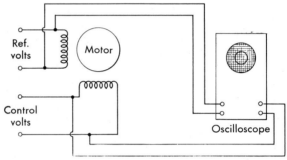

FIG. 7-36. Experimental checking of the phase shift in two-phase a-c motor.

cent of maximum, since the torque is a sine function of the phase shift. Because of unaccounted phase shifts through the system, it is usually necessary to provide additional phase-shifting networks. With the reference and control phases of the servomotor on the X and Y plates of an oscilloscope, as in Fig. 7-36, the pattern is a circle when the oscilloscope channels have the same gain. The chart of Fig. 7-37 shows the ellipses that are seen on the oscilloscope for several phase differences between the X and Y axes. Often an approximate phase shift is suitable for approximating purposes (especially in the laboratory). The student should familiarize himself with this chart. Often poor performance in a-c servos is directly attributable to phase errors between the reference and control phases.

Phase-shift correction can be accomplished in either the control or reference phases. The adjustable network of Fig. 7-38, which is discussed in Sec. 6-8, provides a simple method of inserting an adjustable amount of phase shift in the control phase. Since this network can be placed ahead of the power amplifier, it is required to carry little power.

Shifting the reference phase is conveniently done by a pair of capacitors. One method is shown in Fig. 7-39. Since these capacitors are inserted at a high power level, it is usually not feasible to make them continuously variable. Many manufacturers suggest the size capacitor required for suitable operation of their motor. In any case the final selection of these components is best made in the laboratory.

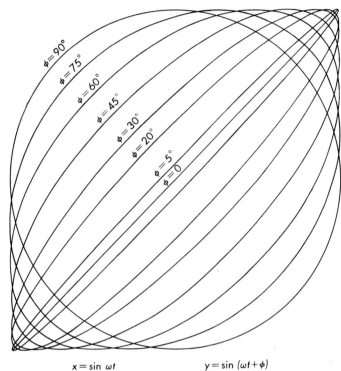

$$x = \sin \omega t \qquad y = \sin (\omega t + \phi)$$

FIG. 7-37. Oscilloscope ellipses for various phase shifts between x and y axes.

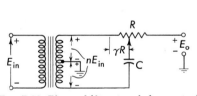
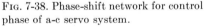

FIG. 7-38. Phase-shift network for control phase of a-c servo system.

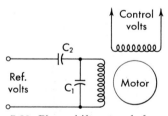

FIG. 7-39. Phase-shift network for reference phase of a-c motor.

In the design of a-c servos, the signal-to-noise ratio is considerably improved by using tuned amplifiers. The design is based upon the concept of eliminating from the response characteristics of the system all frequencies except in the narrow region about the carrier frequency. Careful design of the tuned circuit is necessary, since sharp tuning adds phase lag to the signal. Parallel-tuned LC circuits, as shown in Fig. 7-40a, are inserted in the forward path of the servo and produce a narrow-band system. Tuned transformer coupling, as shown in Fig. 7-40b, produces essentially the same results as Fig. 7-40a, since both methods are inserted in the forward loop of the amplifier.

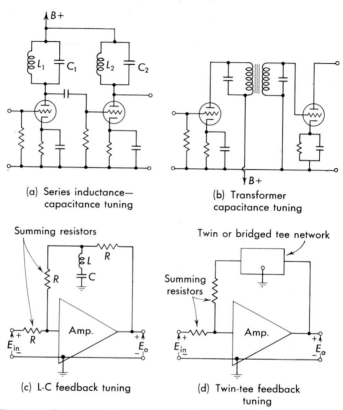

(a) Series inductance—
capacitance tuning

(b) Transformer
capacitance tuning

(c) L-C feedback tuning

(d) Twin-tee feedback
tuning

FIG. 7-40. Tuned amplifiers used to eliminate undesirable frequencies.

An alternate method of tuning the amplifier is shown in Fig. 7-40c. A series LC coil is used in the feedback path of the amplifier. The transfer function of the amplifier with a network $H(p)$ in the feedback is

$$\frac{E_o}{E_{in}} = \frac{A}{1 + AH} \approx \frac{1}{H} \qquad (7\text{-}76)$$

for large values of gain A. The gain of the closed-loop amplifier is large only when H is small. In particular, at a frequency when $H = 0$, the over-all gain is A. Outside this frequency band the gain drops off.

One of the difficulties with all the networks considered thus far is the temperature sensitivity of iron-core inductors. Especially for transistor

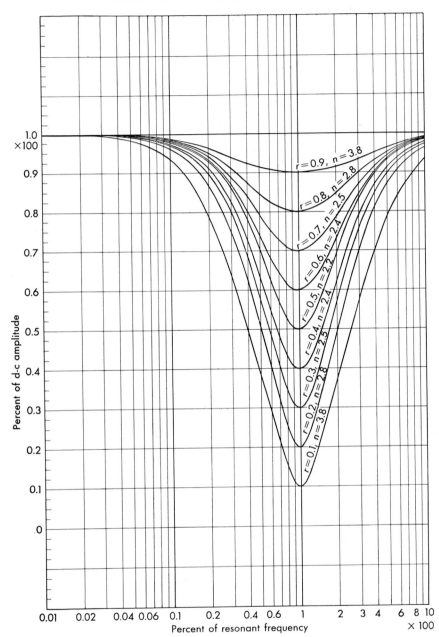

Fig. 7-41a. Amplitude response for the bridged-T networks.

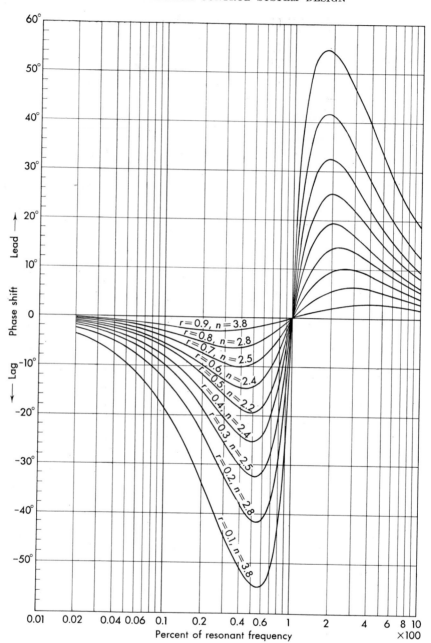

FIG. 7-41b. Phase-angle response for the bridged-T networks.

amplifier, interstage coupling transformers have an input magnetizing inductance which is comparable to the output impedance of the transistor. As the temperature varies, the magnetizing impedance varies and the gain of the stage may vary by a factor of 2. To avoid such problems created by the use of iron-core inductors, RC networks, such as bridged- and parallel-T networks, are used, as shown in Fig. 7-40d. Figure 7-24 shows the frequency response for one bridged-T network. Figures 7-41a and b show the amplitude and phase response for a bridged-T network for various notch depths. The network is driven from a low source impedance and into a large output impedance. A design procedure of bridged- and parallel-T networks is included in Appendix IX.

PROBLEMS

7-1. Determine which of the following two-terminal impedance functions are realizable with only resistances and capacitors:

(a) $\dfrac{7(p+1)(p+6)}{p(p+3)(p+10)}$

(b) $\dfrac{6(p+1)(p+3)}{(p+6)(p+10)}$

(c) $\dfrac{3(p+1)(p+5)}{(p+3)(p+10)}$

(d) $\dfrac{2(p+1)(p-3)}{p(p+2)(p+6)}$

(e) $-4\dfrac{(p+1)(p+3)}{p(p+2)}$

(f) $-3\dfrac{(-p-1)(p+7)}{p(p+5)}$

7-2. Determine which of the functions in Prob. 7-1 can be realized as an RC admittance function.

7-3. Find four RC networks for each of the realizable impedance functions in Prob. 7-1.

7-4. Determine four different networks for the following RC admittance:

$$Y = \frac{(p+1)(p+3)}{(p+2)(p+5)}$$

Each expansion is to possess only positive coefficients.

7-5. Find lattice networks for the following transfer voltage ratios:

(a) $\dfrac{p^2}{(p+6)(p+50)}$

(b) $\dfrac{p(p+1)}{p^2+p+10}$

(c) $\dfrac{p^2+9}{(p+12)(p+20)}$

(d) $\dfrac{p^2+p+10}{(p+10)^2}$

7-6. Find grounded networks for the transfer voltage ratios of Prob. 7-5.

7-7. Synthesize the negative of the transfer voltage ratios of Prob. 7-5 with active networks (as in Sec. 7-8).

7-8. Determine the transfer function for the electromechanical equalizer shown on Fig. 7P-8. Would this system have any practical use?

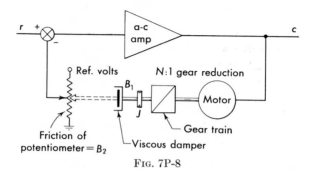

Fig. 7P-8

7-9. Design a resistance shunt and a capacitor shunt bridged-T network with a resonant frequency of 400 cps, a notch depth of 0.2 and a d-c impedance level of $50K$.

7-10. Derive the equation for the phase shifter of Fig. 7-37, and show how this network is useful for a-c servo systems.

7-11. Determine the amplitude and phase response for the LC tuned amplifier of Fig. 7-40c. Assume that the high-gain amplifier has infinite input and zero ouput impedance. Take

$$L = 10h \qquad C = 0.015 \ \mu f \qquad R = 10K\Omega$$

7-12. A light-seeker servo system consists of two photocells mounted on a bracket attached to a shaft which in turn is driven by a motor. The system is shown schematically in Fig. 7P-12. Equalize this system by means of passive element networks. The specification requires an overshoot of 5 per cent and minimum response time (i.e., minimize the rise time).

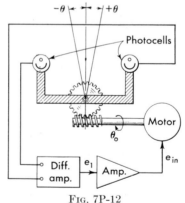

Fig. 7P-12

The output of the differential amplifier is a voltage which is proportional to θ and is positive for positive θ and negative for negative θ. The transfer function of the motor is

$$\frac{\bar{\theta}_o}{E_{in}} = \frac{100}{p(p + 10)}$$

Let $E_1/\theta = 10$ volts/degree and θ_o turns through 20° to cause θ to turn through 1°. The system is to use suppressed-carrier alternating current.

SCHEDULE OF EXPERIMENTS FOR E.E. 486

LABORATORY PERIOD NUMBER	GROUP I	GROUP II	GROUP III	GROUP IV
1	Introduction*	Introduction*	Introduction*	Introduction*
2	2B	1B	13	13
3	1B	2B	6B	6B
4	13	13	2B	1B
5	6B	6B	1B	2B
6	16A	16A	19	19
7	17	17	20†	20†
8	19	19	16A	16A
9	20†	20†	17	17

* There is no formal laboratory instruction sheet.

† Perform experiment during first 1½ hours of the 3 hour period.

The experiment numbers and titles are:

Exp. 486-2B: A study of synchro repeaters.

Exp. 486-13: Operational amplifiers.

Exp. 486-6B: Simulation of a transfer function by means of an analog computer.

Exp. 486-18: Typical servo building block transfer characteristics.

Exp. 486-16A: Analog computer time scale changes.

Exp. 486-17: Simulation of Lead-lag compensation of a closed loop system by means of an analog computer.

Exp. 486-19: Control motor, tachometer, and demodulator transfer characteristics.

Exp. 486-20: Prediction of closed loop performance from the open loop transfer function.

7-13. In a certain industrial application it is desired to keep the flow of liquid from a tank constant and independent of the amount of liquid in the tank. A servo system which performs this operation consists of a motor-driven gate valve, an amplifier, and a flow meter which produces a voltage output proportional to the quantity of liquid flowing [60 volts/(ft³)(sec⁻¹)]. A schematic of the system is shown on Fig.

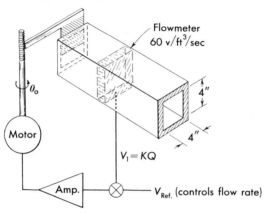

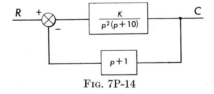

Fɪɢ. 7P-13

7P-13.   For simplicity, the pipe is rectangular.   Assume the flow rate is proportional to the area of the pipe at the gate.   The gate valve travels 1 in./100 rotations of θ_o. The maximum flow rate with the valve completely open is 0.1 ft³/sec.   The transfer function of the motor is $150/p(p + 5)$.   What value of gain would given a ζ of 0.3 for this system?   How would the system be built if an a-c motor and amplifier were to be used?

7-14. The system of Fig. 7P-14 utilizes rate feedback for stability. Set the gain K so that the overshoot produced by a step function input does not exceed 1.20 times the steady-state value.

$$\frac{K}{p^2(p+10)}$$

$$p+1$$

Fɪɢ. 7P-14

CHAPTER 8

SERVOMECHANISM TRANSDUCERS

8-1. Introduction. With increased emphasis on feedback control systems, the need arises for more varied and more accurate "transducers." A transducer is an instrument which converts a signal from one form (mechanical shaft rotation, pressure, angular velocity, etc.) into another form (usually electrical). For example, a shaft position is converted to a voltage for use with an electronic amplifier. Although the approximate mathematical transfer functions and block diagrams are simple, the manufacture of these components is often difficult because of accuracy and reliability requirements.

The characteristics of the transducing element can be summarized as follows:

1. Accuracy: Since the transducer is often placed outside the closed servo loop or in the feedback loop, the accuracy must be the same as that of the over-all closed-loop system.

2. Low power: Transducers are required to handle only low amounts of power (maximum of 2 watts).

3. High quality: The construction is usually of the highest possible quality. Low noise, freedom from harmonics and quadrature, high linearity, low friction are just a few of the requirements usually demanded of these instruments. The harmonics and quadrature which are generated by the transducer must be within limits which prevent saturation of the follow-up amplifiers.

4. Reliability: Because of the wide variety of quantities (acceleration, pressure, angle of attack, Mach number, etc.) that must be transduced into an electrical signal, many "gadgets" have been invented. Because of the importance of reliability in control equipment, considerable emphasis has been placed on transducer reliability by their manufacturers.

This chapter considers some of the important transducers used in the field of feedback control systems. Since it is impossible to cover all types and models of transducers, the more typical and/or important ones are discussed. For convenience, the various types of transducers are grouped according to the quantity measured, for example, position measurement, velocity measurement, acceleration measurement. Other servo components, such as gyros and motors, are postponed until the next chapter, since they do not readily fall into these classifications.

Transfer functions, schematic and block diagrams, typical servo-design data, and photographs of typical units are presented.

8-2. Measurement of Position.   Depending upon the type of system, accuracy desired, power available, and other considerations, the servo designer has a wide class of instruments available for the measurement of position.   The most important types that are considered in this section are conductive instruments (potentiometers) and inductive instruments (synchros, resolvers, E pickoffs).

8-3. Potentiometers.*   A potentiometer, comprising a slider which moves along a resistance element, is shown in Fig. 8-1.   A more useful schematic, with excitation E and output voltage e included, is shown in Fig. 8-2.   The transfer function of a potentiometer is determined from the voltage gradient (volts per radian or volts per inch) along the poten-

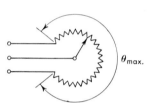

Fig. 8-1. Single-turn potentiometer.

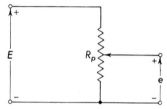

Fig. 8-2. Schematic diagram of a potentiometer.

tiometer.   The potentiometer of Fig. 8-2 has a voltage E applied across a total angle of $\theta_{\max}$ in degrees.   The transfer function is

$$\frac{e}{\theta} = \frac{E}{\theta_{\max}} \tag{8-1}$$

The most common potentiometer, utilizing a linear resistance element, finds wide use in computers and for position comparison in feedback control systems.   Single-turn potentiometers, Fig. 8-1, generally have a usable rotation of less than 360°.   The remaining angle is available for conducting overtravels (10 to 15° arcs at each end of the resistance element).   One typical unit is shown in the photograph of Fig. 8-3 and in the outline drawing of Fig. 8-4.   The accuracy is proportional to the diameter of the potentiometer and to the mechanical precision.   Careful design, precision machining, and choice of optimum materials result in an accurate instrument.

Since the potentiometer slider does not move along a continuous wire, the transfer function is not a continuous curve but a succession of steps.

* Much of the material of this section has been taken from Refs. 26 and 46.

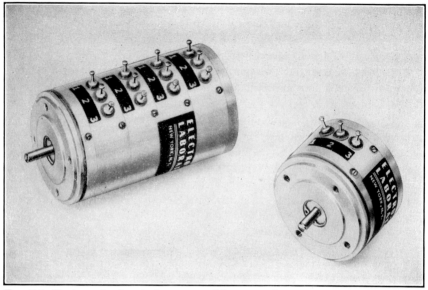

Fɪɢ. 8-3. Photograph of a single-turn precision potentiometer. (*Courtesy of Electro-Mec Laboratory, Inc., Long Island City.*)

As the slider moves from turn to turn, the voltage increases in a step-wise fashion. This step-wise output voltage ΔE is the total voltage E divided by the number of turns n of resistance wire. For a wiper which touches only one wire at a time, the resolution is given by the following definition:

$$\text{Resolution} = \frac{\Delta E}{E} = \frac{E/n}{E} = \frac{1}{n} = \frac{1}{\text{No. of turns on potentiometer}} \quad (8\text{-}2)$$

Since the accuracy of a potentiometer is limited by the size of the voltage steps between wires, and since a system may tend to hunt between two adjacent wires, multi-revolution or multiturn potentiometers have been developed. This type of potentiometer has a resistance element in the shape of a helix. As the slider rotates, it is mechanically caused to move along the helix. The greater length of wire results in improved resolution. A typical unit is shown in the cutaway photograph of Fig. 8-5.

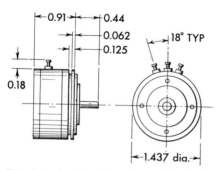

Fɪɢ. 8-4. Outline dimensions of a single-turn precision potentiometer. (*Courtesy of Electro-Mec Laboratory, Inc., Long Island City.*)

Multiturn potentiometers can be more accurate and have a finer resolution but suffer from large size and additional friction referred to the system power source (motor).   Table 8-1 shows a comparison of characteristics of precision potentiometers.   The resolution of the "pot" indicates the accuracy to which any shaft setting can be made.   It is important

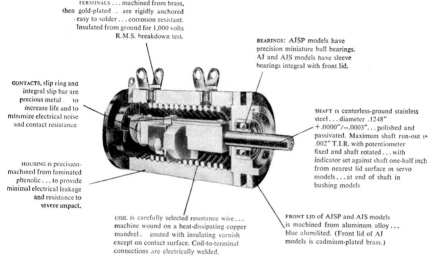

FIG. 8-5. Cutaway view of a typical multiturn precision potentiometer.   (*Courtesy of Helipot Corp., South Pasadena, Calif.*)

to consider this fact in selecting a potentiometer.   Any special accuracy on the part of other components that might be coupled to the pot would be lost if the resolution did not offer equal or greater angular accuracy. The absolute, theoretical accuracy of a potentiometer is one-half the resolution.   This is shown on the curve of Fig. 8-6.

TABLE 8-1. CHARACTERISTICS OF PRECISION POTENTIOMETERS*

No. of turns	1	3	10	25	40
Resistance range..	10–50K	10–75K	25–300K	100–750K	200K–1 Meg
Turns of res. wire	800–4,000	850–5,000	3,000–18,000	8,000–75,000	21,000–135,000
Outside diameter, in............	1¾–3	1½	¾–1¹³⁄₁₆	3⁵⁄₁₆	3⁵⁄₁₆
Coil length, in....	4½–8	14	47	234	374
Max. No. of taps	20–30	14	30	90	100
Best practical linearity, %....	0.10	0.10	0.05	0.025	0.02

* Copyright 1953, by the Helipot Corporation, reprinted by permission.

The transfer function of Eq. (8-1) represents a straight-line input-output relationship.   The deviation of the potentiometer from this straight line is a measure of the linearity accuracy.   Two definitions of linearity are in common use:

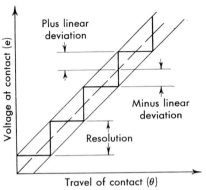

FIG. 8-6. Potentiometer resolution.

Independent linearity (used in connection with precision potentiometers)

Zero-based linearity (used in connection with a rheostat or variable resistance)

Independent-linearity tolerance is the maximum allowable deviation from the best straight line that can be drawn through a plot of the actual points of voltage on the voltage versus rotation curve.   The tolerance is expressed as a percentage of the maximum voltage output. This is shown in Fig. 8-7a, where the straight line has been oriented to fit best the actual output curve.

"Zero-based" linearity is the maximum allowable deviation from the best straight line that can be drawn through the voltage points and also pass through zero voltage at zero shaft displacement.   This is shown in Fig. 8-7b.

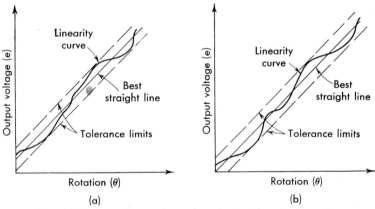

FIG. 8-7. Independent and zero-based potentiometer linearity.

Use of a potentiometer requires that the circuit resistances be considered.   With a constant voltage impressed across the coil of a linear potentiometer, the voltage may not follow the linear transfer function of Eq. (8-1).   As current is drawn through the slider, a so-called "loading error" results. The loading error varies with slider position. The output voltage is given by the expression

$$\frac{e}{E} = \frac{\theta}{1 + (\theta/\beta)(1 - \theta)} \qquad (8\text{-}3)$$

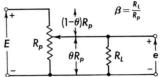

FIG. 8-8. Equivalent circuit for a loaded potentiometer.

where β is the ratio of load resistance R_L to potentiometer resistance R_p. θ is the setting of the potentiometer and is the fraction of the total resistance. The equivalent circuit for a potentiometer working into a load resistance is shown in Fig. 8-8.

The deviation or error from the straight-line curve is given by the expression

$$\frac{\varepsilon}{E} = \frac{(\theta^2/\beta)(1 - \theta)}{1 + (\theta/\beta)(1 - \theta)} \qquad (8\text{-}4)$$

The loading error, shown plotted in Fig. 8-9, varies with slider position. The error is zero at both ends of the coil and has a maximum value at approximately two-thirds rotation. The error varies with load resistance. A load resistance 10 times that of the potentiometer resistance produces a maximum error of 1.5 per cent of the applied voltage. An error of 0.15 per cent results when the load resistance is 100 times the potentiometer resistance. The effect of loading can be reduced by several means:

1. Wind on the potentiometer a slight nonlinear function which compensates for the loading.

2. Locate a tap at the $\frac{2}{3}$ point on the potentiometer. An appropriate resistor connected between the tap and the 100 per cent point compensates for the loading.

The loading error of potentiometers, as shown in Fig. 8-9, is normally considered detrimental. When a potentiometer is loaded appropriately, many nonlinear functions can be obtained with the linear, nontapped potentiometer. In this application, the loading curves

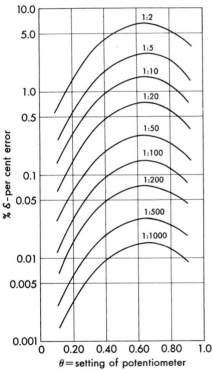

FIG. 8-9. Potentiometer loading error.

become useful.   Equation (8-3) produces the nonlinear curves of Fig. 8-10 for β in the range 0.01 to 1.0.   When the potentiometer is loaded on the top, as shown in Fig. 8-11, the potentiometer transfer function is given by

$$\frac{e}{E} = \frac{1 - \theta + \rho}{1 - \theta + \rho/\theta} \tag{8-5}$$

Equation (8-5) plots into the curves of Fig. 8-10 when ρ is in the range 0.01 to 1.0.

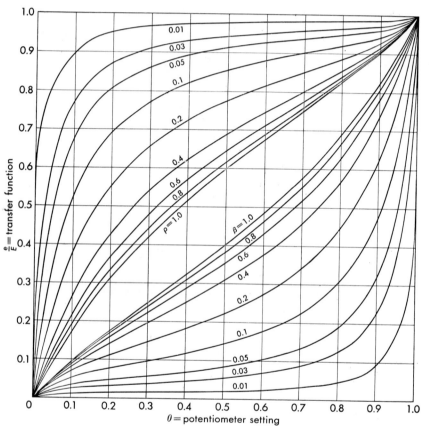

FIG. 8-10. Potentiometer loading curves used to form nonlinear functions.

Other types of nonlinear functions can be obtained by any of the following methods:

1. A standard linear potentiometer with voltage taps and resistance loading

2. A nonlinear winding which incorporates a variation of resistance as θ varies

In general, the same characteristics are inherent in the precision non-linear potentiometer as in precision linear units (i.e., resolution, loading error, etc.). The deviation of the output voltage from the prescribed function is termed "conformity" rather than linearity.

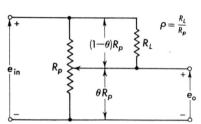

FIG. 8-11. Equivalent circuit for a loaded potentiometer.

FIG. 8-12. A typical multiturn precision potentiometer. (*Courtesy of Helipot Corp., South Pasadena, Calif.*)

The potentiometer offers many advantages in terms of versatility, ease of forming functions, and ability to use either a-c or d-c excitation. Two problems exist in the use of potentiometers—electrical noise generation and reliability.

The physical form of a potentiometer varies with the manufacturer. Figure 8-3 shows a typical single-turn precision potentiometer, and Fig. 8-5 shows a cutaway view of a multiturn unit. This latter unit, which is also shown in Fig. 8-12, is of $7/8$-in. diameter and 1.587-in. body length and is available with a 0.25 per cent linearity tolerance. The construction details of a small ($7/8$-in. diameter by $1/2$-in. length), single-turn potentiometer are shown in Fig. 8-13.

In computer applications it is necessary to "gang," or assemble several potentiometers on a single shaft. The unit shown on Fig. 8-14 permits the ganging of up to 20 units on a single shaft. The individual

FIG. 8-13. A $7/8$-in.-diameter subminiature precision potentiometer. (*Courtesy of DeJur-Ansco Corp., Long Island City.*)

cups are held together with circular clamps. When circuit elements require change, the potentiometers are easily removed and rephased. One manufacturer has produced a "plug-in potentiometer" as shown in Fig. 8-15. A modified terminal board has small, pin-type plugs in place of conventional terminals. Each potentiometer is quickly removed and replaced without disconnecting wires or soldering.

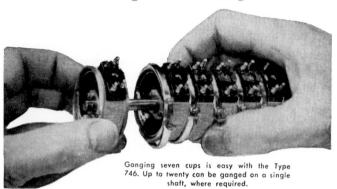

Ganging seven cups is easy with the Type 746. Up to twenty can be ganged on a single shaft, where required.

FIG. 8-14. Ganging several potentiometers on a single shaft. (*Courtesy of Fairchild Controls Corp., Hicksville, N.Y.*)

The problem of resolution in potentiometers, as shown in Fig. 8-6, has been approached in several ways. Smooth and stepless operation, low noise, long life, and low starting torque are some of the characteristics of a slide-wire potentiometer. These potentiometers may have a resistance of 2,500 ohms in a multiturn unit. Another approach to the problem of resolution is through the use of a deposited film potentiometer. Although these units do not have "infinite" resolution, they do exhibit a resolution which is 20 to 70 times better than the comparable wire-wound unit. A resistance material is evaporated and deposited on a ceramic disk. A slider passes over this deposited material to form the potentiometer.

FIG. 8-15. Plug-in potentiometers provide rapid removal and replacement. (*Courtesy of Fairchild Controls Corp., Hicksville, N.Y.*)

Potentiometers for low shaft torque applications (0.003 oz-in.) can be obtained and are useful for direct coupling to low-power transducers such as meter movements and pressure diaphragms. These instruments are usually quite delicate, are less reliable, and possess a high contact resistance.

When translational motion is to be transduced, a linear-motion potentiometer can be used instead of an angular potentiometer with a rack and pinion. Good resolution is possible, and strokes of 1 to 15 in. are available.

A large variety of taps, resistance, shaft extensions, stops, and tapped continuous-rotation units gives a wide latitude to potentiometer applications. The factors to be considered in potentiometer selection can be summarized[12] as follows:

Electrical Suitability.

1. Linearity as required by the application
2. Tolerance on total resistance and shaft angle
3. Resolution error and its effect on servo stability and wear
4. Sufficient electrical insulation strength
5. Freedom from stray capacitive and inductive effects
6. Generation of undesirable radio interference

Mechanical Suitability.

1. Adequate life to meet anticipated performance cycle
2. Adaptability to environmental conditions: temperature, humidity
3. Ability to withstand vibration without excessive contact bounce
4. Precision of mounting surface and shaft extension
5. Provision for easy zeroing and calibration
6. Acceptable starting friction

8-4. Induction-type Position Indicators.* Induction-type transducers are available for position measurement. Although these units are limited to a-c operation and are more costly, they exhibit stepless output, are small in size, and have a high degree of reliability.

The schematic of an induction component which is essentially a transformer with a rotatable secondary is shown in Fig. 8-16. The rotor winding is excited with an a-c voltage, and the output voltages, which are induced in the stator windings, depend on the shaft

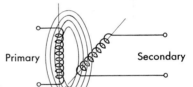

Primary   Secondary

Fig. 8-16. Principle of operation of induction components.

angle. The output voltage is proportional to the fraction of the flux cut by the secondary coil. When the primary and secondary coils are lined up with the flux, the entire primary voltage is transformed. As the second-

* The author is indebted to Mr. Sidney Davis for much of the material in Secs. 8-4, 8-5, and 8-6. The reader is referred to his excellent paper "Rotating Components for Automatic Control" (Ref. 13).

ary is rotated through an angle θ, the output voltage depends upon this angle:

$$E_{out} = K \cos \theta \qquad (8\text{-}6)$$

The advantages of induction units can be listed as follows:

1. High reliability (no contact moving along the sawlike resistance element, only sliding contacts—slip rings).
2. Long life (less wear).
3. Smooth, continuous output voltage.
4. Low noise generated in the system.
5. No radio interference generated.
6. Isolation of input and output circuits because of transformer action.

The disadvantages of these units are summarized:

1. Applicable to a-c signals only.
2. Difficult to obtain good linearity.

Fig. 8-17. Photograph of a typical induction-type transducer. (*Courtesy of Ford Instrument Co., Long Island City.*)

3. Phase shift varies with temperature.

4. Less versatile for forming functions.

5. Generate harmonics and quadrature.

Physically, the induction components have the appearance of small motors. A typical unit is shown on the photograph of Fig. 8-17, and a cutaway view is included on Fig. 8-18. The unit contains a wound rotor

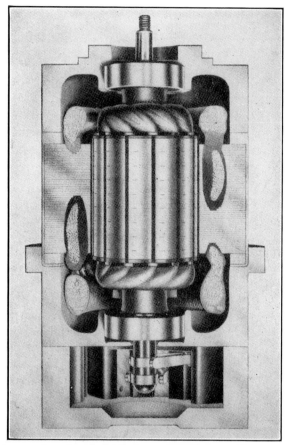

FIG. 8-18. Cutaway view of an induction-type transducer. (*Courtesy of Ford Instrument Co., Long Island City.*)

mounted on bearings. The connections to the rotor are carried through slip rings which are shown in the lower portion of Fig. 8-18. All leads are brought out to connectors mounted at one end of the instrument.

8-5. Resolvers. The induction resolver, shown in the schematic diagram of Fig. 8-19, consists of a rotor and a stator, each with two windings whose axes are 90° apart. The secondary voltages which result are the sine and cosine of the shaft angle. The resolver equations are summarized:

$$E_3 = K(E_1 \cos \theta - E_2 \sin \theta)$$
$$E_4 = K(E_1 \sin \theta + E_2 \cos \theta) \tag{8-7}$$

where E_1 and E_2 are the applied reference voltages, θ is the angle through which the rotor shaft has been mechanically turned from zero with respect

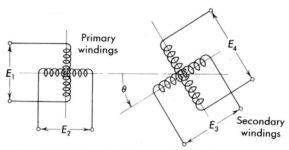

FIG. 8-19. Schematic diagram of induction resolver.

to the case, K is the constant of the resolver, and E_3 and E_4 are the output voltages.

Resolvers are usually designed to function with high accuracy even when one of the input windings (usually the stator) is shorted.

The function of a resolver might be indicated by reference to Fig. 8-20. In many computer and control applications, it is necessary to resolve a vector (e.g., velocity) into its x and y components. V is the input voltage (e.g., 24 volts) impressed across one stator winding, and θ is the angle (0 to 360°) through which the rotor shaft has been mechanically turned from zero. $V \sin \theta$ and $V \cos \theta$ are the output voltages induced in the rotor windings. Both V and θ may be varied, while the resolver continuously provides the resolved velocity components

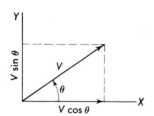

FIG. 8-20. Velocity vector resolved into sine and cosine terms.

$$V_x = V \cos \theta$$
$$V_y = V \sin \theta \tag{8-8}$$

In more complicated applications, the resolver is used to transform coordinates. Suppose that the reference coordinate system in an aircraft is aligned and fixed in an xy coordinate system, as shown on Fig. 8-21. Angular rates or angular velocities are measured about these axes: ω_x and ω_y. These must be transformed or resolved into angular velocities about the roll and pitch axes of the aircraft: ω_r and ω_p. The velocity (see the vector diagram of Fig. 8-22) in the pitch direction is

$$\omega_p = \omega_x \cos \theta - \omega_y \sin \theta \tag{8-9}$$

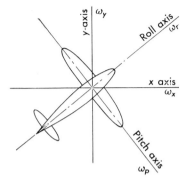

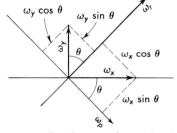

FIG. 8-21. Coordinate transformation from x and y axes to roll and pitch axes.

FIG. 8-22. Resolver used to transform coordinates.

and in the roll direction

$$\omega_r = \omega_x \sin \theta + \omega_y \cos \theta \qquad (8\text{-}10)$$

Since the resolver equations [Eqs. (8-7)] are identical with these, a com-

FIG. 8-23. Photograph of a miniature resolver. (*Courtesy of Reeves Instrument Corp., New York.*)

plicated computation is simply accomplished with this transducer. A typical unit is shown on the photograph of Fig. 8-23, and the nominal dimensions are shown in Fig. 8-24. Since the gain of a resolver-type

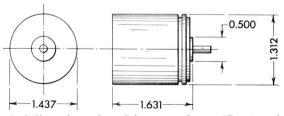

FIG. 8-24. Nominal dimensions of a miniature resolver. (*Courtesy of Reeves Instrument Corp., New York.*)

servo is a function of heading, use of such a unit leads to nonlinear servo design (discussed in Chap. 10).

8-6. Synchros. Depending upon the manufacturer, this unit may be known by any of the following names:

Selsyn
Autosyn
Telesyn

The unit usually consists of a Y-connected stator winding and a single-phase rotor winding. Depending on their function, these units can be used as either torque transmitters or position indicators.

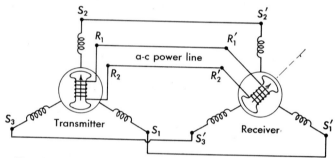

Fig. 8-25. Schematic of two synchros used to transmit torque.

Torque units are connected as in Fig. 8-25. The excitation voltage produces a magnetic field in the synchro transmitter which causes current to flow in the interconnecting wires and hence establishes a magnetic field in the synchro receiver. This receiver field interacts with the field established by the rotor current and aligns the rotor and stator fields. Because of losses in the system, the power at the receiver is less than that at the input. The torque per angle of misalignment is called the synchro torque gradient. When the transmitter shaft is turned, the shaft of the

TABLE 8-2. PERFORMANCE CHARACTERISTICS OF VARIOUS TYPES OF SYNCHROS*
(All units weigh 4 oz)

Type	Voltage gradient, mv/deg	Torque gradient, mg-mm/deg	Error (maximum), min
Transmitter................	204	3,750	10
Control transformer..........	403	.....	10
Repeater...................	...	2,050	30
Differential................	196	.....	10
Resolver...................	439	.....	10

* Courtesy of the Kearfott Company, Inc., Little Falls, N.J.

receiver rotates through the same angle to an accuracy which depends largely upon the load but also upon electrical accuracy. Table 8-2 indicates the performance specifications for typical units.

Synchros are similar in appearance to the other induction components. A typical unit is shown in Fig. 8-26. The transmitters and receiver are similar with the exception of a damping device used on the receiver. An inertia wheel and a dissipation element permit the receiver to follow with a minimum of oscillation or running away. Even with a damper on the receiver, large inertias should not be coupled to the shaft, since they tend to produce oscillations. Large coulomb-friction loads (potentiometers, etc.) are also objectionable, since this type of load causes a positional error.

Another useful synchro for torque or signal transmission is the differential synchro. This unit is similar in objective to a mechanical differential. The differential synchro has a Y-connected stator and rotor and is identified by the three slip rings. The unit is connected between a synchro transmitter and receiver, as shown in Fig. 8-27. The synchro

FIG. 8-26. Photograph of a military-size 15 synchro. (*Courtesy of Doelcam Div., Minneapolis-Honeywell Regulator Co., Boston, Mass.*)

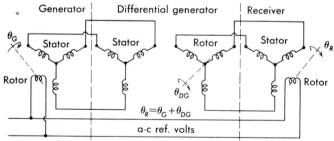

FIG. 8-27. Schematic diagram of a differential generator used in a torque synchro system.

receiver angle θ_r is given by $\theta_r = \theta_g + \theta_{DG}$, where θ_g is the synchro generator angle and θ_{DG} is the differential generator angle.

The standard torque units have certain disadvantages which make them inadequate for most servo design:

1. Poor accuracy when driving a friction load (e.g., potentiometer stack)

2. Poor damping when driving an inertia load

3. Less versatility than a servo system in setting the damping (e.g., by electrical means)

The main use for torque synchros is in the application of presenting display information such as dial readings.

Synchros used as position indicators are connected as in Fig. 8-28 and develop an output-error voltage equal to the sine of the difference in shaft position between the input and the output shaft angles. This error signal is amplified and used to drive a motor that restores input-output correspondence by properly positioning the output shaft. Output torque can be as high as desired. Since the torque is supplied by a

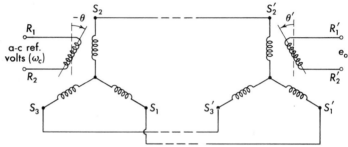

FIG. 8-28. Schematic of synchros used as position indicators.

servomotor driven by an amplifier, mechanical requirements of low bearing friction and built-in damping are not so important as in torque units.

Synchros used in this application are called control synchros and differ from the torque units in the impedance level of the windings. The input impedance is high, so the units do not draw much power. The torque gradient is kept to a minimum in the interest of eliminating the torque transmission of the ordinary torque units. The torque synchro rotor aligns itself with the field. The position synchro is rotated by the servo until the secondary rotor is aligned perpendicular to the magnetic field, since at this position the input to the servoamplifier is zero. Hence the rest position for a torque synchro is 90 electrical degrees with respect to the null position for a position synchro.

With voltages impressed across corresponding stator leads of the synchro transmitter shown in Fig. 8-28, proportional fluxes are produced. These fluxes, which add vectorially to produce a resultant flux, have the same angular position with respect to the synchro receiver stator coils as the transmitter rotor has to its stator coils. With neglect of source impedance, the voltage appearing across $R_1' - R_2'$ (Fig. 8-28) may be expressed as

$$E_{R_1'R_2'} = K_s \sin (\theta - \theta') \qquad (8\text{-}11)$$

For small errors, $\theta - \theta'$ can be substituted for $\sin \theta - \theta'$ with the result

$$E_{R_1'R_2'} = K_s(\theta - \theta') \qquad (8\text{-}12)$$

K_s is the voltage sensitivity of the synchro (volts per radian misalignment) and ω_c is the carrier frequency.

8-7. Reluctance Pickoffs. A large variety of position instruments are built on the variable-reluctance principle. These units are used to measure both angular rotation and linear motion. They are often built into other instruments. For example, pressure transducers, accelerometers, and gyroscopes often utilize a variable reluctance pickoff. A linear motion unit, the so-called " E pickoff," is analyzed in this section. This name comes from its mechanical construction, which is shown in Fig. 8-29.

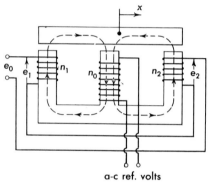

An a-c flux, shown by the dotted lines, is established in the magnetic circuit. The flux at one instant of time is in the direction of the arrows. If the movable portion of

FIG. 8-29. E-type variable-reluctance position pickoff.

the unit (termed an armature) is located symmetrically with respect to the E-shaped unit (termed a stator), the flux in each outer leg is equal. When coils n_1 and n_2 are equal but wound in opposition, the voltage induced across these coils is equal. Hence, with the unit in the symmetrical position the output voltage $e_o = e_1 - e_2 = 0$. If the armature is displaced an amount x, the flux through n_1 decreases and the flux through n_2 increases. The voltage e_2 becomes greater than e_1, and $e_o = e_1 - e_2$ assumes a value. For small displacements and with careful shaping of the magnetic circuit, the transfer function of the unit is

$$e_o = K_s x \qquad (8\text{-}13)$$

where K_s is the pickoff sensitivity expressed in volts per unit length. ω_c is the reference carrier frequency.

When the E pickoff is properly designed, there is no reaction torque on the I member over a wide range of motion. The sensitivity of these variable-reluctance pickoffs is extremely high. It is not uncommon for these units to sense changes of several milli-inches.

8-8. Measurement of Velocity. Velocity pickoffs or tachometers develop an output voltage proportional to the shaft angular velocity.

The tachometer output voltage is used for damping in position servos or as an output comparison unit for velocity servos. Although there are numerous types of velocity pickoffs, the induction or a-c generator and the d-c tachometer have the greatest application.

An ideal tachometer should have the following characteristics:

1. The output voltage is linear with respect to shaft speed.

2. The output is relatively free from harmonics and quadrature.

3. At any one speed the output voltage is proportional to input voltage.

4. High sensitivity, i.e., appreciable output voltage, with small shaft speed.

8-9. Induction Tachometers. The a-c tachometer, schematically shown in Fig. 8-30, resembles a two-phase a-c motor. An a-c reference voltage is applied to one phase of the tach generator, and a voltage of reference frequency and amplitude proportional to shaft speed is generated on the other phase. The sinusoidal reference voltage which is applied to the primary winding sets up in the generator a sinusoidally varying flux of constant amplitude. The secondary winding is located mechanically 90° with respect to this flux, so that with zero velocity no voltage is induced into the secondary. As the shaft is rotated, currents which

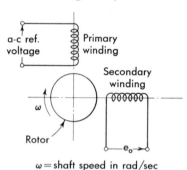

ω = shaft speed in rad/sec

FIG. 8-30. Schematic diagram of an induction tachometer.

generate a flux are induced in the rotor. This rotor flux adds to the reference flux and shifts the direction of the total flux. The total flux now has a component in the direction of the 90° winding, and a voltage is generated in this winding. With proper design the flux component in the 90° winding is made proportional to velocity; hence the output voltage is proportional to velocity.

The characteristics of an a-c generator are best summarized in the following equation:

$$e_o = K_s \omega \qquad (8\text{-}14)$$

where K_s is the voltage gradient in volts per radian per second^{-1} and ω is the shaft speed. A good instrument will have a constant K_s invariant with shaft speed ω, voltage level, and carrier frequency. The phase shift of the output voltage is either 0 or 180° with respect to the reference voltage, depending on whether the shaft direction is positive or negative.

The voltage gradient K_s is found from the manufacturer's literature. Often the manufacturer gives the K_s information as follows: Output volts at 1,000 rpm = 3 volts with rated reference voltage applied. With data in this form the gradient is assumed linear and K_s is computed as follows:

$$K_s = \frac{3}{1,000(2\pi/60)} = 2.87 \times 10^{-2} \text{ volts}/(\text{radian})(\text{sec})^{-1} \quad (8\text{-}15)$$

Equation (8-14) is written alternately as

$$\frac{E_o}{\theta} = K_s p \qquad (8\text{-}16)$$

where p is the Laplace-transform operator.

FIG. 8-31. Alternating-current rate generator. (*Courtesy of Ford Instrument Co., Long Island City.*)

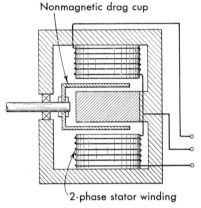

Nonmagnetic drag cup

2-phase stator winding

FIG. 8-32. Sketch of drag-cup a-c tachometer.

The physical size and appearance of any of these rate generators (either alternating or direct current) are similar to the synchros. One type of unit is shown on Fig. 8-31. This rate generator is known as a "drag-cup tachometer." It incorporates a cylindrical drag cup which serves as the rotating element. This cup rotates in the air gap between a cylindrical stator and a core, both of precision-machined laminated-magnetic steel (cf. Fig. 8-32).

The instrument functions as a two-phase induction generator. When one stator phase is excited by a constant-frequency, constant-amplitude voltage source, the output voltage from the other stator phase has an amplitude proportional to the speed of the shaft and a frequency identical with that of the excitation voltage. The unit shown in Fig. 8-31 has the characteristics shown in Table 8-3.

Besides the application of the rate generator to damp closed-loop systems these units are used for integrating and computing. As an example of this latter application consider the block diagram shown in Fig. 8-33.

The over-all transfer function is

$$\frac{C}{R} = \frac{AK_m}{p[(\tau_m p + 1) + AK_s K_m]} \qquad (8\text{-}17)$$

For large amplifier gain the transfer function reduces to

$$\frac{C}{R} \approx \frac{1}{K_s p} \qquad (8\text{-}18)$$

TABLE 8-3. CHARACTERISTICS OF A TEMPERATURE COMPENSATED A-C RATE
GENERATOR*

Frequency, cycles.. 400
Input voltage.. 115
Input power, watts... 4.7 ± 0.3
Input current, ma.. 100 ± 10
Maximum total residual rms voltage (null), mv................. 100
Maximum variation in residual voltage as shaft is positioned, mv   30
Output voltage per 1,000 rpm................................ 3.6 ± 0.4 / ±90°
Maximum deviation of output voltage from linearity at speeds to
  1,800 rpm, %.. 0.1
Output impedance at 1,800 rpm, ohms........................ 26,000
Compensated temperature range, °C......................... 0 to +90
Maximum deviation over full temperature range from output volt-
  age at 25°C, %... ±0.5
Moment of inertia, oz-in.² 0.075

    * Courtesy Ford Instrument Co., Long Island City.

Hence the circuit of Fig. 8-33, which uses a rate generator in the feed-back path, comprises an approximate integrator. The accuracy of such an integrator is limited by the approximation made (that is, $A \gg 1$).

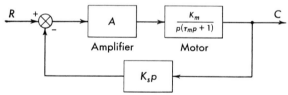

FIG. 8-33. Block diagram of an electromechanical integrator which uses an a-c rate generator.

The accuracy is also limited by the following characteristics of the tachometer:

  1. Threshold (zero output voltage even with some finite shaft velocity)
  2. Variation of K_s with velocity, applied voltage, or environment

8-10. Direct-current Tachometers. Although a-c rate generators are most common, d-c generators are often required for d-c servo applications which are similar to the above-mentioned a-c applications: d-c servo damping, d-c velocity servo comparison, etc. Because of the necessity for brushes and commutation in d-c machines, d-c rate generators are less accurate, exhibit greater friction, produce both electrical and radio noise, are subject to drift, and quite often have a different K_s in one direction from the other.

The d-c generator is similar in appearance and operation to the d-c motor. A fixed field is established with a d-c current through a field coil. As the rotor windings cut the constant magnetic field, a voltage is generated in the rotor windings which is proportional to velocity. The transfer function can be written

$$\frac{E_o}{\theta} = K_s p \qquad (8\text{-}19)$$

where K_s is the d-c generator gradient in volts per radian second^{-1}.

8-11. Permanent-magnet Tachometers. Alnico permanent magnets are often employed as the fixed field in d-c tachometers. These generators are smaller in size, are more reliable, and have a larger gradient K_s than the wound-field units.

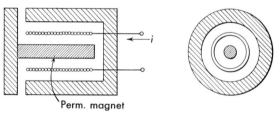

Fig. 8-34. Sketch of d-c–linear-motion rate pickoff.

The permanent magnets are stabilized against demagnetizing effects such as mechanical shock and short circuits by cycling an alternating field, of particular magnitude, through the magnetic circuit after the initial charging of the magnet. The instrument is made insensitive to temperature changes by using a "carpenter metal" shunt in the magnetic path. This shunt has a permeability which changes with temperature in an opposite sense to the permeability changes of Alnico. This technique maintains an essentially uniform flux in the magnetic core. Adjustable magnetic cores (or slugs) permit an adjustment of K_s.

Permanent magnets are often used for measuring linear-motion velocities. This type of pickoff consists of a coil mounted on the fixed member and a magnet mounted on the movable member. A sketch of a linear-motion d-c rate pickoff is shown in Fig. 8-34. As the magnet moves in and out of the coil, a voltage is generated at the output terminals of the coil which is proportional to the linear velocity. The proportionality constant K_s is the voltage gradient in volts per inch second^{-1}. If the magnet is stabilized against demagnetization and compensated for temperature changes, a precise transducer is obtained.

8-12. Capacitor Tachometers. The capacitor tachometer, which is included primarily for interest, comprises a capacitor, a d-c power source, and a switch (or a commutator) connected as shown in Fig. 8-35. The commutator, which is made to rotate with the shaft, alternately charges the capacitor from the source and discharges it through the load. If the

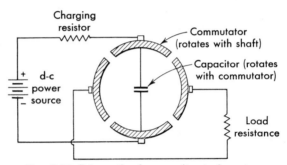

FIG. 8-35. Schematic of a capacitor tachometer.

commutator rotates clockwise (see Fig. 8-35), the discharge current flows through the load from top to bottom. If the shaft rotates counterclockwise, the discharge current flows from bottom to top. Hence the polarity of the load voltage determines the shaft direction.

Figure 8-36 shows the output of the capacitor tachometer for one direction of rotation and for two different angular velocities. The current into the load is a train of sharp pulses (exponential decays), the number of which is proportional to the number of revolutions. If this output is

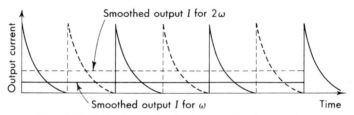

FIG. 8-36. Output waveform of a capacitor tachometer.

smoothed through a filter, an average current which is proportional to speed is obtained. If this output is not smoothed, the capacitor tachometer forms a type of input which can be used with digital systems.

When used as an analogue unit, that is, current proportional to speed, the device is less accurate. For small velocities the "spikes" are widely separated and the averaging process gives rise to large errors.

8-13. Measurement of Acceleration. Although many types of acceleration transducers are manufactured, most of these instruments are based upon a common principle of operation. The instrument measures the motion of a restrained mass when it is subjected to accelerations. Variations as to linear and angular accelerations, a fluid or a solid mass, fluid or pneumatic damping, a-c or d-c output, etc., do not change the fundamental theory underlying the operation of the accelerometer. Two types of accelerometer are considered. One is basically a mechanical unit in which the acceleration measurement depends upon the mechanical system, and the other, a force-balance unit in which a servo corrects some of the inaccuracies in the basic mechanical system.

8-14. Mechanical Accelerometer. A "seismic" or mechanical accelerometer is represented by the schematic of Fig. 8-37. The instrument consists of a mass suspended from the frame by a spring. Damping is provided either mechanically or electrically, and an electrical pick-off measures the position of the mass with respect to the frame. The variable x is the displacement of the frame which is fastened to the body whose acceleration is to be measured. y is the displacement with respect to the frame of the suspended mass M. The position pickoff measures the variable y. K is the spring constant of the suspension, and B is the

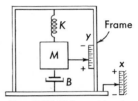

FIG. 8-37. Schematic of a seismic accelerometer.

viscous damping constant. Since y is measured with respect to the frame, the force on the mass due to the spring is $-Ky$ and due to the damper is $-B(dy/dt)$. The motion of the mass in inertial space is $y - x$. The Laplace-transformed equation for the sum of the forces on the mass is

$$Mp^2(Y - X) + BpY + KY = 0 \qquad (8\text{-}20)$$

where zero initial conditions are assumed. Equation (8-20) is rearranged:

$$(Mp^2 + Bp + K)Y = Mp^2X = MA \qquad (8\text{-}21)$$

where $p^2X = A$ is the acceleration to be measured.

The transfer function of the accelerometer is

$$Y = \frac{MA}{Mp^2 + Bp + K} = \frac{A}{p^2 + (B/M)p + (K/M)} \qquad (8\text{-}22)$$

This equation is simplified

$$\frac{Y}{A} = \frac{1}{p^2 + 2\zeta\omega_n p + \omega_n{}^2} \qquad (8\text{-}23)$$

where $\qquad \omega_n = \sqrt{\dfrac{K}{M}} \qquad$ and $\qquad \zeta = \dfrac{B}{2\sqrt{KM}} \qquad (8\text{-}24)$

The output of the accelerometer is measured with any of the position instruments discussed in Sec. 8-2. Commonly, either a linear-motion potentiometer or an E pickoff is used to measure y. If the sensitivity (transfer function) of the position instrument is K_s, then the accelerometer transfer function is

$$\frac{Y}{A} = \frac{K_s}{p^2 + 2\zeta\omega_n p + \omega_n^2} \quad (8\text{-}25)$$

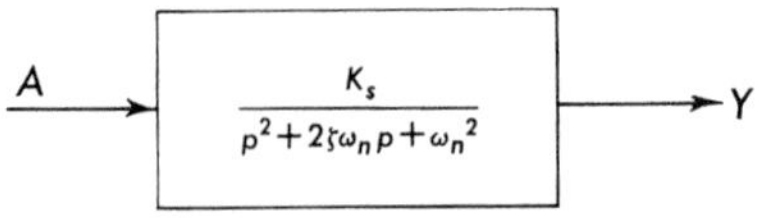

FIG. 8-38. Block diagram of a mechanical accelerometer.

and the block diagram is shown in Fig. 8-38.

Accelerometers of the type just discussed fit in the category of sprung mass instruments. In these instruments the acceleration to be measured appears as a proportional force (or torque) which acts upon a small mass (or moment of inertia). This force is balanced against a spring, and the deflection of this spring then becomes a measure of the force and therefore the acceleration. For static measurements, only a spring and a

FIG. 8-39. A small and rugged seismic accelerometer with potentiometer output. (*Courtesy of Genisco, Inc., Los Angeles, Calif.*)

mass or inertia are necessary. Under dynamic conditions damping is required to dissipate continually vibrational energy. Accelerometers employ liquid, pneumatic, and other forms of damping. They have an accuracy which depends directly upon the accuracy of the spring. Hysteresis, nonlinearities, or nonsymmetrical properties of this spring will result in errors in the instrument. For this and other reasons which are related to open-loop computations, units of this type are generally less accurate and have a smaller range than those of the force-balance or "servo" type, which are described in the next section. Seismic accelerometers are small and rugged, however, and provide a high output voltage from a potentiometer.

Figure 8-39 shows a typical unit that weighs 8 oz and is $1\frac{1}{8}$ by $1\frac{1}{8}$ by $3\frac{1}{8}$ in. over-all size. The output is linear within 1 per cent of full scale with a resolution of 0.3 per cent. Silicone damping provides 0.7 damping ratio. The output is measured with a potentiometer.

Small seismic accelerometers are designed and built for a wide range of accelerations using strain gauges to transduce the motion of the seismic mass. A photograph of a typical unit is shown in Fig. 8-40, and its characteristics summarized in Table 8-4. Because of the step-less character of a strain gauge, the ultimate resolution of these accelerometers is infinite.

FIG. 8-40. Seismic accelerometer with strain-gauge output. (*Courtesy of Statham Laboratories, Inc., Los Angeles, Calif.*)

High-accuracy seismic accelerometers are built for use in various aircraft and missile-control systems. A typical unit is shown in Fig. 8-41.

TABLE 8-4. CHARACTERISTICS OF A SEISMIC ACCELEROMETER*

Range, g	Approximate natural frequency, cps	Excitation d-c or a-c volts	Approximate full-scale open circuit output mv	Approximate full-scale excursion, mv
±2	100	9	±45	90
±5	190	11	±50	100
±10	250	11	±47	94
±15	300	11	±44	88
±20	350	11	±44	88
±25	375	11	±50	100
±50	500	12	±55	110
±100	600	11	±50	100
±200	850	11	±44	88

* Courtesy of Statham Laboratories, Inc., Los Angeles, Calif.

The seismic system consists of a dihedral spring to which a mass is attached at short radius. A magnetic armature is part of the system and is caused to rotate as the acceleration is applied. The displacement of the armature changes circuit inductances in a four-arm variable-reluctance bridge. The units are linear within 0.5 per cent with stepless output (infinite resolution).

The frequency response of seismic instruments [Eq. (8-25) for $p = j\omega$] is shown on Fig. 5-3a (amplitude) and b (phase shift). So that the acceleration measurements will be without waveform change, the widest possible frequency range (bandwidth) is desired. The least requirements

FIG. 8-41. Seismic accelerometer with variable-reluctance output. (*Courtesy of Wiancko Engineering Co., Pasadena, Calif.*)

are a flat amplitude and a linear phase shift. Note that in Fig. 5-3a the $\zeta = 0.707$ curve gives a flat amplitude, within close limits, out to 0.4 of the natural frequency. The phase-shift curve, Fig. 5-3b, is more nearly linear than any on either side of it. For these reasons, accelerometers (and many other instruments) are commonly damped at 0.7 critical damping. As is expected, increased damping will decrease the magnitude of the response peak in the neighborhood of the natural frequency, and thus transient oscillations due to high-frequency excitation are minimized.

8-15. Force-balance Accelerometers. Force-balance accelerometers overcome some of the disadvantages of the previously mentioned instruments. The basic principle underlying the force-balance accelerometer is depicted in Fig. 8-42. In this system a mass is allowed to move along the acceleration-sensitive axis. The position of this mass is measured with a position pickoff, which is generally of the E type, as discussed in Sec. 8-7. The output voltage from this position transducer is amplified with a high-gain amplifier whose output is a current. The current flows through the windings of a forcer* which forces the mass back to its original null position. The forcer current, necessary to zero the position of this mass, is proportional to acceleration. This current is measured as a voltage across a resistor which is in series with the forcer coil. In this system high damping, which is independent of temperature, and good accuracy are obtained by means of appropriate equalization in the servo.

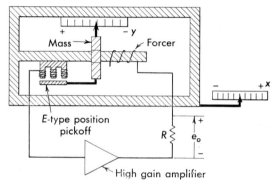

FIG. 8-42. Schematic of force-balance accelerometer.

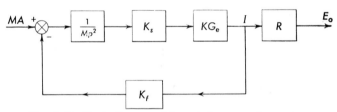

FIG. 8-43. Block diagram of force-balance accelerometer.

The analysis of the force-balance accelerometer of Fig. 8-42 is based upon the block diagram of Fig. 8-43. If the mass is free to move along the rod with essentially zero damping, the force on the mass is related to the displacement as follows:

$$F = Mp^2(Y - X) \qquad (8\text{-}26)$$

or rewritten

$$Y = \frac{1}{Mp^2}(F + Mp^2 X) = \frac{1}{Mp^2}(F + MA) \qquad (8\text{-}27)$$

p is the Laplace-transform operator, and zero initial conditions are assumed. Equation (8-27) is represented by the first block whose output is Y. This quantity is transduced to a voltage through a position pickoff of transfer function K_s and amplified through an amplifier and equalizer KG_e. The current from this amplifier passes through a forcer,

* See Sec. 9-5 for a discussion of a forcer.

with transfer function K_f in force units per milliampere. This current forces the mass back to a null position. The output voltage is taken at the output of a final block with transfer function R. The servo force fed back cancels the input acceleration.

With an equalizer of the form

$$G_e(p) = \alpha p + 1 \tag{8-28}$$

that is, position plus rate compensation, the system is made stable. The damping is electrically controllable (as α is varied), so is independent of temperature effects. The closed-loop system has the equation

$$\frac{E_o}{MA} = \frac{\dfrac{RK_sK(\alpha p + 1)}{Mp^2}}{\dfrac{K_sK(\alpha p + 1)K_f}{Mp^2} + 1} \tag{8-29}$$

which reduces to

$$\frac{E_o}{A} = \frac{RK_sK(\alpha p + 1)}{p^2 + (K_sKK_f\alpha/M)p + (K_sKK_f/M)} \tag{8-30}$$

where

$$\omega_n{}^2 = \frac{K_sKK_f}{M} \quad \text{and} \quad \zeta = \frac{\alpha}{2}\sqrt{\frac{K_sK_fK}{M}}$$

The closed-loop force-balance accelerometer transfer function becomes

$$\frac{E_o}{A} = \frac{RK_sK(\alpha p + 1)}{p^2 + 2\zeta\omega_n p + \omega_n{}^2} \tag{8-31}$$

Besides a controlled damping, the resonant frequency is proportional to the square root of the loop gain. Hence a high resonant frequency is possible with the force-balance units.

Force-balance instruments, which are applicable to many types of measurement, have great advantages in that the inaccuracies in the mechanical system, such as spring hysteresis, are replaced by fewer electrical inaccuracies, such as forcer errors. The accuracy of the force-balance system depends, to a large extent, on the accuracies with which one can built a forcer. In essence, the feedback system makes possible the use of an electrical standard (forcer) rather than a mechanical standard (spring).

If temperature compensation, such as a Curie shunt* across the magnetic path of the forcer, and appropriate equalization to account for variations of the copper with temperature are used, an accelerometer of high

---

* A Curie shunt is the name usually given carpenter metal whose reluctance varies with temperature in the opposite direction as does that of iron. See Sec. 9-5 for more information on forcers.

accuracy and fine resolution can be obtained.   Instruments of this type are capable of measuring accelerations of the order of 0.001 g.   Since the unit is always operating about a null, the linearity can be improved, by factors of 10, over completely mechanical accelerometers.

8-16. Pressure Transducers.   Static and differential pressure transducers are built in a variety of forms but most are based upon a similar principle of operation.   A mechanical motion is produced by the expansion of a diaphragm or a Bourdon tube.*   Transducers used for servo applications produce an output voltage which is proportional to pressure.

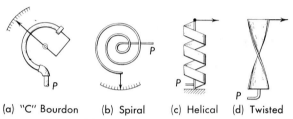

(a) "C" Bourdon   (b) Spiral   (c) Helical   (d) Twisted

FIG. 8-44. Sketch of four different Bourdon-tube arrangements.

For pressure ranges of 0 to 1 in. of water up to 30 psi† diaphragms are commonly used.   For ranges from 0 to 30 up to 0 to 10,000 psi Bourdon tubes are usually used.

Four general types of Bourdon tubes are used for measuring pressure (Fig. 8-44):

1. *C-type.*   Tube is bent in the form of a circular arc.
2. *Spiral type.*   Tube is wound on itself in the form of a spiral.
3. *Helical type.*   Tube is wound in the form of a helix.
4. *Twisted type.*   Tube is twisted in a helix.

The principle of operation of all types is identical.   Practical considerations dictate the type used by the gauge manufacturers.

The C-type Bourdon tube, which is shown in Fig. 8-44a, takes the form of a circular arc, having one end rigidly anchored and the other end free. With the application of pressure to the inside of the tube, it tends to straighten out so that the free end will rotate.   When this free end is linked to a pointer, the angle of rotation can be read on a scale which is graduated in pressure units.   Figure 8-45 shows a typical C-type Bourdon-tube pressure transducer.

For measurement of either high-pressure liquid or high-pressure gas, the stainless-steel or beryllium-copper helical element, shown in Fig. 8-46, can be operated up to 10,000 psi.

* This tube takes its name from a French engineer, Eugene Bourdon, who, in 1849, patented a metallic tube designed to deflect proportionally to a change in pressure.

† Pounds per square inch.

FIG. 8-45. C-type Bourdon-tube pressure transducer.   (*Courtesy of G. M. Giannini and Co., Inc., Pasadena, Calif.*)

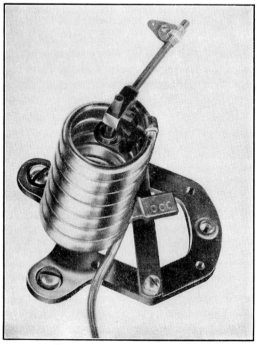

FIG. 8-46. High-pressure helical element used in a pressure transducer.   (*Courtesy of The Bristol Co., Waterbury, Conn.*)

To obtain an electrical signal proportional to pressure, altitude, air speed, and other quantities required for modern flight-control systems, a sensitive and accurate instrument is needed. A twisted Bourdon tube, which is shown in the photograph of Fig. 8-47, used in conjunction with a

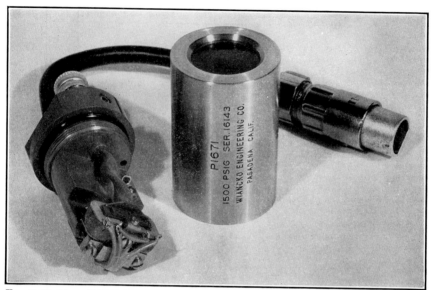

FIG. 8-47. Aircraft-type pressure transducer using a twisted Bourdon tube. (*Courtesy of Wiancko Engineering Co., Pasadena, Calif.*)

variable-reluctance, a-c pickoff, produces a voltage proportional to pressure. Both absolute and differential pressure are available. One unit has the following characteristics:

Scale factor	100 mg/(volt/mm Hg)
Pressure range	0–1,500 psig
Size	2¼ by 2¼ by 4½ in.
Excitation volts	30 volts at 400 cps
Linearity	±2%

Diaphragm pressure elements, which are shown in Fig. 8-48, find wide application in aircraft control systems. Elements are constructed by first forming capsule shells. These shells are then welded into capsules which are built into elements. The number of capsules per element is determined by the travel or stroke required for a given pressure range. Multiple-capsule elements do not require internal springs, as do formed bellows, since the elements themselves act as springs. The number of flexings (life span) which any element will withstand is dependent on several factors—percentage of rated range through which the element operates, magnitude of pressure involved, frequency of operation, operating temperature, etc. Laboratory tests at room temperature and at a frequency of 30 cpm have given over 200,000 flexings without changing over-all characteristics of the element more than 1 per cent. Linearity of these elements is better than ½ per cent. A multiple-diaphragm pressure-measuring element is shown in Fig. 8-49. This unit responds with

Fig. 8-48. Two-capsule diaphragm element.   *(Courtesy of The Bristol Co., Waterbury, Conn.)*

Fig. 8-49. Multiple-diaphragm pressure element. *(Courtesy of The Bristol Co., Waterbury, Conn.)*

a large deflection for a small pressure change. The stack has a high accuracy, high sensitivity, and long life.

Of the many varieties of pressure transducers the unit of Fig. 8-50 is interesting because of its size. This miniature pressure transducer uses an unbonded strain gauge for transduction. The unit has a total non-linearity plus hysteresis less than ± 1 per cent full scale. The range of absolute pressures is 0 to 5 to 0 to 150 psi. The unit is less than $\frac{3}{4}$ in. long and 0.610 in. in diameter.

FIG. 8-50. Miniature pressure transducer. (*Courtesy of Statham Laboratories, Inc., Los Angeles, Calif.*)

8-17. Conclusions. The field of servo transducers is ever increasing. Thousands of instrument companies are continually spending time and money on research into new methods of measuring the quantities discussed in this chapter. Also, as the field of automatic control expands, more quantities, e.g., temperature, altitude, angle of attack, and Mach number, must be transduced over wider ranges for use in control systems.

PROBLEMS

8-1. For the circuit of Fig. 8P-1, determine the loading error as a function of potentiometer setting for the following values of θ: 0.2, 0.4, 0.6, 0.8, and 1.00. Let $R_p = R_L$.

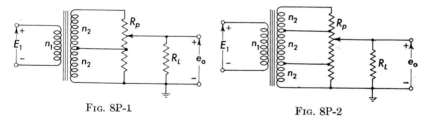

FIG. 8P-1 FIG. 8P-2

8-2. Repeat Prob. 8-1 for two equally spaced taps, as shown in Fig. 8P-2, with $R_p = R_L$. As a result, generalize the problem to i taps and determine the effect of taps on potentiometer loading.

8-3. For the loading curve of the circuit of Fig. 8-8, with $\beta = 0.2$, fit a power series equation of the form

$$\frac{e}{E} = A\theta^n$$

Determine A and n for the best fit, and find the greatest error. n is not necessarily an integer.

8-4. Design an electromechanical integrator utilizing an a-c rate generator with a $K_s = 2.87 \times 10^{-2}$ volts/(radian)(sec^{-1}). Lay out the system block diagram such that an output rate of 0.1 radian/sec results when a step of 1.0 volt is applied to the input.

8-5. Find a passive-circuit equalizer to stabilize the accelerometer which is described by Fig. 8-43.

8-6. Lay out a block diagram for a force-balance pressure transducer. Discuss the advantages and disadvantages of such a unit.

8-7. Mach number is defined by the ratio of true air speed to the speed of sound measured in the same units and under the same conditions. Hence the equation

$$M = \frac{V_t}{C} = \frac{\text{true air speed}}{\text{speed of sound}}$$

If P_s is the static atmospheric pressure and P_p is the stagnation or pitot pressure, the Mach number is defined by the following equations:

$$\frac{P_p}{P_s} = (1 + 0.2M^2)^{3.5} \qquad \text{for } M \leqslant 1.0$$

$$\frac{P_p}{P_s} = \frac{167M^2}{[7 - (1/M^2)]^{2.5}} \qquad \text{for } M \geqslant 1.0$$

Design a servo comprising two pressure transducers, amplifier, motor, and function potentiometers which will compute Mach number.

CHAPTER 9

SERVO COMPONENTS AND APPLICATIONS

9-1. Introduction. The units discussed in the previous chapter fall into the category of transducers. This chapter deals with other servo components. As the field of automatic control expands, the types and number of components increase. Some of the more common components—control motors, gear trains, gyroscopes, and subtractors—are discussed here.

9-2. Control Motors.* The output torque required for many servo systems is supplied by control motors. These motors are commonly

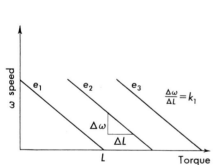

Fig. 9-1. Linearized torque-speed characteristics for a servomotor.

Fig. 9-2. Miniature control motor. (*Courtesy of Servomechanisms, Inc., Westbury, N.Y.*)

driven by an electronic, transistor, or magnetic amplifier. For servo applications the motor performance is specified not only in terms of the power requirements of the load but also in terms of the special servo requirements. Both a-c and d-c control motors are manufactured. The torque-speed characteristics of both types, to a first approximation, are represented by the ideal curves of Fig. 9-1. For proper operation control motors should not deviate appreciably from these straight lines. A typical servo-control motor is shown on Fig. 9-2. This unit operates at 400 cps and is a two-phase induction motor. The dimensions are approx-

* See Ref. 1, chap. 9, for additional discussion of motors.

273

imately 1.06-in. diameter, 1.296-in. length.   Typical load characteristics for the motor of Fig. 9-2 are shown in Fig. 9-3.   When the torque-speed curve of Fig. 9-3 is linearized, an approximate transfer function is obtained.

Before the transfer function is determined, the performance of the motor will be considered from a physical point of view.   The two phases of an a-c motor are termed excitation, or fixed, phase and control, or variable, phase.   Normally a reference voltage is applied to the fixed phase and the amplified error voltage is applied to the control phase.

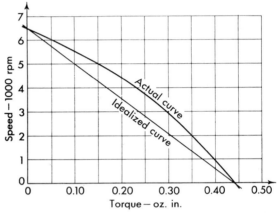

FIG. 9-3. Typical torque-speed characteristics for a control motor.

If the fixed field is excited and the control field is shorted, the output torque is zero.   If, while in this state, the shaft is turned with the fingers, a distinct tendency to drag is felt.   This is "internal" electrical damping; the motor shaft feels as if someone dipped the whole motor into molasses.   As the shaft is turned, currents are induced in the rotor. The magnitude of these currents is proportional to the velocity in the same manner as in the a-c rate generator which is discussed in the previous chapter.   This internal damping is reduced unless the control winding is driven from a low-impedance source.

Suppose full reference voltage is applied to the fixed phase while a variable voltage is applied to the control phase.   As the control voltage is increased, the stall torque increases uniformly.   The greater the control voltage, the greater is the torque.

Hence the motor produces a damping torque proportional to velocity and another torque proportional to the control voltage.   This physical reasoning is borne out by the following analysis which is based on the torque-speed curves of Fig. 9-1.   These curves, together with a knowledge of load conditions and motor inertia, are sufficient for determining the motor transfer function.   Often, a pure inertia load J is assumed, and a transfer function is found from the linearized torque-speed curves of Fig. 9-1, from which the expression is written

$$\omega = k_1L + k_2e \tag{9-1}$$

where k_1 is the slope of the torque-speed curve and k_2 is found from the intersection of the torque-speed curves with the $L = 0$ axis.   Equation (9-1) is easily rewritten in the form

$$L + m\omega = ke_{in} \tag{9-2}$$

where m is the slope $= -1/k_1 = -\Delta L/\Delta\omega$ and k is the ratio k_2/k_1.   Suppose the motor drives an inertia load $\bar{L} = Jp^2\bar{\theta}$, where $\bar{\theta}$ is the angle of the motor shaft.   The shaft velocity $\bar{\omega}$ is

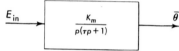

$$\bar{\omega} = p\bar{\theta} \tag{9-3}$$

FIG. 9-4. Block diagram for a motor driving an inertia load.

The equation is obtained by combining the above expressions

$$Jp^2\bar{\theta} = kE_{in} - mp\bar{\theta} \tag{9-4}$$

which is rearranged as follows:

$$\bar{\theta} = \frac{kE_{in}}{p(Jp + m)} \tag{9-5}$$

Both a-c and d-c motors can be approximated by this expression, but with d-c motors, brush friction near $\omega = 0$ causes a larger error.   Figure 9-4 shows the block diagram of a motor.   In this figure, $K_m = k/m$ and $\tau = J/m$.   It must be emphasized that the block diagram of Fig. 9-4 and the transfer function of Eq. (9-5) are applicable for a motor driving an inertia load.

In the actual design of a servo system it is necessary to obtain numerical values for the transfer function of Eq. (9-5) from the manufacturer's literature.   A torque-speed curve similar to Fig. 9-3 together with a table of performance data similar to Table 9-1 is usually supplied by the manufacturer.   Since the torque-speed curve is given only for full rated applied voltage, approximations must be made to obtain the transfer function. Since a position servo generally operates about a null, that is, for values of control voltage near zero, the slope of the zero voltage torque-speed curve is more accurate than the slope of the rated voltage curve.   This slope, as is shown later, is approximately one-half the slope of the full rated voltage curve.   Hence as a first approximation take

$$m = \frac{1}{2}\frac{\text{stall torque (rated voltage)}}{\text{no-load speed (rated voltage)}} \tag{9-6}$$

TABLE 9-1. PERFORMANCE DATA ON A TYPICAL A-C CONTROL MOTOR*

Reference Phase:

Voltage	115 volts rms
Current at stall	85 ma
Input power at stall	7.2 watts
Power factor at stall	75%
Impedance at stall	1,400 ohms

Control Phase:

Voltage	115 volts rms
Current at stall	38 ma
Input power at stall	2.1 watts
Power factor at stall	50%
Impedance at stall	3,000 ohms
Tuned impedance at stall	6,300 ohms
Tuning capacitor at stall	0.12 μf
Minimum stall torque	0.42 oz-in.
No-load speed	6,500 rpm
Maximum power output	0.70 watts
Maximum power output	3,700 rpm
Winding temperature rise at stall	65°C
Rotor inertia	0.9 g-cm²

* Courtesy of Servomechanisms, Inc., Westbury, N. Y.

where the $\frac{1}{2}$ accounts for the difference in slope between the zero voltage and rated voltage torque-speed curve. The other constant is

$$k = \frac{\text{stall torque}}{\text{rated control voltage}} \qquad (9\text{-}7)$$

The stall torque is read from the torque-speed curve at the point where the speed is zero, and the no-load speed is read at the point where the torque is zero. For the motor of Fig. 9-3

$$\text{Stall torque} = L_o = 0.42 \text{ oz-in.}$$

$$\text{No-load speed} = \omega_o = 6,500 \text{ rpm} = \frac{(6,500)(2\pi)}{60}$$

$$= 680 \text{ radians/sec}$$

$$\text{Rated control voltage} = 115 \text{ volts}$$

The constants are

$$k = \frac{0.42}{115} = 3.65 \times 10^{-3} \text{ oz-in./volt}$$

$$m = \frac{1}{2}\frac{0.42}{680} = 0.309 \times 10^{-3} \text{ oz-in. sec} \qquad (9\text{-}8)$$

For an inertia load which is equal to the inertia of the motor

$$J = 2(0.9) = 1.8 \text{ g-cm}^2$$

$$= \frac{1.8}{980} \text{ g-cm sec}^2 = \frac{1.8}{980}(0.0137) \text{ oz-in. sec}^2$$

$$= 2.51 \times 10^{-5} \text{ oz-in. sec}^2$$

FIG. 9-5. Low-inertia 60-cycle servomotor.   (*Courtesy of Diehl Mfg. Co., Somerville, N.J.*)

The transfer function quantities are

$$\text{Time constant} = \tau = \frac{J}{m} = \frac{2.51 \times 10^{-5} \text{ oz-in. sec}^2}{0.309 \times 10^{-3} \text{ oz-in. sec}} = 0.0813 \text{ sec} \quad (9\text{-}9)$$

$$\text{Motor constant} = K_m = \frac{k}{m} = \frac{3.65 \times 10^{-3} \text{ oz-in. volt}}{0.309 \times 10^{-3} \text{ oz-in. sec}}$$

$$= 11.8 \text{ per volt sec} \quad (9\text{-}10)$$

The approximate transfer function is

$$\frac{\bar{\theta}}{\bar{e}} = \frac{11.8}{p(0.0813p + 1)} \quad (9\text{-}11)$$

Figure 9-5 shows a good quality 60-cps servomotor.

If a family of torque-speed curves is available or can be run, a more accurate transfer function can be obtained. A typical servomoter was run on a dynamometer.* Torque-speed curves for various control voltages are plotted on Fig. 9-6. The intersections with the $\omega = 0$ axis of the various curves are taken from Fig. 9-6 and plotted in Fig. 9-7.

* The dynamometer consists of a d-c motor coupled to the test motor through a calibrated torsion wire. The angular deviation between the two motors (which is converted into torque units) is read by the apparent stopping of the motion with a stroboscope, from which the speed is also read. The d-c motor acts as a variable load. This makes an excellent servolab experiment.

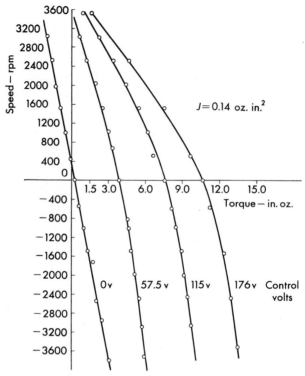

FIG. 9-6. Torque-speed curve for 5-watt 115-volt 60-cps two-phase control motor.

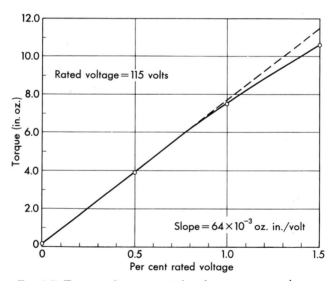

FIG. 9-7. Torque-voltage curve taken from torque-speed curve.

The slope of the torque-speed curve for zero control voltage is used for m, since the servo operates near the null (zero control volts)

$$m = \frac{+1.5 - (-1.5)}{(2\pi/60)[-1,700 - (2,350)]} = -\frac{3}{(4,050)(6.28/60)}$$
$$= 7.09 \times 10^{-3} \text{ oz-in. sec} \quad (9\text{-}12)$$

The slope of the linear portion of Fig. 9-7 is used to determine the second constant

$$k = \frac{3.9 - 0.2}{(0.5)(115)} = 64 \times 10^{-3} \text{ oz-in./volt} \quad (9\text{-}13)$$

The transfer function quantities are found from these values and the motor inertia $(J_m = 0.14 \text{ oz-in.}^2)$. For an inertia load which is equal to the motor inertia

$$J = \frac{2(0.14)}{(32)(12)} \frac{\text{oz-in.}^2}{\text{in./sec}^2} = 0.73 \times 10^{-3} \text{ oz-in. sec}^2 \quad (9\text{-}14)$$

The time constant and motor constant are

$$\tau = \frac{J}{m} = \frac{0.73 \times 10^{-3}}{7.09 \times 10^{-3}} = 0.103 \text{ sec} \quad (9\text{-}15)$$

$$K_m = \frac{k}{m} = \frac{64 \times 10^{-3}}{7.09 \times 10^{-3}} = 9.04 \text{ per volt sec}$$

It is interesting to compare the values of k and m found accurately with those found approximately. The approximate values are found from the manufacturer's literature as follows:

$$k = \frac{7.5}{115} = 65.2 \times 10^{-3} \text{ oz-in./volt}$$

$$m = \frac{1}{2} \frac{7.5}{(3,600)(2\pi/60)} = 9.95 \times 10^{-3} \text{ oz-in. sec}$$

$$(9\text{-}16)$$

Notice that although the torque-voltage constant k compares closely, the slope of the torque-speed curve m shows some error.

Use of the $\frac{1}{2}$ factor is justified on the basis of the slope of the torque-speed curves of Fig. 9-6. The nonlinear shape of any motor torque-speed curves and the change of slope with voltage preclude a high degree of accuracy.

9-3. Alternating-current Control Motors. The advantages of a-c servo systems, as outlined in Chap. 7, have resulted in widespread use of a-c components. The two-phase a-c servomotor, shown in the schematic diagram of Fig. 9-8, satisfies the requirements for the output unit of an a-c system. The main or "fixed" field is continuously excited from the reference line. The voltage is adjusted to give a maximum torque per control field watt.   The control field is spaced 90° in space from the fixed field.   The control field is driven with a suppressed-carrier signal, which must be 90° phase-shifted in time with respect to the reference voltage.   The control field and the reference field are usually similar in

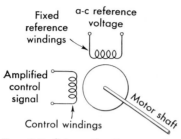

FIG. 9-8. Schematic diagram of a two-phase servomotor.

power rating.   Often, however, the control field is of a higher impedance level, so that a good impedance match to the amplifier is achieved.

A variety of special motor designs is available to the control engineer.   A partial list of a-c motor types includes

a. Squirrel Cage.   This is an induction motor which has a series of shorted conducting bars located around the periphery of the rotor.   This type of motor has excellent performance characteristics and has a high ratio of output to input power.   A typical Mark 8 unit is shown on Fig. 9-9. The stall torque is 2.35 oz-in., and the rotor inertia 4.0 g-cm^2.

b. Drag Cup.   This type of motor is similar to the squirrel-cage motor except that the rotor is a drag cup of conducting material.   The mechanical construction is similar to the rate generator shown in the schematic of Fig. 8-32.   All the heavy iron laminations which provide the low-reluctance flux path are stationary, and only a light cup is rotating.   The advantages of this type of motor are constant developed torque independent of rotor position, high torque-to-inertia ratio, and low bearing friction.

c. Solid-iron Rotor.   For less expensive applications, a compromise between the high-efficiency squirrel-cage motor and the high torque-to-inertia ratio drag-cup unit is reached with a motor that has a rotor of solid, unlaminated iron.   This motor, however, finds less application than the previous units.

FIG.   9-9.   High-performance squirrel-cage servomotor. (*Courtesy of Doelcam Div., Minneapolis-Honeywell Regulator Co., Boston, Mass.*)

d. Motor Plus Damper.   Frequently it is possible to stabilize a feedback system by adding viscous damping to the motor shaft. Motors are available which have adjustable eddy-current dampers.   Units of this type usually are built for small-size motors, since a large waste of power would occur in larger (20-watt and greater) applications.   Damping is accomplished by the relative motion between a low-inertia drag cup connected to the rotor and a fixed magnetic field. As the cup cuts lines of flux set up by the magnetic field, eddy currents are induced in the cup. These currents create a drag or damping effect proportional to the speed of the rotor. The degree of damping is varied by adjusting the strength of the fixed magnetic field. This is accomplished by a screw-driver adjustment on the back cup of the motor. This type of damping, which is included on the motor of Fig. 9-10, is simple and rugged. In contrast to network damping, this viscous-drag damping is insensitive to line frequency changes. It is cheaper and more compact than tachometer-generator feedback but not always equivalent.

Fig. 9-10. Damped control motor utilizing an adjustable eddy-current disk. (*Courtesy of Servomechanisms, Inc., Westbury, N.Y.*)

Frequently viscous damping is used in small servomotors. A small paddle wheel is affixed to the shaft and caused to move through grease or heavy oil.

An integral motor and a-c tachometer provide a power source with an output velocity voltage available to be fed back for damping in large

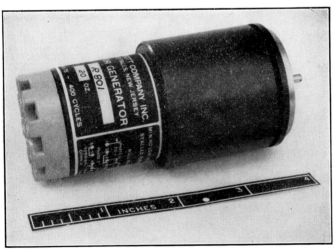

Fig. 9-11. Combination servomotor generator. (*Courtesy of Kearfott Company, Inc., Clifton, N.J.*)

power systems. Since these units utilize one housing and one shaft, a saving in size and cost results. The resulting servo has a greater adjustability of damping. A typical combination unit is shown on Fig. 9-11.

Direct-current motors and tachometers on one shaft are also available for use in d-c systems.

e. Motors for Plate-to-plate Operation. High-impedance, center-tapped control field windings are often used in a-c motors. These units eliminate the need for an output transformer, since the motor can be driven directly from the plates of two vacuum tubes (or power transistors) in push-pull operation. Since the quiescent plate current cancels out for push-pull operation, there is no net direct current through the a-c motor. Care must be exercised in the choice of d-c plate supply to avoid voltage breakdown in the motor.

FIG. 9-12. Direct-current, permanent-magnet-field servomotor. (*Courtesy of Servo-Tek Products Co., Hawthorne, N.J.*)

9-4. Direct-current Servomotors. To a first approximation, the transfer function of Eq. (9-5) is applicable to d-c control motors. A more accurate but more complicated transfer function includes the effects of winding time lags, armature inductance, etc. The torque-speed characteristics are greatly affected by the type of excitation, that is, series, shunt, or fixed excitation. Direct-current machines develop large power output in a small size. Extreme environmental conditions are withstood by sealing the units.

The major application of d-c motors in aircraft control systems is in power actuators, where weight and space limitations demand a unit with a large power-to-volume ratio.

The disadvantages of d-c motors can be listed as follows:

1. Brush and commutator maintenance.
2. Radio interference generated.
3. d-c amplifier drift (develop an output with no input).
4. Difficult to match amplifier to motor, since it is impossible to use a transformer.

Permanent-magnet excitation finds wide application in d-c servomotors since it overcomes some of the above-cited disadvantages. A typical unit is shown in Fig. 9-12.

9-5. Forcers. In many applications, such as the force-balance accelerometer, a force (or a torque) is required with no appreciable motion involved. The term "forcer" or "torquer" is applied to such a unit. Figure 9-13 shows a simplified diagram of a forcer. A permanent magnet is free to move a small distance through the field coil. A current through the field coil produces a flux which interacts with the fixed flux of the permanent magnet and hence develops a force whose sign depends upon the polarity of the magnet and direction of current through the field winding. Frequently the magnet is fixed and the coil moves.

Careful stabilization of the magnet and compensation of the magnetic path for temperature changes can result in a precision instrument whose equation can be written

$$f = K_s i \qquad (9\text{-}17)$$

where K_s is the sensitivity of the instrument in force units per ampere. The unit resembles the d-c rate pickoff which is described in Sec. 8-11. The methods of stabilization are similar.

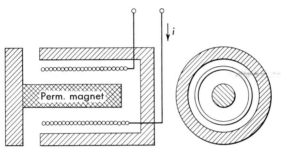

Fig. 9-13. Simplified diagram of a forcer.

9-6. Gear Trains.[12] Feedback control systems make wide use of high-quality gear trains for the following reasons:

1. Mechanically matching the motor to the load. Since a servo-motor often operates at high speed but low torque, a gear train is required to drive the load with a greater torque but less speed.

2. Gain adjustment in the closed loop.

3. Adding and subtracting mechanical signals.

4. Scale changing; for example, a two-speed system.

5. Reversing direction of rotation.

For many systems which use a potentiometer for transducing the position of the shaft, the motor must

Fig. 9-14. Precision miniature speed reducer. (*Courtesy of Bowmar Instrument Corp., Fort Wayne, Ind.*)

run at a reasonable velocity while the potentiometer can turn only 1 to 10 turns. A precision miniature speed reducer is shown in Fig. 9-14. The dimensions are 1.062-in. diameter and 1.656 in. long. The unit drives a load torque of 25 in.-oz. The backlash of this unit is 30 min maximum at the output shaft. Gear ratios up to 3,000:1 are possible.

Gear-head motors incorporate the gear reduction and the motor in one integral unit. A typical unit, which is shown in Fig. 9-15, features savings in size, weight, and cost. Gear ratios in the range 12:1 to 3,000:1 are available on many of the standard control motors. A universal design allows a wide variety of gear ratios in the same basic configuration. On the individual gear clusters, gear heads are supplied with either precision stainless-steel ball bearings or sleeve bearings.

Fig. 9-15. Gear-head motor. (*Courtesy of Servomechanisms, Inc., Westbury, N.Y.*)

9-7. Choice of Optimum Gear Ratio. The first and perhaps simplest method of selecting gear ratios for simple servo systems is merely to arrange for the maximum load power demand to match the maximum motor output capabilities. Suppose the maximum load demand is 1.6 watts at 100 rpm. The torque-speed curve of a typical two-phase a-c induction servomotor, such as shown in Fig. 9-16, is essentially a straight line between zero torque, maximum speed and zero speed, maximum torque. Somewhere on this line the product of torque and speed will be maximum, and this is actually the maximum power-output point of the motor. Since the torque-speed characteristic is assumed a straight line, the maximum power point is halfway up that line. If, however, it is not a straight line and has some curved shape, the maximum power point will

have to be calculated.   In the case of Fig. 9-16 the maximum power point
is 2,600 rpm.   Therefore, knowing that the maximum power demand of the
load occurs at 100 rpm and the maximum motor power delivery is 2,600
rpm, the quotient of motor speed divided by load speed yields the gear
ratio for this match—26:1.

Although the maximum-power-point method is adequate for many simple servomechanism design problems, it is often wise to check it by

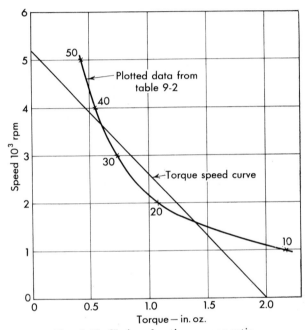

FIG. 9-16. Choice of optimum gear ratio.

another method.   This method is based on a mechanical impedance
match.   The load-speed and torque conditions for maximum power
demand are known.   The speed is 100 rpm, and the torque is given by
the expression

$$L = \frac{1.356P \times 10^3}{\omega} \qquad (9\text{-}18)$$

where P = mechanical power, watts
      L = torque, in.-oz
      ω = speed, rpm
For this application,

$$L = \frac{(1.356)10^3(1.6)}{100} = 21.7 \text{ in.-oz} \qquad (9\text{-}19)$$

In this method various possible gear ratios between motor and load are arbitrarily assumed. Based on each assumption, the motor speed and motor torque are calculated and arranged in tabular form. As an example of this, Table 9-2 shows the calculation of a series of assumed gear ratios and motor conditions. Each gear ratio results in motor-speed and motor-torque points which are plotted directly on the motor-speed-torque curve. Each assumed gear ratio yields a point on the curve.

TABLE 9-2. OPTIMUM GEAR RATIO

Assumed gear ratio	Motor speed, rpm	Motor torque, in.-oz
10	1,000	2.17
20	2,000	1.08
30	3,000	0.724
40	4,000	0.543
50	5,000	0.434

These are connected to form a curve that has a relation to the motor-torque-speed curve such as shown in Fig. 9-16.

All portions of the gear-ratio curve that lie beneath the motor-torque-speed curve represent satisfactory gear ratios. Any gear ratios above the normal motor-torque-speed curve are unusable and will not give the required load performance. If the whole gear-ratio curve lies outside the motor-torque-speed curve, the motor has insufficient power and will not do the job. It can readily be seen from this curve that the gear-ratio value of 26 calculated by method 1 is adequate for the job and would work satisfactorily. This curve is useful in that if the gear-ratio curve barely penetrated the motor-speed-torque characteristic, it would indicate that the motor was marginal.

With the over-all gear ratio chosen the best ratio for each gear mesh is usually required. This is accomplished with the nomogram* of Fig. 9-17, which helps to determine the individual stage ratios that will give minimum reflected gear train inertia for any given over-all ratio and any given number of stages. Although the minimum reflected inertia results only for an infinite number of meshes, the nomogram gives the best mesh ratios for any given number of meshes while keeping the reflected inertia to a minimum.

Suppose a gear ratio of 75 is desired in four meshes. Referring to the nomogram, place a straightedge through the point which represents the total number of stages (four) and also through the point which corre-

---

* This nomogram is taken from Reeves Catalog RICO-10. The derivation is available from Reeves Instrument Corp., New York, N.Y.

sponds to the over-all gear ratio on the right-hand scale (75:1). From the left-hand scale it can be seen that the gear ratio of the first stage is 1.72. Round this off to 1.75, and determine the remaining gear ratio; 75/1.75 equals about 43. To determine the second-stage ratio repeat this process, using 43 as the over-all ratio and three as the number of stages. The subsequent stage ratios are found in a similar fashion.

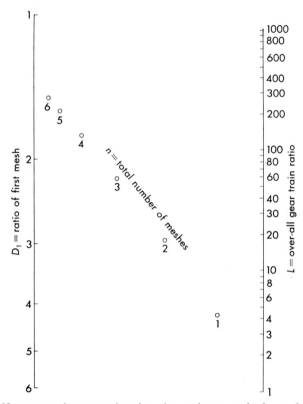

Fig. 9-17. Nomogram for approximating the optimum ratio for each gear mesh.

9-8. Gyroscopes. * Essentially, a gyroscope consists of a wheel mounted on a shaft and arranged to be spun at high angular velocity. Frequently, the wheel is mounted in a system of gimbals, which permits it freedom to take up any orientation in space.

The most useful characteristic of a gyroscope is its tendency to maintain its axis in a fixed direction in space. This phenomenon is best explained by a consideration of the concepts of rotational dynamics.

A simple example will help to gain insight into the operation of the gyroscope. In this example the effects of moments of inertia of the wheel

* See chap. 9 of Ref. 34 for more information on gyroscopes.

and gimbal system about axes other than the spin axis are neglected. The resulting equation will fail to show certain behavior characteristics. For many purposes, however, the results are adequate. For this derivation the following nomenclature is needed:

M_x, M_y, M_z = components of angular momentum about the x, y, and z axes

I_s = moment of inertia of wheel about spin axis

ω_s = angular velocity of wheel

$H = I_s\omega_s$ = angular momentum of wheel

These quantities are demonstrated in Fig. 9-18.

At time $t = 0$, suppose the torque Q_x is applied about the x axis. This may be accomplished by pressing down on the gyro housing at point p. Initially, $M_z = I_s\omega_s = H$ and $M_x = M_y = 0$. Originally, the angular momentum of spin lies along OZ and has a magnitude H. Since the rate of change of angular momentum of a system is equal to the applied torque,* the following expression can be written:

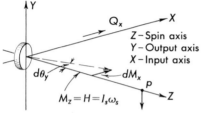

Z – Spin axis
Y – Output axis
X – Input axis

$$Q_x = \frac{dM_x}{dt} \qquad (9\text{-}20)$$

This is expressed in different form,

$$dM_x = Q_x\,dt \qquad (9\text{-}21)$$

FIG. 9-18. Vector diagram for a simplified gyro system.

If this term is added vectorially to the initial angular momentum (see Fig. 9-18), a new value is obtained. $M_x + dM_x$ is separated from the initial value by an angle $d\theta_y$ which, from Fig. 9-18, is given by

$$d\theta_y = \frac{dM_x}{H} = \frac{Q_x\,dt}{H} \qquad (9\text{-}22)$$

This is rewritten as follows:

$$\omega_y = \frac{d\theta_y}{dt} = \frac{Q_x}{H} \qquad (9\text{-}23)$$

The gyro is thus rotating about the OY axis with a velocity ω_y. Equation (9-23) demonstrates the fundamental gyroscopic law: A torque about any axis other than the spin axis produces a velocity about the axis which is orthogonal to the applied torque axis. Because of this property the gyro is an important instrument for measuring torques ($Q_x = H\omega_y$) by measuring precession velocity.

Alternately a large gyroscope can be used to obtain a stabilizing countertorque. For applied torques about the x or y axis, the gyro supplies

* In linear mechanics, the rate of change of linear momentum equals the applied force $F = dmv/dt$.

an equal countertorque which prevents motion in the direction of the applied torque as long as the gyro can precess. Once the precession angle θ has reached 90°, the gyroscope is in a state of "gimbal lock" and ceases to function as described. In the state of gimbal lock the OZ axis has precessed into the OX axis, about which the torque is being applied. With a torque applied about the OX or spin axis, the gyro ceases to produce a countertorque.

9-9. More Complete Mathematical Treatment of a Gyroscope. In this section the more general gyroscopic equations are derived. Such quantities as spring constant, damping, and moment of inertia about the two axes of interest are considered, and their effects discussed. The equations of this section are aimed at the single-degree-of-freedom gyroscope. In the subsequent derivation, the following assumptions are made:

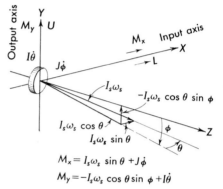

1. Small-angle assumption (that is, $\sin \theta \approx \theta$ and $\cos \theta \approx 1$).

2. Moments of inertia about the x and y axes are considered constant during the period studied.

3. The gimbal system is sufficiently symmetric so that products of inertia are negligible.

$$M_x = I_s\omega_s \sin \theta + J\dot\phi$$
$$M_y = -I_s\omega_s \cos \theta \sin \phi + I\dot\theta$$

Fig. 9-19. Coordinate system for more complete gyro equations.

If the gyroscope is mounted in a gimbal system and the position of the spin axis is displaced from the OZ axis by small angles, θ in azimuth and ϕ in elevation (Fig. 9-19), the following additional nomenclature is needed:

J = moment of inertia of wheel, case, and gimbal system about x axis. This includes inertia of platform or other mounting of gyroscope

I = moment of inertia of wheel, case, and gimbal system about y axis

L = torque applied about x axis

U = disturbing torque applied about y axis

The remaining symbols are identical with those given earlier. The inertial torques which act in the two directions x and y are first obtained. The remaining torques are summed about appropriate axes, and application of Newton's law yields the desired equations. The desired equations are the precession angle θ and the gimbal angle ϕ as functions of L and U.

Because a single-degree-of-freedom gyro is considered here, the only axis capable of moving is the y axis of Fig. 9-19. For this reason this axis is called the output axis. The gyro input, which is a torque, appears about the input axis. The applied torque L is the desired input, and the precession velocity ϕ the desired output.* Undesired torques appearing about the output axis are called disturbing torques, since they produce drift of the gyroscope. The greatest limitation in the use of gyroscopes lies in the random disturbing torques U which cause undesired velocities ϕ. Such torques as caused by spring constant K and damping D about this axis are especially important. A sketch of a gyro gimbal system is included in Fig. 9-20.

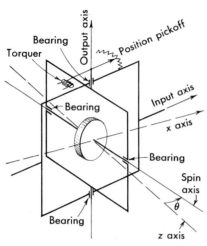

FIG. 9-20. A sketch of a gyro gimbal system.

Consider the angular momentum of the spin axis $H = I_s \omega_s$ as shown in Fig. 9-19. For small angular displacements θ and ϕ about the y and x axes, the projection of H in the direction of the x and y axes is, respectively,

$$H \sin \theta \qquad \text{and} \qquad -H \cos \theta \sin \phi \tag{9-24}$$

When combined with the angular momentum due to the precession velocity,

$$M_x = H \sin \theta + J \frac{d\phi}{dt} \tag{9-25}$$

$$M_y = -H \cos \theta \sin \phi + I \frac{d\theta}{dt} \tag{9-26}$$

Since the angles are small, $\sin \theta$ can be replaced by θ and $\cos \theta$ by 1. Use of this simplification, together with Laplace transformation, results in the following:

$$\bar{M}_x = H\bar{\theta} + Jp\bar{\phi} \tag{9-27}$$
$$\bar{M}_y = -H\bar{\phi} + Ip\bar{\theta} \tag{9-28}$$

The bars over the variables indicate that the equations have been transformed where p is the Laplace-transform operator. Since the time rate of change of momentum is equal to the applied torque,

$$\bar{Q}_x = \mathcal{L} \frac{dM_x}{dt} = p\bar{M}_x = Hp\bar{\theta} + Jp^2\bar{\phi} \tag{9-29}$$

$$\bar{Q}_y = \mathcal{L} \frac{dM_y}{dt} = p\bar{M}_y = -Hp\bar{\phi} + Ip^2\bar{\theta} \tag{9-30}$$

* A dot over the variable means differentiation with respect to time—$\dot{\phi} = d\phi/dt$.

The damping and spring torque about the input axes are negligibly small compared with the applied torque, so these are neglected with the result $Q_x = L$. The damping and spring restoring torques about the output axis are included:

$$\bar{Q}_y = \bar{U} - Dp\bar{\theta} - K\bar{\theta} \tag{9-31}$$

where D is the damping coefficient and K the restoring torque coefficient, both about the output axis. Upon substituting into Eqs. (9-29) and (9-30),

$$\bar{L} = (Jp^2)\bar{\phi} + (Hp)\bar{\theta} \tag{9-32}$$
$$\bar{U} = (-Hp)\bar{\phi} + (Ip^2 + Dp + K)\bar{\theta} \tag{9-33}$$

where p denotes the Laplace-transform operator (zero initial conditions). Solution by Cramer's rule (a ratio of two determinants) yields the following two equations:

$$\bar{\phi} = \frac{(\bar{L}/J)(Ip^2 + Dp + K) - \bar{U}(H/J)p}{p^2\{Ip^2 + Dp + [K + (H^2/J)]\}} \tag{9-34}$$

$$\bar{\theta} = \frac{\bar{L}(H/J) + \bar{U}p}{p\{Ip^2 + Dp + [K + (H^2/J)]\}} \tag{9-35}$$

Equations (9-34) and (9-35) are the gyro equations. Depending upon the gimbal system and the particular use of the gyro, various of the terms can be neglected.

Since $\bar{U}$ in Eqs. (9-34) and (9-35) is the disturbing torque, the transfer function from torque input to precession angle output is given by

$$\frac{\bar{\theta}}{\bar{L}} = \frac{H/J}{p\{Ip^2 + Dp + [K + (H^2/J)]\}} \tag{9-36}$$

when $\bar{U}$ is set equal to zero.

9-10. The Free Gyro.   If there are no restraining gimbals in any direction on the gyro, the gyro wheel remains fixed in space and the gyro measures the angular position of the aircraft with respect to the gyro as a reference.   Gyros used in this manner establish an inertial reference of relatively low accuracy.   In order to obtain the approximate transfer functions for a gyro in this mode of operation, set $\bar{L}$, I, D, and K equal to zero in Eq. (9-34), obtaining

$$\mathcal{L}^{-1}\, p\phi = \frac{d\phi}{dt} = \frac{U}{H} \tag{9-37}$$

Similarly, setting $\bar{U}$, I, D, and K equal to zero in Eq. (9-35), a simplified equation results for the other axis:

$$\mathcal{L}^{-1}\, p\theta = \frac{d\theta}{dt} = \frac{L}{H} \tag{9-38}$$

When the gyro is used in this form, various mechanical members must remain constant with respect to time, temperature, and hysteresis.

Hence, used in this mode, gyro drift rates of fractions of a degree per minute are common.

Figure 9-21 shows a cutaway view of a two-degree-of-freedom gyro measuring displacement about two axes by means of a pickoff placed on each gimbal axis.   The gyro motor and inner gimbal assembly are symmetrical.   The complete symmetry of motor and inner gimbals enables this unit to sustain high vibrational requirements up to 9 g at 1,000 cps,

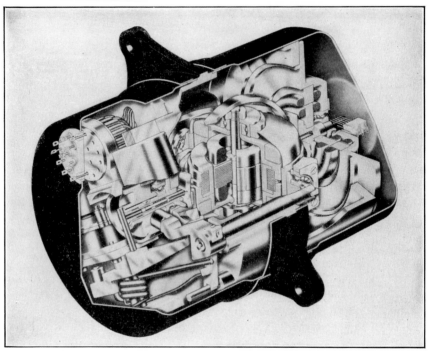

FIG. 9-21. Cutaway view of a free gyro.   (*Courtesy of Summers Gyroscope Co., Santa Monica, Calif.*)

with a drift of less than 2°/min.   A unique and positive "caging" device is used with an extremely fast time response.   When a gyro is caged, electrical or mechanical torques are applied to the gyro to prevent any motion of the gyro gimbals.   Caging is accomplished within a maximum period of 30 sec when the gimbal is at its maximum displacement.   The gyro is fully uncaged in less than 0.1 sec.   The drift rate is less than 0.2°/min under normal operation.   The unit has 360° continuous rotation on the outer gimbal and ±85° on the inner gimbal.   A thin, pancakelike synchro is used on the outer gimbal, and a potentiometer on the inner gimbal.   The gyro fits into a hermetically sealed case $3\frac{5}{8}$ in. in diameter and $5\frac{1}{4}$ in. long.

9-11. The Rate Gyro. In many aircraft maneuvers it is necessary to measure the rate of roll, pitch, or yaw, and these measurements are used to damp out certain undesirable oscillations of the aircraft about these axes. A low-accuracy gyro, called a rate gyro, is used for this purpose. In order to understand the operation of a rate gyro, set $\bar{U}$ equal to zero and equate Eqs. (9-34) and (9-35), eliminating $\bar{L}$. In so doing, the following expression results:

$$p\bar{\phi} = \frac{1}{H}(Ip^2 + Dp + K)\bar{\theta} \qquad (9\text{-}39)$$

For small I and D or also with slowly varying time functions, Eq. (9-39) reduces to

$$\theta = \frac{H}{K}\frac{d\phi}{dt} \qquad (9\text{-}40)$$

Equation (9-40) indicates that a signal which is proportional to the rate $d\phi/dt$ is obtained. Practically, the large value of K is obtained by supporting the output axis in a torsional spring.

A rate gyro produces velocity signals; that is, it yields a voltage proportional to the time derivative of the input axis angle. Any low rate drift of this angle is differentiated and hence of little importance. Also, since gyros of this type are used primarily for damping in systems, high accuracy and low drift are not essential.

A cutaway view of a rate gyro is shown in the sketch of Fig. 9-22. This unit utilizes an induction-type pickoff with a linearity of ± 1 per cent. The gyro resolution is less than $0.1°/\text{sec}$. The unit is 3.3 in. long with a 2.0-in. diameter.

9-12. The Restrained Gyro. If only one axis is free to move with respect to the case, the gyro becomes a restrained gyro, or single-degree-of-freedom gyro. If K, D, and U are set equal to zero in Eq. (9-34) (note that H^2/JK is much larger than 1), the approximate transfer function for a gyro in this mode is given by

$$\bar{\theta} \approx \frac{\bar{L}}{pH} \qquad (9\text{-}41)$$

Because of the form of this transfer function, that is, the $1/p$ multiplying the torque, this gyro is often called an "integrating gyro." A more complete transfer function can be found by setting U and K to zero as follows:

$$\frac{\bar{\theta}}{\bar{L}} = \frac{H/J}{p[Ip^2 + Dp + (H^2/J)]} \qquad (9\text{-}42)$$

Gyroscopes of this type are the most accurate of those discussed and are used to measure angular accelerations. Drift rates in the order of 0.05 to 0.1°/hr are possible. These gyros are generally used in conjunction with a platform for "inertial guidance" systems, which are discussed in the next section.

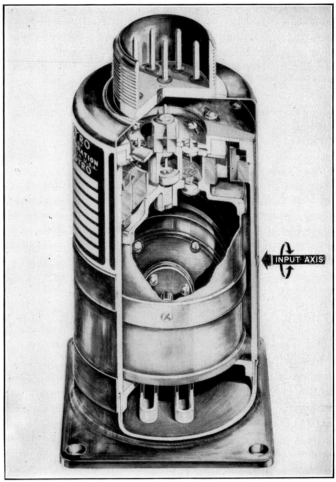

FIG. 9-22. Cutaway view of a rate gyro. *(Courtesy of American Gyro Div., Daystrom Pacific Corp., Santa Monica, Calif.)*

Because of the high accuracy of these components, considerable care must be taken in the design of the output axis. Any spring or damping torques that appear about the output axis U of the gyro produce a precession velocity $\dot{\phi}$ about the input axis [cf. Eq. (9-34)]. The output axis spring rate K is especially important, since from Eq. (9-39)

$$\bar{\phi} = \frac{K}{H} \frac{1}{p} \bar{\theta} = \mathcal{L} \frac{K}{H} \int_0^t \theta \, dt \qquad (9\text{-}43)$$

Since the gimbal angle ϕ is the integral of the precession angle θ, K must be kept small and H as large as possible.

The wheel and gyro rotor of many precision gyroscopes are encased in a fluidtight sphere which is floated in fluid. The gas within the sphere may be nitrogen or some other inert gas at atmospheric pressure. The case should be made of magnetic material so that any stray fields produced by the motor are shielded from the sensitive pickoff on the gyro.

The wheel and motor are dynamically balanced as a unit to a high degree of accuracy. The entire gyro (wheel, motor, and inner housing) is statically balanced to a degree of accuracy (less than 10 dyne-cm) about the output axis for both weight and buoyancy. During the static balance, the wheel is stationary so that no gyroscopic action is included in the balance.

Single-degree-of-freedom gyros are often supported in a hydraulic or pneumatic bearing. The gyro weight is often buoyed up with a flotation fluid. The flotation fluid has a viscosity that is stable with temperature and is large enough to produce a high damping. The flotation fluid reduces the gimbal bearing loading, which in turn lowers the gimbal bearing friction. It also provides good shock cushioning for the gimbal during vibration and acceleration conditions. An expansion device is incorporated on the side of the gyro to provide for expansion of the fluid with temperature and altitude. The fluid must be inert so it does not react with any of the exposed wiring or metal within the unit.

Typical values for an accurate gyroscope are

$$\omega_s = 24{,}000 \text{ rpm} = 2{,}515 \text{ radians/sec}$$

(In actual practice the frequency used to drive the wheel should be different from 400 cps to prevent interaction with other a-c quantities.)

$$I_s = 1.2 \times 10^3 \text{ g-cm}^2 = 1.2 \times 10^3 \text{ dyne-cm sec}^2$$
$$H = I_s\omega_s = 3 \times 10^6 \text{ dyne-cm sec}$$
$$I = 10^4 \text{ g-cm}^2 = 10^4 \text{ dyne-cm sec}^2$$
$$D = 10^5 \text{ dyne-cm sec}$$
$$J = 10^6 \text{ g-cm}^2 = 10^6 \text{ dyne-cm sec}^2$$
$$K = 4 \times 10^4 \text{ dyne-cm/radian}$$

Some of the typical terms are

$$\frac{H^2}{J} = 9 \times 10^6 \text{ dyne-cm/radian} \qquad (9\text{-}44)$$

Notice that this is considerably larger than the output axis spring rate $H^2/J = 9 \times 10^6 \gg K = 4 \times 10^4$.

$$\sqrt{\frac{H^2}{JI}} = \text{nutation frequency} = 30 \text{ radians/sec} \qquad (9\text{-}45)$$

The nutation frequency is the undamped natural resonant frequency of the characteristic equation. With $D = 0$ in the denominator of either Eq. (9-34) or (9-35), the characteristic equation is

$$Ip^2 + \frac{H^2}{J} = 0 \tag{9-46}$$

The roots of this equation are

$$p_i = \pm j\omega_n = \pm j \frac{H}{\sqrt{IJ}} \tag{9-47}$$

ω_n is the frequency at which the undamped gyro would oscillate and is

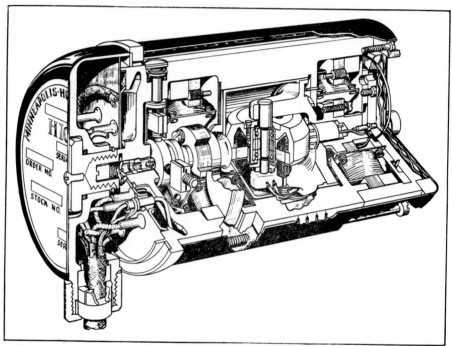

Fig. 9-23. Cutaway view of a single-degree-of-freedom gyro—the HIG gyro. (*Courtesy of the Aeronautical Division, Minneapolis-Honeywell Regulator Co., Minneapolis, Minn.*)

termed the nutation frequency. The nutation frequency is a figure of merit of the gyroscope.

Figure 9-23 shows a cutaway sketch of one integrating gyroscope. This unit, like others of its type, is a single-degree-of-freedom gyro with a floated gimbal construction. The gyro element, a symmetrical wheel, is mounted in a sealed container. It is powered by a three-phase hysteresis-type motor which is operated from a precisely controlled frequency source. A precise frequency source is required to keep $H(= I\omega_s)$ constant and hence induce little error into the torque equations—Eqs. (9-34) and (9-35).

The position of the gyro gimbal is indicated by an electromagnetic pickoff. Torque is applied to the gimbal by an electromagnetic (permanent-magnet type) torque generator (torquer). The sensitivity of the gimbal pickoff varies with the primary excitation current and frequency. The drift rate is less than 0.1°/hr.

The gyro is maintained at an elevated temperature by an electric heater. A built-in temperature-sensitive resistance element measures and controls the gyro temperature. Operating temperature is maintained by cycling the heater on and off by means of an external relay or by proportional temperature control. A photograph of the unit of Fig. 9-23 is included in Fig. 9-24.

9-13. Inertial Navigation.[30,34,49] One of the applications of single-degree-of-freedom gyros is in connection with a stable platform. Although it is not possible to describe completely this electromechanical form of automatic navigation, a brief description is presented.

Fig. 9-24. A high-accuracy single-degree-of-freedom gyroscope. (*Courtesy of the Aeronautical Division, Minneapolis-Honeywell Regulator Co., Minneapolis, Minn.*)

Inertial navigation is based upon an accurate measurement of acceleration. Velocity is obtained as the first time integral, and position is found from a second integration of acceleration. Unlike other forms of air-borne navigation, the system is insensitive to wind, aircraft maneuvers, magnetic storms, enemy jamming, or any other outside disturbance.

An inertial guidance system typically includes the following:

1. A pair of translational accelerometers which are oriented at right angles to each other, e.g., one in the north-south and the other in the east-west direction.

2. A gyroscopically stabilized platform which keeps the accelerometers oriented in a particular direction regardless of the orientation of the vehicle.

3. A computer which corrects the acceleration signals for Coriolis, gravitational, and other accelerations; corrects the platform orientation for the rotation of the earth (15°/hr, which can be established with a clock); and doubly integrates the acceleration signals. This latter function is often performed directly by the accelerometer.

Three single-degree-of-freedom gyroscopes, which are discussed in Sec.

9-12, are utilized to establish a direction in space (item 2 above). The stable element, which is shown in the schematic of Fig. 9-25, comprises three gyroscopes in a frame which is gimbal-mounted to provide three degrees of freedom. The stable element together with the gimbals and gimbal servo systems is termed a stable platform. The single-degree-of-freedom gyro senses a torque about its input axis (platform gimbal). The

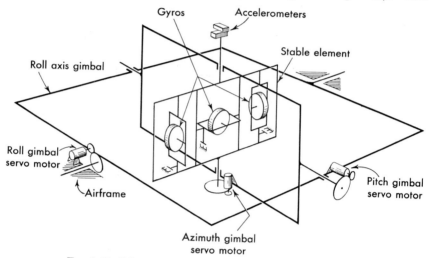

FIG. 9-25. Schematic diagram of a gyro-stabilized platform.

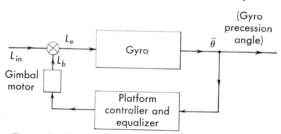

FIG. 9-26. Block diagram of platform servo system.

gyro precesses in response to the applied torque, and a sensitive pickoff senses the precession. The precession angle is amplified, equalized, and applied to a gimbal motor which provides the countertorque on the platform. A simple block diagram of a single-axis platform servo system is shown in Fig. 9-26.

An accuracy requirement of 1-mile error after a 1-hr flight is not uncommon for inertial guidance systems. Besides this performance requirement the space and weight problem is serious. An inertial system with the above accuracy may weigh 200 lb. To meet such requirements very precise gyro, platform, and system design is required.

9-14. The Vertical Gyro.   The vertical gyro is a special class of free gyro which contains a pendulous body.   This pendulous body applies torques electrically, hydraulically, or pneumatically to the appropriate free gyro axis, such that the gyro is caused to precess so that one of its axes is aligned with respect to local gravity.   The process of aligning the

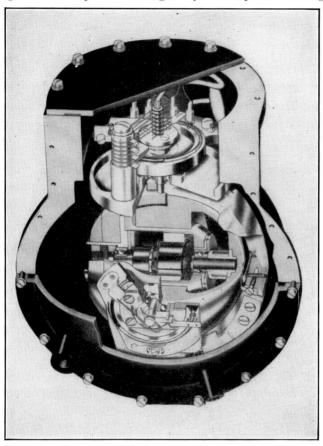

FIG. 9-27. Cutaway view of a vertical gyro.   (*Courtesy of Summers Gyroscope Co., Santa Monica, Calif.*)

axis with respect to gravity is termed erection.   In order that a gyro will respond in a negligible fashion to accelerations (other than the earth's gravitation) of the aircraft, various schemes are employed, such as erection cutouts, limiters, and filters.   These schemes make the gyro less sensitive to spurious accelerations.

Erection rates may vary from 10 to 20 min, and drift in these gyros may be from $\frac{1}{2}$ to $1°$/min.   Vertical gyros are commonly used to detect or to control changes in attitude about the pitch and roll of axes of an airborne vehicle.   Sensitivity is obtained in these two axes by mounting the gyro with its spin axis vertical.

A cutaway view of a roll-and-pitch vertical gyro is shown on Fig. 9-27. This unit is approximately 4-in. diameter by $5\frac{1}{2}$ in. long and weighs $3\frac{1}{2}$ lb.   Potentiometers on the inner and outer gimbals yield pitch and roll angles with an accuracy of $1\frac{1}{2}°$.

To get an idea of the order of magnitude of the precession rates and torques involved in a gyro, consider the following example: Assume a wheel with 3-in. radius, 1-in. thickness, made of brass.   If the angular velocity is 10,000 rpm and its mass is 0.03 lb/in.^{3}, then I is equal to 0.098 in.-lb sec^2; ω_s is equal to 1,057 radians/sec; then H, the angular momentum, is equal to 103.7 in.-lb sec; and the precession rate is equal to 0.55°/sec for a 1-lb-in. applied torque.

From a practical point of view the precession direction of a gyro can be determined as follows: When a torque is applied about a particular axis of the gyro (any axis other than the spin axis), the gyro will rotate in such a fashion that the spin axis will precess into the axis about which the torque is applied.

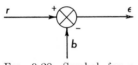

FIG. 9-28. Symbol for a subtractor.

9-15. Subtractors.   The symbol shown in Fig. 9-28, which is always seen in servo applications, is defined in Chap. 1 to be a subtractor. This element symbolizes the property that the signal to the right is equal to the input minus the fedback quantity.   In equation form this is written as

$$\epsilon = r - b \qquad (9\text{-}48)$$

Since the error introduced by the comparison unit goes directly into the system error, the subtractor is an important item in servo design.

In practice this subtractor can take many forms.   Sometimes the subtraction takes place as a difference of torques applied to an axis (as in the gyro-stabilized platform).   Often the subtraction takes place in the magnetic field (synchro transmitter and receiver).   Often, however, special components must be used to perform this function. Some of these, which are included here, are differential gear boxes, transformers, difference amplifiers, and resistance networks.

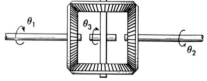

FIG. 9-29. Mechanical subtractor—a differential.

9-16. The Differential Gear Box. Figure 9-29 indicates, in schematic form, a differential gear system which yields an output shaft position equal to the difference between

θ_1 and θ_2.   If $\omega_1 = \omega_2$, then the inner shaft velocity will be zero.   If $\omega_1 \neq \omega_2$, then θ_ε assumes a value proportional to the difference of position as follows:

$$\theta_\varepsilon = \tfrac{1}{2}(\theta_1 - \theta_2) \tag{9-49}$$

where θ_1 and θ_2 are the angles of rotation of the end gears, θ_ε is the angular rotation of the spider gears or differential casing.

Fig. 9-30. Gear assembly utilizing differentials.   (*Courtesy of Bowmar Instrument Co., Fort Wayne, Ind.*)

The gear assembly of Fig. 9-30 shows two differentials.   The units possess the following characteristics:

1. *Low friction:* breakaway torque as low as 0.01 oz-in.
2. *Low backlash:* 5 to 7 min of arc depending upon the size.
3. *High speeds:* 500 to 800 rpm.   Differentials can be operated temporarily at higher speeds.

The units are built to a high degree of precision and are often made from stainless steel to resist wear and corrosion.

9-17. Transformers.   For a-c systems, transformers are used in a variety of ways to obtain a subtraction.   In Fig. 9-31 are indicated three methods of transformer subtraction.   The transfer function for all these connections is identical; that is,

$$e_\varepsilon = N(e_{in} - e_f) \tag{9-50}$$

The choice of one particular circuit of Fig. 9-31 is a compromise between size (Fig. 9-31c is the smallest) and the null condition (Fig. 9-31a is most desirable). In Fig. 9-31a the difference is taken in the voltages at the secondary of the transformer. Even in the null condition ($e_\varepsilon = 0$), the flux in each transformer core is maintained at a large value because the e_{in} and e_f may be large. In Fig. 9-31b the difference is taken in the flux within the inner core. Since the fluxes from the primary windings cancel, the excitation of the transformer is so small that near the null condition the output e_ε is often distorted.

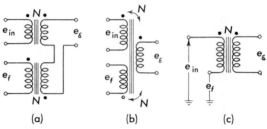

FIG. 9-31. Alternating-current servo subtraction using transformers.

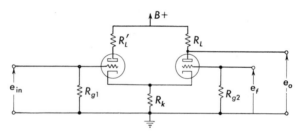

FIG. 9-32. Schematic diagram of a difference amplifier.

Figure 9-31c is the smallest configuration, but it has less desirable characteristics. The subtraction takes place in the voltages at the primary to the transformer. Near the null condition, the transformer excitation is small and the output voltage e_ε is distorted from sinusoidal. Also, for appropriate operation, the internal impedance of the sources e_{in} and e_o must be nearly equal.

The use of transformers in computer and servo applications has changed the design and appearance of these units. Low phase shift, constant transfer function (turns ratio) with changing load and changing temperature, and small size are characteristic of these units. Both laminated and toroidal cores are used. Phase shift of 10 milliradians and transfer function (turns ratio) accuracy of 1 part in 10,000 are available with high-quality toroids.

9-18. Difference Amplifier. The schematic of a difference amplifier for either a-c or d-c signals is shown in Fig. 9-32. The gain expressions for the difference amplifier can be obtained by reference to a text* on vacuum-tube circuits. For $(R_L + r_p)/(1 + \mu) \ll R_K$ the transfer function is given by

$$e_o = \frac{\mu R_L}{R_L + 2r_p} (e_{in} - e_f) \qquad (9\text{-}51)$$

where μ is the plate resistance and r_p is the amplification factor of both tubes. Careful adjustment of circuit values (especially R'_L) results in a good subtracter. It is important that the common cathode resistor be large for good subtracting.

9-19. Resistance Subtraction. Very common in feedback amplifier design is resistance differencing, which is shown schematically in Fig.

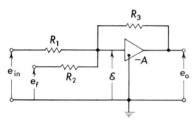

FIG. 9-33. Resistance subtraction using a high-gain amplifier.

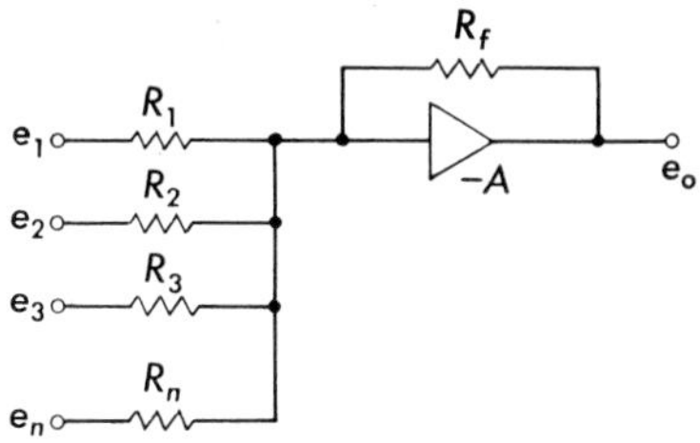

FIG. 9-34. Addition of many inputs.

9-33. The amplifier, either direct or alternating current, has high negative gain $-A$. If ε is the voltage of the node at the amplifier input, the sum of the currents into the node can be written as

$$\frac{e_{in} - \epsilon}{R_1} + \frac{e_f - \epsilon}{R_2} + \frac{e_o - \epsilon}{R_3} = 0 \qquad (9\text{-}52)$$

Since the amplifier has large gain, ϵ is small and the output is

$$e_o = -\frac{R_3}{R} (e_{in} + e_f) \qquad (9\text{-}53)$$

where $R_1 = R_2 = R$. If e_{in} and e_f are fed into the summing point with opposite signs, a difference is obtained. If $R_1 \neq R_2$, the gain of the fed-back signal can be changed with respect to the gain of the input signal

$$e_o = -\frac{R_3}{R_1} e_{in} - \frac{R_3}{R_2} e_f \qquad (9\text{-}54)$$

Any number of signals can be added or subtracted at the input simply by bringing more resistors into the summing point, as shown in Fig. 9-34. An amplifier of this type finds wide application in analogue computers.[50]

When the subtraction is performed on d-c signals (for d-c servos), a d-c amplifier must be used. For suppressed-carrier summing, an a-c

* Reference 47, pp. 111–117.

amplifier can be used. Just as the other servo components—motors, gear trains, synchros, potentiometers—are available from manufacturers, so also can packaged amplifiers be obtained. Figure 9-35 shows a photograph of one of a series of amplifiers which are capable of driving a corresponding series of servomotors. This particular amplifier is hermetically sealed and designed to control a 2-watt 400-cycle two-phase servomotor. The size is 3 by 1¾ by 4⅛ in., and the unit weighs 1 lb. With an input of 0.01 volt alternating current the voltage gain is 7,300. Three 1-megohm inputs are available for summing three a-c signals.

Fig. 9-35. Plug-in a-c servoamplifier. (*Courtesy of Servomechanisms, Inc., Westbury, N.Y.*)

9-20. Demodulators and Modulators. Suppressed-carrier signals, which are found in many a-c systems, are converted to d-c with a phase-sensitive demodulator. A modulator converts the d-c signal to alternating current. Application of both phase-sensitive demodulators and modulators is indicated in Chap. 7. The output d-c signal from a "phase-sensitive" demodulator is proportional to the amplitude of the a-c input. The polarity, however, depends upon the phase of the signal with respect to the reference. If the suppressed-carrier signal is in phase with the reference, the output is positive; if the signal is 180° out of phase with the reference, the output is negative.

The operation of a phase-sensitive demodulator is explained with the aid of Fig. 9-36. An a-c signal which is suppressed-carrier-modulated with a sinusoid is shown in Fig. 9-36a. When a reference signal, which is shown in Fig. 9-36b, is added, the waveform of Fig. 9-36c is obtained. Rectification of the signal shown in Fig. 9-36c yields a signal, presented in Fig. 9-36d, which is filtered to produce the low-frequency sinusoid of Fig. 9-36e.

Many practical circuits* exist which accomplish the demodulation shown in Fig. 9-36. Three typical circuits are shown in Fig. 9-37. A half-wave diode demodulator is shown in Fig. 9-37a. The reference voltage is applied symmetrically to both diodes. When the input signal is

* Reference 1, pp. 68–86.

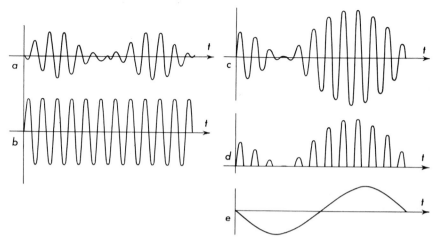

FIG. 9-36. Waveforms demonstrating phase-sensitive demodulation.

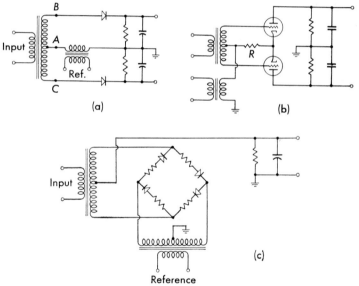

FIG. 9-37. Various demodulator circuits.

zero, the diodes conduct when points *B* and *C* are positive. During conduction equal currents flow through the load resistors, but in opposite directions. Hence the output voltage is zero. During the negative half cycle the diodes do not conduct and the output voltage is zero.

As an a-c signal is applied, the voltage on the secondary of the transformer adds to the reference voltage on one side of the center tap and subtracts from the reference on the other side of the center tap. During the positive (conducting) cycle one diode conducts more than the other. The voltages dropped across the load resistors are no longer equal. Hence, the net voltage across the output assumes a value. The output voltage is smoothed with an RC filter. This voltage is proportional to the input provided the reference voltage is larger than the amplitude of the signal voltage. The output is a push-pull signal.

Figure 9-37b shows a half-wave demodulator which uses triodes instead of diodes. In addition to demodulation, this circuit provides amplification.

The "ring demodulator" of Fig. 9-37c provides a full-wave rectified voltage with respect to ground. The analysis of the circuit is similar to that of Fig. 9-37a. The upper diodes conduct during the first half cycle, and the lower diodes during the second half cycle. An RC filter is again used to smooth the output.

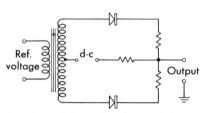

Fig. 9-38. Schematic of a modulator.

Most phase-sensitive demodulator circuits can be reversed and used as modulators. A phase-sensitive modulator produces an a-c voltage which is proportional to the input d-c voltage magnitude and has a phase, either 0 to 180° with respect to the reference, depending upon the polarity of the d-c input. Figure 9-38 shows a circuit for a modulator which is opposite in operation to the demodulator of Fig. 9-37a.

9-21. Magnetic Amplifiers.* This type of amplifier is often superior to a vacuum-tube amplifier because of its greater dependability and reliability, longer life, and, in many cases, smaller size and lighter weight than an equivalent vacuum-tube circuit. Magnetic amplifiers are essentially variable-impedance devices. Their operation depends in general on their insertion between a source of a-c power and a load in a circuit such as that shown in Fig. 9-39. By virtue of the controllable impedance offered by the magnetic amplifier, the output circuit current and, therefore, the load power and voltage can be controlled.

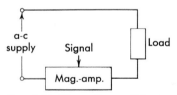

Fig. 9-39. Magnetic amplifier inserted between source and load.

Variation of the impedance offered by the amplifier may be achieved by an independent source of control power. Amplification occurs, since the power requirements of the control source may be many times less than the controlled power supplied to the load.

Magnetic amplifiers may be either the self-saturating type or the sim-

* Most of the material in this section is taken from Ref. 57, and Ref. 1, chap. 11.

ple saturable-reactor type. The simple saturable-reactor magnetic amplifier has been used for many years, but with the development of modern dry-type rectifiers and rectangular loop core materials, the self-saturating type has come into greater prominence. The self-saturating magnetic amplifier is differentiated from the simple saturable-reactor type by the addition of the self-saturating rectifier, which prevents demagnetization of the reactor by the a-c supply voltage. The self-saturating magnetic amplifier has a greater ratio of power amplification to response time than the simple saturable-reactor type and has a smaller physical size for an equivalent power rating. Although the self-saturating magnetic amplifier has generally more desirable characteristics, the

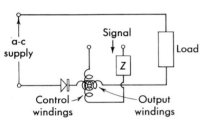

Fig. 9-40. Half-wave self-saturating magnetic amplifier.

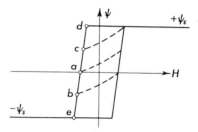

Fig. 9-41. Idealized ψ-H curve.

simple saturable-reactor type can be used to a greater advantage in some cases, in particular in those applications requiring a high degree of linearity.

The theory of operation of a self-saturating magnetic amplifier can be described in terms of a half-wave circuit. Figure 9-40 shows a half-wave self-saturating circuit with a resistive load. Assuming the magnetic core to have the idealized ψ-H relationship shown in Fig. 9-41, and also assuming the rectifier to have zero back leakage, the steady-state operation of the circuit is as follows: At the end of a negative half cycle of supply voltage ($E_m \sin \omega t$), the rectifier will block and the load current will be zero. H will be determined by the control ampere turns, and ψ by the magnetic characteristics of the core. Assuming a negative control H applied to the core, the initial operating point at the start of a positive half cycle will be on the left flank of the hysteresis loop at a point determined by the value of control ampere turns. Such a point might be point a of Fig. 9-41. As the supply voltage increases positively, the operating point proceeds along the dashed line toward $+\psi_s$ and a small magnetizing current flows through the load. A high impedance Z prevents control-circuit current flow as a result of voltage induced by transformer action from the output winding.

At a definite time t_f during the positive half cycle, the flux will reach a value ψ_s. This time is defined approximately by the equation

$$\int_0^{t_f} E_m \sin \omega t \, dt = N(\psi_s - \psi_a) \times 10^{-8} \text{ volt-sec} \qquad (9\text{-}55)$$

where N is the number of output winding turns, ψ_s the saturation flux, and ψ_a the value of flux at point a. From the time t_f until voltage zero, the entire supply voltage is transferred to the load because the saturated core cannot support voltage. This is shown in the load voltage plot of Fig. 9-42. With the negative half cycle of supply voltage, the operating point proceeds toward point a along the left flank of the hysteresis loop.

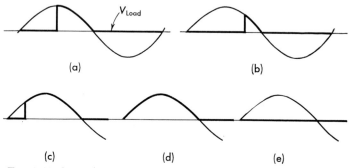

FIG. 9-42. Operation of half-wave self-saturating magnetic amplifier.

During this period a small and steadily decreasing load current flows. When the operating point reaches a, the load current falls to zero, the rectifier blocks the supply voltage for the remaining portion of the negative half cycle, and the operating point remains at a (assuming no rectifier leakage). Adjustment of the control ampere turns will set the initial operating point at a corresponding point on the left flank of the hysteresis loop. Load voltage waveforms corresponding to initial operating points at a, b, c, d, and e are shown in Fig. 9-42a, b, c, d, and e. If the reactor is properly designed, no current other than magnetizing current flows through the load when the initial operating point is at e, the cutoff point, since the full half cycle of supply voltage is absorbed in changing the flux from $-\psi_s$ to $+\psi_s$. This is expressed by the equation

$$\int_0^{\pi/\omega} E_m \sin \omega t \, dt = 2N\psi_s \, 10^{-8} \qquad \text{volt-sec} \qquad (9\text{-}56)$$

Conversely, when the initial operating point is at d, corresponding to full output, the entire positive half cycle of supply voltage appears at the load. Thus the load current is a direct function of the control winding ampere turns; this relation is shown in the amplifier control characteristics of Fig. 9-43.

The undesirability of the high control-circuit impedance Z renders the half-wave self-saturating magnetic amplifier impractical. Full-wave magnetic amplifiers provide a means for "bucking" induced control winding voltages and, in addition, permit load current to flow on both halves of the cycle of supply voltage.

In any magnetic amplifier, there will be a time delay between a change of control voltage and the response of the output current to this change. For operation within the linear range of the control characteristic curve, a step-function change of the control signal voltage will cause the output to change exponentially with time. This is the result that would be expected if the control winding of an amplifier were represented by a series resistance and inductance. The exponential response to a step-function change in input voltage in such a circuit is characterized by a time constant. The response time or time constant for a Magamp is defined as the time, in cycles of amplifier a-c supply frequency, for the output current to reach 63 per cent of its final value in response to a step-function change of control voltage.

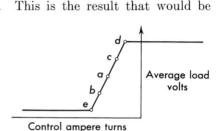

FIG. 9-43. Magnetic amplifier control characteristics.

The response time is a function of the ratio of the square of the number of control turns to the control-circuit resistance. In the general case of multiple control and bias windings the coupling between windings is sufficiently close to unity that the response time will be a function of the total of the turns squared per ohm of each winding. That is, the total effective turns squared per ohm will be given by

$$\frac{N^2}{R} = \frac{N_{c1}^2}{R_{s1}} + \frac{N_{c2}^2}{R_{s2}} + \cdots + \frac{N_b^2}{R_b} \qquad (9\text{-}57)$$

where N_{c1}, N_{c2}, . . . , N_b are the number of turns of the various control and bias windings and R_{s1}, R_{s2}, . . . , R_b are the total resistances in the corresponding control and bias circuits. (Generally, sufficient bias power is available to make this last term negligible.)

The relation between response time τ and the effective control circuit N^2/R is

$$\tau = k_1 \frac{N^2}{R} + k_2 \qquad \text{cycles} \qquad (9\text{-}58)$$

where k_1 and k_2 are constants. The constant k_2 is the minimum possible, or inherent, response time. In full-wave amplifier circuits the value of k_2 will vary from a minimum of $\frac{1}{2}$ cycle to as much as 3 or 4 cycles depending on the amplifier output circuit. The value of k_1 is dependent on the supply frequency, the core size, and magnetic properties.

A series of magnetic amplifiers, together with the associated rectifiers, is shown in Fig. 9-44.

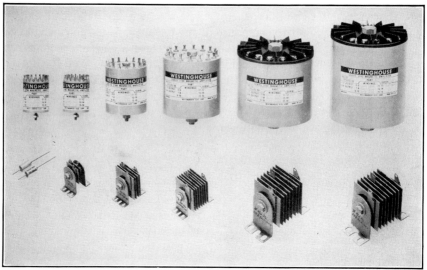

FIG. 9-44. Magnetic amplifier components. (*Courtesy of Westinghouse Electric Corp., Pittsburgh, Pa.*)

PROBLEMS

9-1. Obtain the transfer function for the motor shown in Fig. 9P-1. The total inertia is 2.28×10^{-4} oz-in. sec².

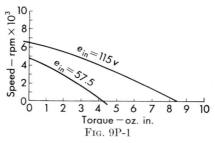

FIG. 9P-1

9-2. Derive the equations for the difference amplifier of Fig. 9-32.

9-3. The following numerical values represent a single-degree-of-freedom gyro:

$H = 1 \times 10^6$ dyne-cm sec

$I = 10^4$ g-cm²

$D = 10^5$ dyne-cm sec

$J = 10^6$ g-cm²

$K = 5 \times 10^4$ dyne-cm/radian

(a) Find the gyro nutation frequency.

(b) Obtain the transfer function $\bar{\theta}/L$, and locate the poles in the p plane.

9-4. Use the gyro of Prob. 9-3 in the block diagram of Fig. 9P-4.

(a) Take $G_2(p)$ = constant, and determine stability and steady-state errors.

(b) Take $G_2(p) = 1 + \alpha p$, and choose α and A for the optimum system.

(c) Take $G_2(p) = 1 + \alpha p + (\gamma/p)$, and choose α, γ, and A for the optimum system.

NOTE: An optimum system has zero steady-state error in θ.

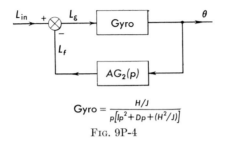

$$\text{Gyro} = \frac{H/J}{p[Ip^2 + Dp + (H^2/J)]}$$

FIG. 9P-4

CHAPTER 10

NONLINEARITIES IN SERVO DESIGN

10-1. Classification of Servo Nonlinearities. In the previous chapters, the control-system equations have been assumed to be linear. In these chapters, amplifiers are assumed to operate only in their linear ranges; motor torque-speed curves are linearized (cf. Chap. 1). The systems discussed in the first few chapters of this book are described by a linear differential equation of the form

$$a_n \frac{d^n y}{dt^n} + a_{n-1} \frac{d^{n-1} y}{dt^{n-1}} + \cdots + a_1 \frac{dy}{dt} + a_o y = f(t) \qquad (10\text{-}1)$$

where the a_i are constants, independent of time or the dependent variable. These systems are assumed linear for purposes of design. Since the performance may deviate from that predicted from linear theory, this assumption is further considered in this chapter.

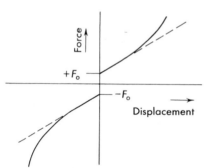

Fig. 10-1. Force versus displacement of a preloaded spring.

Actually the springs and viscous dampers (Fig. 1-6) and all the equations of Chap. 2 are linear only in regions. For values near the origin, or null, and for large excursions, these units may deviate from linearity. A spring actually may have the characteristics shown in Fig. 10-1. This spring has a preload force which produces a discontinuity near the origin. For large displacements the spring rate $\Delta f/\Delta x$ increases because of interference in the coils.

Familiar stress-strain diagrams, gas-expansion laws, and even the simple pendulum cannot be described in all regions with linear equations. The electrical engineer is familiar with the saturation of iron-core inductors and rotating components using iron magnetic circuits. Nonlinear vacuum-tube and transistor characteristics are further examples. These are just a few of the common relations with which servo engineers grapple in the design of feedback control systems.

312

Why does the solution of nonlinear differential equations require special treatment? Basically the answer is that the principle of superposition is invalid. The solution of differential equations by either Laplace transform or the classical method depends upon superposition. For example, the classical method requires that the solution be divided into transient and steady-state components (cf. Appendix II). Each of these is found separately, and their sum is the complete solution for linear systems. This summation is not valid when the equation is nonlinear.

Even when the driving function is zero, a transient component cannot be found by the techniques used for the linear case. For example, suppose it is desired to find the solution to the equation

$$a_2 \frac{d^2c}{dt^2} + a_1 \frac{dc}{dt} + a_0 c^2 = 0 \tag{10-2}$$

Following the technique of Appendix II and assuming a solution $c = Ae^{pt}$,

$$a_1 A p^2 e^{pt} + a_2 A p e^{pt} + a_3 A^2 (e^{pt})^2 = 0 \tag{10-3}$$

The quantity Ae^{pt} does not cancel out of this expression as in linear equations:

$$a_1 p^2 + a_2 p + a_3 A e^{pt} = 0 \tag{10-4}$$

Equation (10-4) cannot be solved to find the values of p, and hence other methods must be used.

Nonlinearities in control systems are conveniently divided into two classes: (a) those which are in the system of necessity and (b) those which are purposely inserted into the system to improve the design. The first class includes all the unavoidable phenomena such as saturation, threshold, and backlash. Component manufacturers spend considerable time and money to reduce these nonlinearities in their equipment.

Nonlinearities of the second class—intentionally inserted—are finding increased application in extending the control possibilities of all-linear systems. Automatic gain control, which changes the gain of the system with signal level, and aircraft acceleration limiter, which limits the maximum fin displacement depending upon the acceleration loads, are two examples of the second type of nonlinearity.

Control-system nonlinearities are also classed according to their magnitude, small or large. Unavoidable nonlinearities are often small, since every attempt is usually made to reduce them. The nonlinearities which are purposely inserted into the system are usually in the large class. The differences between these two are summarized:

1. Analysis of systems with large nonlinearities is usually more difficult than for small nonlinearities.

2. New phenomena such as sudden jump in frequency response, sub-

harmonic resonance, etc., often result when the nonlinearity is large. The response of systems containing small nonlinearities usually deviates little from the linear design.

No *general* method of analysis and design has been developed for solving nonlinear systems.   Methods have been developed to treat certain nonlinearities.   For this reason the nonlinearities have been divided into the two basic types—small and large.   With few reservations, small nonlinearities are generally treated in an indirect manner.   An analysis or design is made upon the linear system, with constant coefficients.   The effect of the nonlinearity is considered as a deviation from this linear result.

For large nonlinearities not only is there no general analysis of these systems but even a given analysis of a given system does not reveal all the details of the system operation.   For instance, an entirely different mode of attack is used to demonstrate subharmonic frequency response from that used to demonstrate the jump phenomena.   Since nonlinear system behavior depends upon the input, it is not sufficient to design for simple functions such as a step or ramp.   In fact, deliberately introduced nonlinearities may improve the system for certain inputs and degrade its performance for others.

The field of nonlinear systems is quite broad and is continually expanding as a result of research activity in this field.   The material presented in this chapter is intended as an outline, and the reader is referred to the bibliography included at the end of this book for additional information (Refs. 2, 32, 33, 35, 36, 37, 39, 51).

10-2. Linearization of Small Nonlinearities.   Because of the additional complexity in designing nonlinear feedback control systems, the first analysis given here is based upon a linearized, although approximate, equation. For example, the motor torque-speed curves were linearized (cf. Chaps. 1 and 9) by drawing straight lines in the region of use.

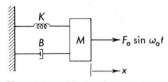

Fig. 10-2. Mechanical system used to demonstrate equivalent viscous damping.

10-3. Equivalent Damping.   As an aid to linearizing nonlinear functions, energy techniques are often applied.   For example, suppose it is desired to find the equivalent viscous damper which will replace another type of damper. Figure 10-2 shows a mechanical system containing a viscous damper.   The response x is found from impedance techniques (cf. Chap. 2):

$$x = A \sin (\omega t + \theta) \tag{10-5}$$

where A is the amplitude of the displacement and depends upon F_0, B, K, and M as follows:

$$A = \frac{F_0}{\sqrt{(K - M\omega^2)^2 + B^2\omega^2}} \qquad (10\text{-}6)$$

The energy dissipated per cycle, which, in this system, is only in the damper B, is

$$\int_0^{2\pi/\omega} F_B \, dx = \int_0^{2\pi/\omega} F_B \frac{dx}{dt} \, dt \qquad (10\text{-}7)$$

where F_B is the damping force and dx/dt is the velocity. Since all quantities are sinusoidal, the energy dissipated is

$$W_B = \int_0^{2\pi/\omega} \left(B \frac{dx}{dt} \right) \frac{dx}{dt} \, dt = B \int_0^{2\pi/\omega} \left(\frac{dx}{dt} \right)^2 dt \qquad (10\text{-}8)$$

Since $dx/dt = A\omega \cos(\omega t + \theta)$, the integral of Eq. (10-8) becomes

$$W_B = B \int_0^{2\pi/\omega} A^2\omega^2 \cos^2(\omega t + \theta) \, dt \qquad (10\text{-}9)$$

which upon integration becomes

$$W_B = BA^2\omega\pi \qquad (10\text{-}10)$$

As an example of the use of this expression [Eq. (10-10)], consider the problem of finding an equivalent viscous damper (force versus velocity) to represent the coulomb or dry friction shown in Fig. 10-3. The energy dissipated per cycle with this type of damping is calculated and equated to Eq. (10-10). Solution for B yields the equivalent damping. The energy dissipated per $\frac{1}{4}$ cycle is

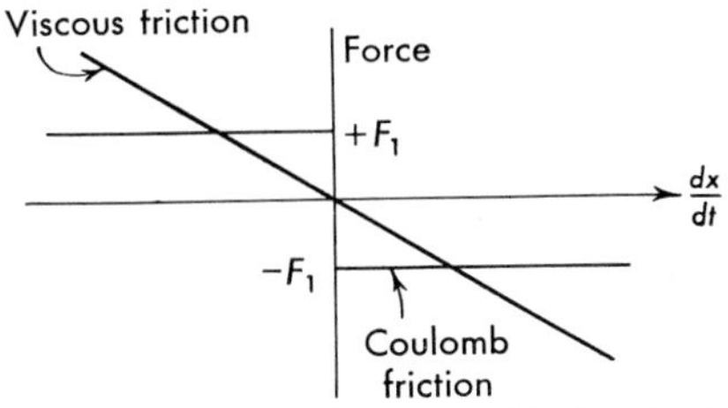

FIG. 10-3. Coulomb or dry friction force curve.

$$W_B = \int_0^{\pi/2\omega} F \, dx = F_1 A \qquad (10\text{-}11)$$

The energy dissipated in the complete cycle is $4F_1A$, and the equivalent viscous damping constant is found by equating Eq. (10-10) to Eq. (10-11):

$$B_{eq} = \frac{4F_1 A}{A^2\pi\omega} = \frac{4F_1}{A\pi\omega} \qquad (10\text{-}12)$$

This expression for B_{eq} depends upon the amplitude A of the motion. For sinusoidal, steady-state motion, the amplitude is easily found from Eq. (10-6):

$$A = \frac{F_0}{\sqrt{(K - M\omega^2)^2 + [(4F_1/A\pi\omega)\omega]^2}} = \frac{F_0}{\sqrt{(K - M\omega^2)^2 + (16F_1^2/A^2\pi^2)}} \qquad (10\text{-}13)$$

Solving for A,

$$A = \frac{F_0/F_1[1 - {}^{16}\!\!/_2(F_1{}^2/F_0{}^2)]^{1/2}}{K - \omega^2 M} \qquad (10\text{-}14)$$

10-4. Equivalent Spring Constant. For small displacements from an operating point, the slope of the restoring force near the point can be used to predict performance. Consider, for example, the amplifier saturation curve of Fig. 10-4. Suppose, because of bias, noise, quadrature voltages, etc., the operating point occurs at 20 mv. For stability analysis the incremental slope $\Delta e_o/\Delta e_{in}$ at the operating point can be used. This gain is considerably less, as can be seen from Fig. 10-4, than the gain at null.

As another example of a spring force, consider the pendulum of Fig. 10-5. Suppose the performance about an operating point $\theta = \theta_0$ is to

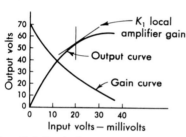

FIG. 10-4. Equivalent gain for a saturated amplifier.

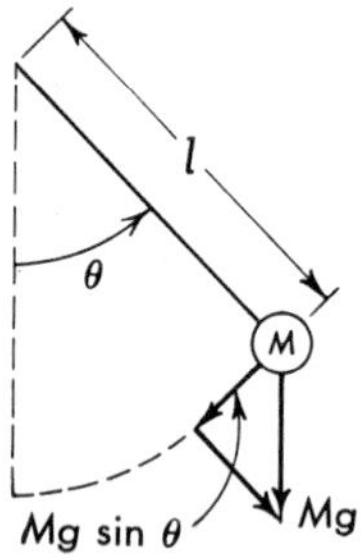

FIG. 10-5. Pendulum behaves as a nonlinear-spring restrained system.

be found. The spring force is $Mg \sin \theta = Mg \sin (\theta_0 + \delta)$, where δ corresponds to the small displacements about the operating point θ_0 and $\theta = \theta_0 + \delta$. The equation is

$$\frac{Mld^2(\theta_0 + \delta)}{dt^2} + Mgl(\sin \theta_0 \cos \delta + \cos \theta_0 \sin \delta) = L(t)$$

$$\frac{d^2\delta}{dt^2} + (g \cos \theta_0)\delta = L(t) - g \sin \theta_0 \qquad (10\text{-}15)$$

The effective gain for small inputs depends upon the slope of the function at the operating point: $\cos \theta_0$.

10-5. The Describing-function Method.* If a sinusoidal function is the input to an element that comprises a nonlinearity, the output is periodic. A Fourier series of the output waveform can be made, as shown in the schematic of Fig. 10-6. The higher harmonics can be neglected for either of the following reasons:

1. The transmission of the higher harmonics in the system is less than

---

* The first presentation of this work in the United States is credited to R. J. Kochenburger. See Ref. 31.

the transmission of the fundamental. This is the behavior of a system whose frequency response resembles a low-pass filter.

2. The signal amplitude is such that the effect of the nonlinearity is small and the higher harmonics present are negligible.

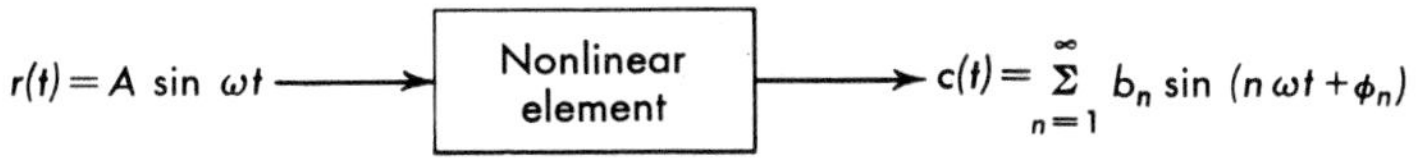

$$r(t) = A \sin \omega t \longrightarrow \boxed{\begin{array}{c}\text{Nonlinear}\\\text{element}\end{array}} \longrightarrow c(t) = \sum_{n=1}^{\infty} b_n \sin (n\omega t + \phi_n)$$

FIG. 10-6. Block diagram which demonstrates the describing-function method.

If either or both of these characteristics are present, the nonlinearity can be represented by an equivalent linear transfer function. This transfer function is called the describing function and depends upon the signal amplitude:

$$G_n = \frac{\text{complex amplitude of output fundamental}}{\text{complex amplitude of input sinusoid}} \qquad (10\text{-}16)$$

G_n is called the describing function and may be real or complex. It is represented by the block diagram of Fig. 10-7.

If the nonlinearity is single valued, as in the case of amplifier saturation shown in Fig. 10-8, G_n is a real quantity whose magnitude depends upon the amplitude of the input

$$r \longrightarrow \boxed{G_N(A)} \longrightarrow b_1$$

FIG. 10-7. Block diagram of describing function.

signal. If the nonlinearity is double valued, as in the case of backlash shown in Fig. 10-9, G_n is a complex quantity whose magnitude and phase both depend upon the amplitude of the input signal. If the nonlinearity occurs in one part of a differential equation, like a nonlinear damper, an

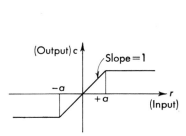

FIG. 10-8. Saturation—single-valued nonlinearity.

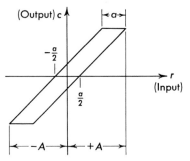

FIG. 10-9. Backlash—double-valued nonlinearity.

iron-core inductor, the describing function depends upon frequency and amplitude.

The nonlinear system is approximated by a linear system, and a block diagram for the system is drawn as in Fig. 10-10 with certain limitations. The frequency-analysis technique of Chap. 5 is now applicable. As the amplitude of the sinusoidal input to the nonlinear element varies, the gain and phase of G_n change and hence produce a change in gain and phase in the closed-loop system.

10-6. Describing Functions for Common Nonlinearities.* The most important types of unavoidable nonlinearities that are encountered in servo design are considered in this section. The describing functions are computed and plotted for saturation, threshold, and backlash.

10-7. Describing Function for Saturation. The phenomenon of saturation, or limiting, exists in many physical systems. Figure 10-8 depicts an idealized form of saturation. The output is proportional to

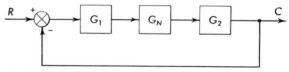

Fig. 10-10. Block diagram for describing-function approximation.

the input, with unity proportionality constant, until the output reaches $\pm a$. For larger amplitudes the output remains at the value $\pm a$. If the amplifier should have a gain K rather than unity, the amplifier can be broken into two blocks placed in series:

1. A linear block with transfer function K (the amplifier gain in the unsaturated region)
2. A nonlinear block consisting of G_n, the describing function for an amplifier of unity gain and limited at $\pm a$

When a sinusoidal input (for example, a voltage) $r(t) = A \sin \omega t$ is applied to the input to the saturating element (for example, an electronic amplifier), the output has the form shown on Fig. 10-11. The peaks of the sinusoid, above the amplitude $\pm a$, are clipped off. The output $c(t)$ has the form

$$c(t) = \sum_{n=1}^{\infty} b_n \sin n\omega t \qquad (10\text{-}17)$$

Since the output (shown in Fig. 10-11) is antisymmetrical with respect to the origin, only the $\sin n\omega t$ terms appear in the output Fourier series.† Because the sinusoid is symmetrical about $\pi/2$ in the interval 0 to π, only the odd harmonics appear. The coefficients b_n are found from the Fourier series expansion

$$b_n = \frac{4}{\pi} \int_0^{\pi/2} c(t) \sin n\omega t \, d\omega t \qquad n = 1, 3, 5, \ldots \qquad (10\text{-}18)$$

---

* See also Ref. 21 on this same topic.
† See Appendix X for a review of Fourier series.

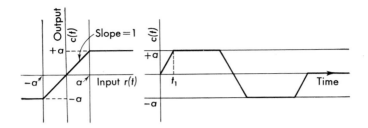

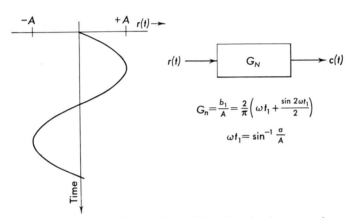

$$G_n = \frac{b_1}{A} = \frac{2}{\pi}\left(\omega t_1 + \frac{\sin 2\omega t_1}{2}\right)$$

$$\omega t_1 = \sin^{-1}\frac{a}{A}$$

Fig. 10-11. Waveform and describing function for saturation.

where
$$c(t) = A \sin \omega t \qquad \text{for } 0 < t < t_1$$
$$= a \qquad \text{for } t_1 < t < \frac{\pi}{2} \qquad (10\text{-}19)$$

When Eq. (10-19) is substituted into Eq. (10-18), the values of b_n are found:

$$\frac{b_n}{A} = \frac{2}{\pi}\left[\frac{\sin (n-1)\omega t_1}{n-1} - \frac{\sin (n+1)\omega t_1}{n+1}\right] + \frac{4}{n\pi}\frac{a}{A}\cos n\omega t_1 \qquad (10\text{-}20)$$

where t_1 is given by

$$\sin \omega t_1 = \frac{a}{A} \qquad (10\text{-}21)$$

Substituting Eq. (10-21) into Eq. (10-20) and simplifying,

$$\frac{b_n}{A} = \frac{2}{n\pi}\left[\frac{\sin (n-1)\omega t_1}{(n-1)} + \frac{\sin (n+1)\omega t_1}{(n+1)}\right] \qquad (10\text{-}22)$$

The describing function b_1/A is given by the expression

$$\frac{b_1}{A} = \frac{2}{\pi}\left(\omega t_1 + \frac{\sin 2\omega t_1}{2}\right) \qquad (10\text{-}23)$$

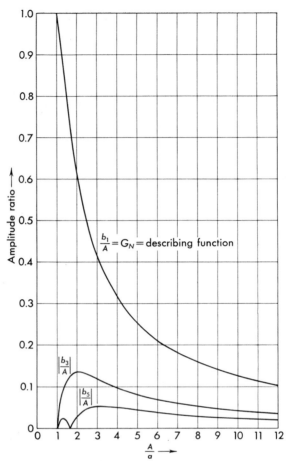

FIG. 10-12. Plot of the describing function for saturation. Third and fifth harmonics are also included.

The equations for the two higher harmonics b_3/A and b_5/A are

$$\frac{b_3}{A} = \frac{2}{3\pi}\left(\frac{\sin 2\omega t_1}{2} + \frac{\sin 4\omega t_1}{4}\right) \tag{10-24}$$

and

$$\frac{b_5}{A} = \frac{2}{5\pi}\left(\frac{\sin 4\omega t_1}{4} + \frac{\sin 6\omega t_1}{6}\right) \tag{10-25}$$

Since the output fundamental is in phase with the input sinusoid, the describing function is a real quantity, with zero phase shift. It depends only upon the signal level a/A. The describing function b_1/A and the third and fifth harmonics are plotted in Fig. 10-12.

10-8. Describing Function for Threshold. In many control systems, the input to a component must exceed a certain minimum value before any output is realized. A motor, for example, requires a finite voltage (possibly 2 volts) before any motion results. This phenomenon is termed dead space or threshold. This undesirable effect is shown on

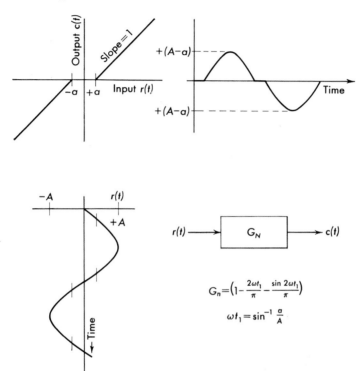

$$G_n = \left(1 - \frac{2\omega t_1}{\pi} - \frac{\sin 2\omega t_1}{\pi}\right)$$

$$\omega t_1 = \sin^{-1} \frac{a}{A}$$

FIG. 10-13. Waveform and describing function for threshold.

Fig. 10-13. The output is given by

$$c(t) = \sum_{n=1}^{\infty} b_n \sin n\omega t \qquad (10\text{-}26)$$

and is included in Fig. 10-13. The coefficients b_n are found from the Fourier expansion

$$b_n = \frac{4}{\pi} \int_0^{\pi/2} c(t) \sin nt \, dt \qquad n = 1, 3, 5 \ldots \qquad (10\text{-}27)$$

where
$$c(t) = 0 \qquad \text{for } 0 < \omega t < \omega t_1$$
$$= A \sin \omega t - a \qquad \text{for } \omega t_1 < \omega t < \frac{\pi}{2} \qquad (10\text{-}28)$$

and
$$\omega t_1 = \sin^{-1} \frac{a}{A}$$

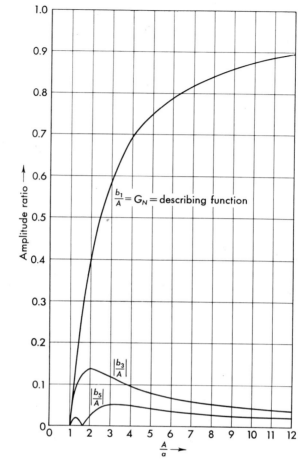

FIG. 10-14. Plot of describing function and third and fifth harmonic for threshold.

The output is represented by a sine series only, since $c(t)$ has odd symmetry with respect to the origin. Because the output is symmetrical about $\pi/2$ in the interval 0 to π, only odd harmonics occur. When Eq. (10-28) is substituted into Eq. (10-27), the following equation results:

$$\frac{b_n}{A} = \frac{-2}{n\pi}\left[\frac{\sin (n-1)\omega t_1}{n-1} + \frac{\sin (n+1)\omega t_1}{n+1}\right] \qquad \text{for } n = 1, 3, 5, \ldots$$

(10-29)

where $\omega t_1 = \sin^{-1} a/A$. The describing function b_1/A is given by

$$\frac{b_1}{A} = \frac{2}{\pi}\left(\frac{\pi}{2} - \omega t_1 - \frac{\sin 2\omega t_1}{2}\right)$$

(10-30)

and is plotted in Fig. 10-14 along with the third and fifth harmonics. Because the output fundamental is in phase with the input, the describing function is a real number, independent of frequency. Notice that the third and fifth harmonics are the same in magnitude for threshold and saturation. Since the higher harmonics are used to indicate the error in approximating the nonlinear function, only the magnitude is plotted.

10-9. Describing Function for Backlash. When the output load is connected to the motor with a loose gear train, the phenomenon of backlash occurs. A plot of the input-output relation results in a closed curve called a hysteresis loop.

FIG. 10-15. Schematic of backlash between two moving members.

Backlash, or hysteresis, exists between two mechanically coupled elements. Figure 10-15 shows a schematic for a mechanical coupling. As the lower piece moves, the upper portion does not follow until the lower

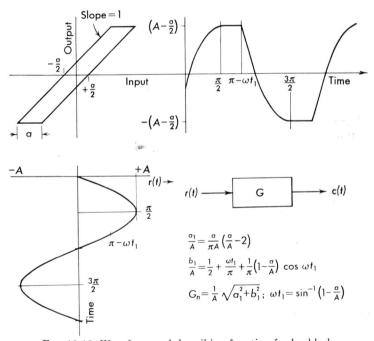

$$\frac{a_1}{A} = \frac{a}{\pi A}\left(\frac{a}{A} - 2\right)$$

$$\frac{b_1}{A} = \frac{1}{2} + \frac{\omega t_1}{\pi} + \frac{1}{\pi}\left(1 - \frac{a}{A}\right)\cos \omega t_1$$

$$G_n = \frac{1}{A}\sqrt{a_1^2 + b_1^2}; \quad \omega t_1 = \sin^{-1}\left(1 - \frac{a}{A}\right)$$

FIG. 10-16. Waveform and describing function for backlash.

piece has moved through the distance a. The backlash, which is shown in the sketch of Fig. 10-16, is assumed to be symmetrical. With a sinusoidal input $r(t) = A \sin \omega t$, the output has the form of Fig. 10-16. The output is written as two equations:

$$c(t) = A - \frac{a}{2} \qquad \text{for } \frac{\pi}{2} < \omega t < \pi - \omega t_1$$
$$= \frac{a}{2} + A \sin \omega t \qquad \text{for } \pi - \omega t_1 < \omega t < \frac{3\pi}{2} \qquad (10\text{-}31)$$

where $\omega t_1 = \sin^{-1}[1 - (a/A)]$. Because the waveform is shifted in phase with respect to the input sinusoid, both a_1 and b_1 must be computed for the Fourier series which represents the output

$$c(t) = \sum_{n=1}^{\infty} (a_n \cos n\omega t + b_n \sin n\omega t) \qquad (10\text{-}32)$$

where
$$a_n = \frac{2}{\pi} \int_{\gamma}^{\gamma + \pi} c(t) \cos n\omega t\, d(\omega t) \qquad (10\text{-}33)$$

$$b_n = \frac{2}{\pi} \int_{\gamma}^{\gamma + \pi} c(t) \sin n\omega t\, d(\omega t)$$

The quantity $c(t)$ is given by Eq. (10-31). When Eq. (10-31) is substituted into Eq. (10-33), the describing function is obtained:

$$\frac{a_1}{A} = \frac{a}{\pi A}\left(\frac{a}{A} - 2\right) \qquad (10\text{-}34)$$

and
$$\frac{b_1}{A} = \frac{1}{\pi}\left[\frac{\pi}{2} + \omega t_1 + \left(1 - \frac{a}{A}\right)\cos \omega t_1\right] \qquad (10\text{-}35)$$

The amplitude and phase of the describing function are plotted in Fig. 10-17 from Eqs. (10-34), (10-35), and the following:

$$Z_n = \sqrt{a_n{}^2 + b_n{}^2} \qquad \text{and} \qquad \phi_n = \tan^{-1}\frac{a_n}{b_n} \qquad (10\text{-}36)$$

The higher harmonics Z_3 and Z_5 are also found from Eq. (10-36), where the components a_3 and b_3 are

$$\frac{a_3}{A} = \frac{1}{6\pi}\left[\cos 2\omega t_1 + \frac{1}{2}(1 + \cos 4\omega t_1)\right]$$
$$\frac{b_3}{A} = \frac{1}{6\pi}\left(\frac{1}{2}\sin 4\omega t_1 + \sin 2\omega t_1\right) \qquad (10\text{-}37)$$

and the fifth harmonic is found from

$$\frac{a_5}{A} = \frac{1}{10\pi}\left[\frac{1}{6} - \frac{1}{2}\cos 4\omega t_1 - \frac{1}{3}\cos 6\omega t_1\right]$$
$$\frac{b_5}{A} = \frac{1}{10\pi}\left(\frac{1}{3}\sin 6\omega t_1 + \frac{1}{2}\sin 4\omega t_1\right) \qquad (10\text{-}38)$$

These are plotted, in magnitude, in Fig. 10-18.

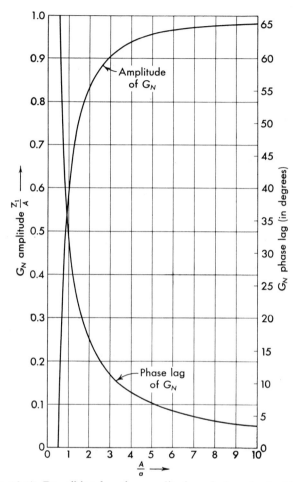

FIG. 10-17. Describing-function amplitude and phase for backlash.

10-10. Use of the Describing Function in Servo Design. In order to understand the use of the describing-function method in servo design, consider the effect of the three nonlinearities of the previous sections upon the simple position servo shown in Fig. 10-19. The system consists of an amplifier with a transfer function

$$G_1 = \frac{K}{1 + 0.2p} \tag{10-39}$$

and a motor gear train with a transfer function

$$G_2 = \frac{1}{p(1 + 0.5p)} \tag{10-40}$$

Each of three nonlinearities is included in the system:

1. Amplifier saturation
2. Threshold in the motor
3. Backlash in the gear train

The system whose open-loop transfer function is

$$G_1 G_2 = \frac{K}{p(1 + 0.2p)(1 + 0.5p)} \tag{10-41}$$

is analyzed for each of these three nonlinearities.

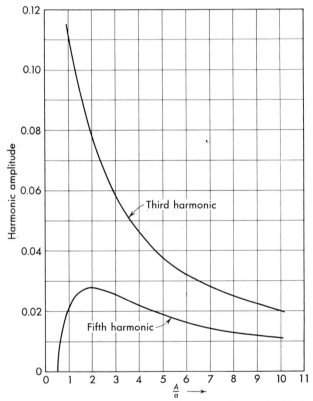

FIG. 10-18. Third and fifth harmonic amplitudes for backlash.

Since the describing function is derived for an element with a sinusoidal input, the use of this method is valid only near the $j\omega$ axis. Care must be used to extend the method to find transient information. The frequency-response method is most applicable, since it is based upon sinusoidal driving functions. For applications on or near the $j\omega$ axis, the root-locus method can be applied. Both root-locus and frequency methods are used in the example.

The gain K is set at 1.60, and the system is redrawn to include G_n in Fig. 10-20. The describing function G_n for amplifier saturation is simply a gain change (cf. Fig. 10-12). The use of the describing-function method with frequency analysis is shown in Fig. 10-21. Since the describing function is simply a gain change, the response is found by shifting the 0-db axis. The gain margin for each of the amplitude ratios is included in the figure.

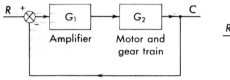

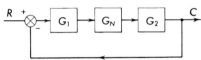

FIG. 10-19. Block diagram of a simple position servo.

FIG. 10-20. Block diagram of a position servo.

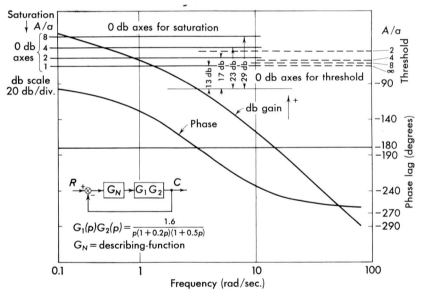

FIG. 10-21. Frequency analysis of a simple position servo using the describing-function approximation of the nonlinear amplifier. Plot of $G_1G_2G_N(j\omega)$.

The root-locus diagram, shown in Fig. 10-22, is found in the standard manner (cf. Chap. 4). The gain changes as a function of the signal level A/a, as shown by the describing function of Fig. 10-12, and the response of the system changes with signal level. The loop gain versus the amplitude ratio A/a is included in Fig. 10-22.

The describing function for threshold is similar to G_n for saturation, since both are simply gain changes. The frequency response, shown in Fig. 10-21, is made to reflect the effect of threshold by changing the 0-db axes. The root-locus method is applied to this system, as shown in Fig. 10-23. As the signal level A/a changes, the system operates at new values of loop gain with a corresponding change in system response. As the system approaches a null, $A/a \rightarrow 1$, the loop gain decreases, and when

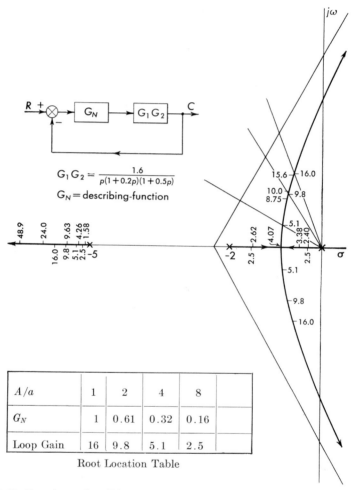

$$G_1 G_2 = \frac{1.6}{p(1+0.2p)(1+0.5p)}$$

G_N = describing-function

A/a	1	2	4	8	
G_N	1	0.61	0.32	0.16	
Loop Gain	16	9.8	5.1	2.5	

Root Location Table

Fig. 10-22. Root-locus–describing-function solution of a simple position servo containing a saturating amplifier.

A/a becomes less than 1, the loop gain reduces to zero. The case of amplifier saturation is different in that as the system approaches a null, the gain increases and the system operates linearly.

Since the describing function for backlash includes both an amplitude and a phase change with signal level (cf. Fig. 10-17), the application to the position servo of Fig. 10-20 is more complex. The frequency-response method more readily lends itself to analysis of systems wherein the describing function has both an amplitude and phase change. The linear portion of the open-loop transfer function is

$$G_1G_2(p) = \frac{1.6}{p(1 + 0.2p)(1 + 0.5p)}$$

$$G_1G_2(j\omega) = \frac{1.0}{(j\omega/1.6)(1 + 0.2j\omega)(1 + 0.5j\omega)}$$

(10-42)

The amplitude and phase for the system of Eq. (10-42) are shown in Fig. 10-24. As G_n varies, owing to signal level, the amplitude scale or the

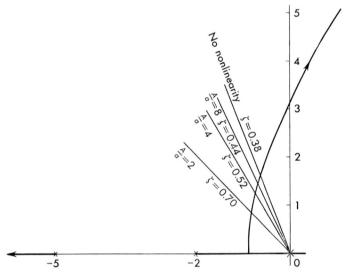

FIG. 10-23. Root-locus diagram for threshold.

$A/a = 1$	$G_N = 0$ (No output)
$A/a = 2$	$G_N = 0.38$
$A/a = 4$	$G_N = 0.68$
$A/a = 8$	$G_N = 0.84$

0-db axis is moved to account for the amplitude change in G_n. The change in the phase angle of G_n is accomplished by shifting the phase-shift scale. For example, when A/a equals 4, G_n is read from Fig. 10-17:

$$G_n = 0.94\angle - 9°$$

(10-43)

The 0-db line is moved up 0.56 db, and the phase scale is shifted 9°. For $A/a = 2$, $G_n = 0.84\angle - 17°$ and the 0-db line is shifted up 1.54 db and the phase scale changed $-17°$. In this system the response is deteriorated by the inclusion of backlash. Even in the worst case, however, $A/a = 1$, this system is stable. The phase margin is 40°, and the gain margin is 8 db. The low loop gain accounts for this stability.

The analysis of backlash using the describing function with the root-locus method is less significant. Its inclusion at this point is primarily for academic interest. The equation that is solved is

$$1 + K(|G_n|\angle\phi)G_1G_2(p) = 0 \qquad (10\text{-}44)$$

or rewritten

$$K|G_n|G_1G_2(p) = -1\angle - \phi = 1\angle - (180 + \phi) \qquad (10\text{-}45)$$

In the usual root-locus construction the angle criterion is

$$\arg KGH = 180° \qquad (10\text{-}46)$$

The normal root locus is constructed with the aid of the rules of Chap. 4.

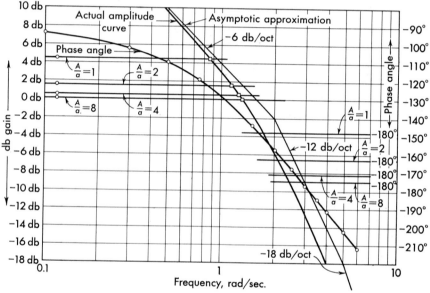

Fig. 10-24. Describing-function analysis for backlash.

The plot is symmetrical about the real axis, and all roots, for any value of gain, appear in complex conjugate pairs.

When the angle criterion of Eq. (10-45) is used, the construction must be accomplished with a Spirule or drafting machine. The rules for sketching the root-locus plots are no longer valid. For example, when summing the angles to 180°, roots move along the real axis until they coalesce. As the gain is further increased, the roots leave the real axis in complex conjugate pairs. When the argument of $KGHG_n$ is some angle other than 180°, the roots do not move along the axis. The roots no longer occur in complex conjugate pairs, so a root can leave the real axis and move alone around the p plane.

For the problem of backlash in the position servo of Fig. 10-19, the root-locus diagram for various signal levels is shown in Fig. 10-25. Ratios of signal level A to backlash a of 1, 2, 4, 8, and infinite (no backlash) are plotted. As an example of the plotting consider the case of

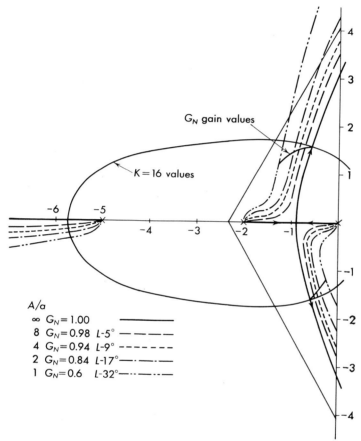

G_N gain values

$K = 16$ values

A/a

∞ $G_N = 1.00$ ————

8 $G_N = 0.98$ $\angle$-5° — — — —

4 $G_N = 0.94$ $\angle$-9° - - - - - - -

2 $G_N = 0.84$ $\angle$-17° —·—·—·—

1 $G_N = 0.6$ $\angle$-32° —··—··—

Fig. 10-25. Root-locus diagram for system with backlash.

$A/a = 2$, where

$$G_n = 0.84\angle - 17° \qquad (10\text{-}47)$$

The root locus is found by locating points in the p plane where

$$KG_1G_2G_n = -197° \qquad (10\text{-}48)$$

The plot of Fig. 10-25 was plotted with the Spirule (cf. Chap. 4). For the transfer function

$$KG_1G_2G_n = \frac{16G_n}{p(p + 0.5)(p + 0.2)} \qquad (10\text{-}49)$$

the gain at the operating point is $16G_n$. This diagram serves no practical value, since the results (i.e., non-conjugate roots) are meaningless. Figure 10-25 is simply an interesting exercise.

10-11. Limitations of Describing Functions. The basic assumption underlying the describing-function approach to the analysis of nonlinear systems is: If the input to the nonlinear element is a sinusoidal signal, the fundamental component of the output is sufficient to describe the nonlinearity. Use of the fundamental component is justified on the grounds that

1. The servo usually acts like a low-pass filter which attenuates the higher harmonics.

2. The harmonics generated from the nonlinearities are usually of smaller amplitude than the fundamental.

Since the input is sinusoidal, the describing function is best suited to the frequency-analysis stability method. However, the Nyquist criterion, i.e., the number of encirclements of the point $-1 + j0$ corresponds to the number of roots in the right half plane, is derived for linear systems. The extension to nonlinear systems, especially where G_n is a complex quantity and the -1 point changes to $-1/G_N \angle \phi$, is not well defined.

For cases where G_n is simply a change in gain, i.e., saturation and threshold, frequency methods give reasonable information. The root locus is less valuable, since the describing function is not valid away from the $j\omega$ axis. For the case of backlash, the root locus yields information that is of little use. Reference to Fig. 10-25 indicates the root-locus plot for a system with backlash. Although a gain can be found for which the roots curve into the right half plane, this does not give useful information about the transient response, since it would appear that non-complex conjugate roots exist.

Another difficulty in using the describing function for analysis of closed-loop systems lies in the nature of the signal amplitude into the nonlinear element. A stable servo tends to reduce the error, or signal into the nonlinearity, to zero. The describing-function analysis requires a sinusoidal input. This condition exists only if the system is oscillating or is being driven with a sinusoid. The describing function is not easily extended to a system whose input varies. As the system approaches null, the amplitude and hence G_n change. As the loop gain varies, the response changes with signal level.

The describing function must be considered as an approximate method of analysis.

10-12. Topological Solution of Feedback Control Systems.[2,37,51] The previous sections consider methods of analysis of systems based upon sinusoidal inputs. Subsequent sections are concerned with the transient analysis of nonlinear systems. The topological, or "phase plane,"

methods presented in these next few sections are subject to the following
limitations:

1. They are easily applicable to second-order systems only.
2. Only driving functions that can be represented by initial conditions
are applicable.

In practice, of course, few feedback control systems can be represented
by a second-order differential equation.   Often, however, a complex system can be approximated by a second-order system comprising a pair of
"least damped roots."   In any case the investigation of the effects of
nonlinearities on the response of second-order systems sheds light on
effects of nonlinearities in higher-order systems.

The limitation on the driving function is less serious.   Since step,
ramp, and impulse functions can usually be represented by initial conditions, the more important inputs can be studied.

Under the above limitations, topological methods, and especially the
all-graphical methods of Sec. 10-15, provide a practical means of investigating some nonlinear equations.

10-13. The Phase Plane.   The
response of a second-order system,
after the application of a disturbance, can be described by the variable x* and the first derivative $\dot{x}$.
The differential equation solution
can be reduced to a form where time

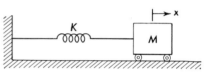

FIG. 10-26. Undamped mechanical system.

is a parameter.   The response of the system is conveniently plotted on a
"phase plane" on which the vertical axis is the velocity $y = \dot{x}$ and the
horizontal axis the displacement x in the phase plane.   The path which
represents the motion x and $\dot{x}$ is termed the phase trajectory.

To demonstrate the solution in the phase plane consider the undamped
mechanical system of Fig. 10-26.   The second-order differential equation
for the nonforced motion is

$$M \frac{d^2x}{dt^2} + Kx = 0 \qquad (10\text{-}50)$$

Time is eliminated from this equation by multiplying through by x and
integrating with respect to time:

$$M \int_0^t \dot{x}\ddot{x}\, dt + K \int_0^t \dot{x}x\, dt = 0$$

which reduces to

$$\frac{M\dot{x}^2}{2} + \frac{Kx^2}{2} = h \qquad (10\text{-}51)$$

---

* The dependent variable is labeled x, and its derivative $dx/dt = \dot{x} = y$.   Any
particular variable c or ε can be later substituted for x.

where h is the constant of integration and depends upon the initial conditions. Equation (10-51), which represents the first integral or energy of the system, can be rewritten

$$\frac{y^2}{a^2} + \frac{x^2}{b^2} = 1 \qquad (10\text{-}52)$$

where $y = \dot{x}$, $a^2 = 2h/M$, and $b^2 = 2h/K$. Equation (10-51) is the sum of the kinetic ($\frac{1}{2} M\dot{x}^2$) and potential ($\frac{1}{2}Kx^2$) energies. For a conservative system, that is, one which has no energy loss (i.e., no damping), the sum at any time of the kinetic and potential energies is constant. This

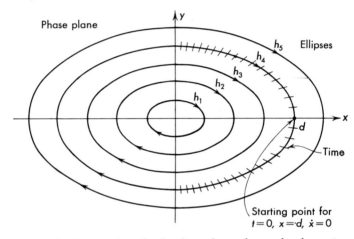

FIG. 10-27. Phase trajectories for the undamped second-order system.

constant h_i depends upon the amount of energy supplied to the system by the initial conditions.

The phase trajectories, for various initial conditions, h_i are plotted from Eq. (10-52) in Fig. 10-27. This equation represents a family of ellipses which have minor and major axes a and b. These ellipses are plotted with time indicated by time markers (small marks shown on the h_2 trajectory). These time marks are placed on the curve such that the time solutions

$$x = A \sin\left(\sqrt{\frac{K}{M}}\, t + \phi\right)$$
$$y = \dot{x} = A\sqrt{\frac{K}{M}} \cos\left(\sqrt{\frac{K}{M}}\, t + \phi\right) \qquad (10\text{-}53)$$

are satisfied. Motion in the phase plane is always in a clockwise direction if the positive directions of x and $\dot{x}$ are assumed as shown in Fig. 10-27.

For the example of Fig. 10-27 a point continues to rotate indefinitely, since the contours on the phase plane are closed. The time solution, that is, x versus t or $\dot{x}$ versus t, is found by projecting the motion of the point on the phase trajectory (the time markers) on the x axis to yield x versus t and projecting the motion on the y axis to yield $\dot{x}$ versus t. The initial conditions determine the point at which the motion begins. For example, if the system has, as initial conditions, $\dot{x} = 0$ and $x = +d$ at $t = 0$, the starting point would be as shown in Fig. 10-27. Similarly, any desired initial velocity and position determine a trajectory.

The method of determining the phase plane and hence the solution for this system (Fig. 10-26) offers little advantage in the solution of nonlinear equations. For many systems this analytic method is impossible. The phase plane becomes useful when it is plotted by graphical techniques. The following sections present two graphical methods for constructing phase-plane solutions.

10-14. The Method of Isoclines. Suppose that the entire phase plane is covered with line segments and that each has a slope which is the slope at some point of the phase trajectory. With these "slope lines" plotted, the phase trajectories are readily constructed by connecting the slope lines.

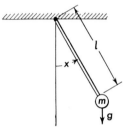

Fig. 10-28. Simple pendulum under the influence of gravity.

The slope at a point (x,y) in the phase plane is

$$\lambda = \frac{dy}{dx} = \frac{dy}{dt}\frac{1}{dx/dt} = \frac{\dot{y}}{\dot{x}} \qquad (10\text{-}54)$$

The lines along which λ is a constant are termed "isoclines." In the general case both $\dot{y}$ and $\dot{x}$ can be represented as functions of x and y:

$$\dot{x} = P(x,y) \qquad \text{and} \qquad \dot{y} = Q(x,y) \qquad (10\text{-}55)$$

where P and Q are functions of x and y, not necessarily linear. The time variable is eliminated by forming the slope of the phase trajectory.

$$\frac{dy}{dx} = \lambda = \frac{\dot{y}}{\dot{x}} = \frac{Q(x,y)}{P(x,y)} \qquad (10\text{-}56)$$

For various constant values of λ the isoclines (a line along which the slope is a constant $\lambda = \lambda_i$) are plotted from Eq. (10-56) as follows:

$$\lambda_i P(x,y) = Q(x,y) \qquad (10\text{-}57)$$

By connecting the slope lines, the desired phase trajectories are constructed.

Consider as an example a pendulum, shown in Fig. 10-28, under the influence of gravity. The equation for the angular position of the pendulum is

$$\ddot{x} + \frac{g}{l}\sin x = 0 \qquad (10\text{-}58)$$

Let $\dot{x} = y$, then $\dot{y} = \ddot{x} = -(g/l)\sin x$ and $\lambda = \dot{y}/\dot{x} = -(g/ly)\sin x$. This equation is rearranged:

$$y = \frac{g}{l\lambda_i}\sin x \qquad (10\text{-}59)$$

This is the equation for the isoclines. When various values of λ_i are substituted, $\lambda_i = 0,\ \pm\frac{1}{2},\ \pm 1,\ \pm 3,\ \infty$ the curves along which λ_i is a constant are found and plotted as shown in Fig. 10-29. As the sine curves are drawn, the small slope lines are drawn at the slope λ_i that corresponds to

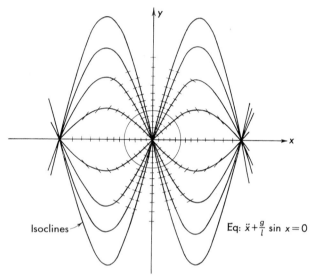

FIG. 10-29. Solution of pendulum problem by method of isoclines.

the particular isocline. The phase trajectories are constructed by connecting the slope lines, as shown by the one trajectory in Fig. 10-29. With $g/l = 1$, the trajectory is a circle for small oscillations.

The complete family of phase trajectories is plotted in Fig. 10-30. The closed curves correspond to finite oscillatory motion, while the upper curves represent the motion of the pendulum rotating in a complete circle about the pivot. The set of trajectories that separates these two types of motion is termed the "separatrix." This trajectory corresponds to the motion which follows the application of initial conditions

$$x = \pi \text{ radians} \qquad \dot{x} = 0 \qquad (10\text{-}60)$$

The motion in the phase plane is clockwise, as can be verified by considering the relation between x and $\dot{x}$. When x is at x_0 and $\dot{x}$ is zero, the point on the trajectory corresponds to the point a in Fig. 10-30. At this position, the pendulum is displaced to the right (cf. Fig. 10-28) an angular distance x_0. When the pendulum moves, x decreases and $\dot{x}$ begins to increase in the negative direction. When the pendulum reaches $x = 0$, the velocity is maximum negative. This point corresponds to the point b in Fig. 10-30. Continuing on, the velocity starts to decrease and x becomes negative. When the pendulum has reached its maximum angular displacement to the left, which is the negative direction, the velocity is zero and the point on the trajectory is c. The motion continues in this fashion.

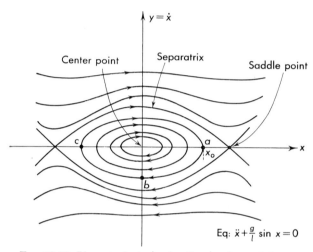

FIG. 10-30. Phase trajectories for the simple pendulum.

10-15. The Lienard Construction. This construction is a more direct method of plotting the phase trajectories. The accuracy is about comparable to that obtained from the method of isoclines. The construction described in this section is applicable to the following types of nonlinear second-order differential equations:

$$\ddot{x} + F(\dot{x}) + x = 0 \tag{10-61}$$
$$\ddot{x} + \dot{x} + g(x) = 0 \tag{10-62}$$
$$\ddot{x} + F(\dot{x}) + g(x) = 0 \tag{10-63}$$
$$\ddot{x} + f(x)\dot{x} + g(x) = 0 \tag{10-64}$$

The method consists of constructing graphically the slope of the phase trajectory. For example, the slope for Eq. (10-61) is found by first eliminating time

$$\dot{x} = y \tag{10-65}$$
$$\dot{y} = \ddot{x} = -[F(y) + x]$$

and the slope is

$$\lambda = \frac{\dot{y}}{\dot{x}} = \frac{-[F(y) + x]}{y} \tag{10-66}$$

The normal slope λ_n is related to λ as follows:

$$\lambda_n = -\frac{1}{\lambda} = \frac{y}{x + F(y)} = \frac{y}{x - [-F(y)]} \quad (10\text{-}67)$$

The last form of Eq. (10-67) is used for the graphical construction. The auxiliary curve $x = -F(y)$ is plotted, as shown in Fig. 10-31, with $+F(y)$ horizontal and y vertical. The scales of both axes are the same, and $F(y)$ has the same scale as x. The slope of the trajectory at the point x_0,y_0 is constructed in Fig. 10-31. The normal slope λ_{n0} at the

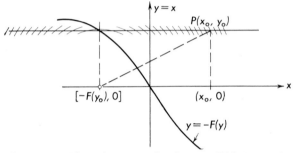

Fig. 10-31. Lienard construction for $\ddot{x} + F(\dot{x}) + x = 0$.

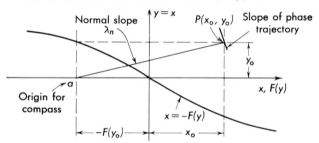

Fig. 10-32. Lienard construction for all points along the line $y = y_0$.

point x_0,y_0 is found from the ratio

$$\lambda_{n0} = \frac{y_0}{x_0 - [-F(y_0)]} \quad (10\text{-}68)$$

The denominator consists of two terms. $-F(y_0)$ is found by projecting y_0 back along a line $y = y_0$ until the curve of $-F(y)$ is intersected as shown in Fig. 10-31. The distance from the point $(x_0,0)$ to $-[F(y_0),0]$, as determined graphically, is the denominator of Eq. (10-68). The numerator y_0 is the vertical distance from the point y_0,x_0 to the x axis. Hence the normal slope is along the line from the point $-[F(y_0),0]$ to $P(x_0,y_0)$ as shown in Fig. 10-31. The desired slope of the phase trajectory is found by constructing a small line perpendicular to λ_{n0} at $P(x_0,y_0)$. This is easily accomplished with a compass.

As an example, suppose the slope lines for all points along the line $y = y_0$ are constructed. This is accomplished in Fig. 10-32 by putting the point of the compass at $[-F(y_0),0]$ and drawing all intersections with $y = y_0$. The solution for particular initial conditions is found by following one trajectory around. In this case, start at the initial condition $P(x_0,y_0)$ and go step by step until the trajectory is traced out. Each slope line is constructed as shown in Fig. 10-31. It is not necessary to draw the line that represents λ_{n0}, since only the origin for the compass, point a, is needed to strike the small slope line λ_0 at the point $P(x_0,y_0)$.

The method for constructing the solution of Eq. (10-62) is similar to that for Eq. (10-61). Again let

$$\dot{x} = y$$
$$\dot{y} = \ddot{x} = -y - g(x) \qquad (10\text{-}69)$$

and the normal slope is

$$\lambda_n = -\frac{1}{\lambda} = -\frac{\dot{x}}{\dot{y}} = \frac{y}{y - [-g(x)]} \qquad (10\text{-}70)$$

The auxiliary curve $y = -g(x)$ is plotted on the phase plane to the same scale as y. Both x and y axes must have the same scale so that angles

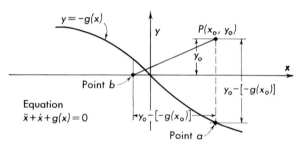

FIG. 10-33. Lienard construction for $\ddot{x} + \dot{x} + g(x) = 0$.

are preserved. For a point $P(x_0,y_0)$, the numerator of Eq. (10-70) represents the distance from the point $P(x_0,y_0)$ to the x axis. The denominator of Eq. (10-70) for $x = x_0$ and $y = y_0$ is composed of two parts: y_0, which is the distance from the point $P(x_0,y_0)$ to the x axis, and $-g(x_0)$, which is the distance from the x axis to the point where the line $x = x_0$ intersects the $-g(x_0)$ curve (point a on Fig. 10-33). The algebraic sum $y_0 - [-g(x_0)]$ is measured with a pair of dividers or a compass and is transferred to the x axis, as shown in Fig. 10-33. This locates the center point of the compass, point b in Fig. 10-33. A small line drawn through $P(x_0,y_0)$ with the center at point b is the slope of the phase trajectory at that point.

As an example of this construction, consider the position servo of Fig.

10-34.   The motor transfer function is

$$\frac{4.1}{p(0.016p + 1)} \tag{10-71}$$

and the amplifier transfer function A is set for a damping ratio of 0.20 with no threshold.   The open-loop transfer function with this setting of

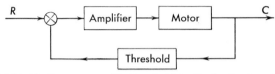

FIG. 10-34. Position servo with threshold in the feedback path.

gain is

$$KG = \frac{24,400}{p(p + 62.5)} \tag{10-72}$$

The threshold transfer function is plotted in Fig. 10-35 and is represented by $H(c)$.   The closed-loop response is

$$\frac{C}{R} = \frac{KG}{1 + KGH(c)} = \frac{24,400}{p(p + 62.5) + 24,400H(c)} \tag{10-73}$$

The differential equation is

$$\ddot{c} + 62.5\dot{c} + 24,400H(c) = 24,400r \tag{10-74}$$

The response to a step input into this system is desired.   Since the phase plane can be used only for zero driving functions, a set of initial conditions must be found that will duplicate the step input.   This is done, in this case, by setting $r = 0$ and taking for initial conditions the following:

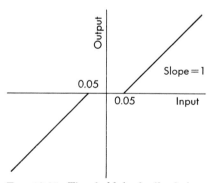

FIG. 10-35. Threshold in feedback loop of position servo.

$$\text{at } t = 0 \qquad c = c_0 \qquad \dot{c} = 0 \tag{10-75}$$

These initial conditions are such that as c returns to the null position the solution passes back and forth across the nonlinearity.   This duplicates the response to an input step function.   Making the usual substitutions,

$$\begin{aligned} y &= \dot{c} \\ \dot{y} &= \ddot{c} = -62.5y - 24,400H(c) \end{aligned} \tag{10-76}$$

and the normal slope is

$$\lambda_n = \frac{\dot{c}}{\dot{y}} = \frac{y}{62.5y + 24{,}400H(c)} \tag{10-77}$$

Equation (10-77) is put in a more suitable form by dividing out the constant 62.5:

$$\lambda_n = \frac{1}{62.5}\,\frac{y}{y + 391H(c)} \tag{10-78}$$

Dividing numerator and denominator by 62.5 and rearranging,

$$62.5\lambda_n = \frac{y/62.5}{(y/62.5) + 62.5H(c)} \tag{10-79}$$

The normalized phase plane is plotted with the variables $y' = y/62.5$ and

$$\lambda'_n = x/y' = x/(y/62.5)$$
$$= 62.5x/y = 62.5\lambda_n$$

with the equation

$$\lambda'_n = \frac{y'}{y' + 62.5H(c)}$$
$$= \frac{y'}{y' - [-62.5H(c)]} \tag{10-80}$$

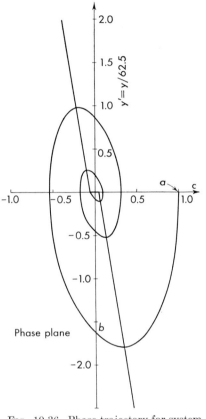

FIG. 10-36. Phase trajectory for system with threshold.

Both axes y' and c on the phase plane now have the same dimension—radians (since 62.5 has the units 1/sec). The resulting construction for a step change of 1 radian is shown in Fig. 10-36. The threshold function $-62.5H(c)$ is plotted first, and the construction follows the scheme outlined in Fig. 10-33. The response of the system for large amplitude is similar to a linear system because of the relatively small threshold. As the signal becomes smaller, the nonlinear effect becomes more pronounced. The system does not return to a complete null but sticks at a point where the phase trajectory passes through the threshold with zero velocity (cf. Fig. 10-36).

The solution for Eq. (10-63) is constructed in a manner similar to the previous two cases. The normal slope is found from the equation

$$\lambda_n = \frac{-\dot{x}}{\dot{y}} = \frac{y}{x - [x - g(x) - F(y)]} \tag{10-81}$$

where $\dot{x} = y$ and $-\dot{y} = F(y) + g(x) = x - \{[x - g(x)] - F(y)\}$. The construction is similar to the two previous cases except that the procedure is more complicated, since the horizontal position of the center of the compass is located at $[x - g(x)] - F(y)$. Both the curves $x' = x - g(x)*$ and $x = F(y)$ are plotted on the phase trajectory, and the distances measured and summed with a compass.

The solution of Eq. (10-64) is constructed in the phase plane by defining the variable y, not as $y = \dot{x}$, but through the equation

$$\dot{x} = y - \int_0^x f(x) \, dx = y - F(x) \tag{10-82}$$

where $F(x) = \int_0^x f(x) \, dx$. When Eq. (10-82) is differentiated with respect to time,

$$\ddot{x} = \frac{d}{dt}\dot{x} = \dot{y} - \frac{d}{dt}F(x) = \dot{y} - \frac{d}{dx}F(x)\frac{dx}{dt} = \dot{y} - \dot{x}f(x) \tag{10-83}$$

Substituting Eq. (10-83) into Eq. (10-64) gives

$$\dot{y} = -g(x) \tag{10-84}$$

The normal slope is found from Eqs. (10-82) and (10-83). The normal slope at a point x_0, y_0 is given by the ratio

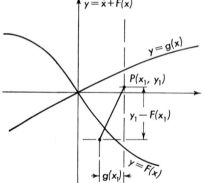

$$\lambda_{n0} = \frac{y_0 - F(x_0)}{x_0 - [x_0 - g(x_0)]}$$
$$= \frac{y_0 - F(x_0)}{x_0 - x'(x_0)} \tag{10-85}$$

The denominator construction is similar to previous cases [cf. the construction of Eq. (10-62)]. The numerator is constructed by subtracting the lengths y_0 and $F(x_0)$. The desired center is found from the ratio of Eq. (10-85) with the graphical construction shown on Fig.

Fig. 10-37. Graphical construction for $\ddot{x} + f(x)\dot{x} + g(x) = 0$.

10-37. Both $F(x) = \int_0^x f(x) \, dx$ and $g(x)$ are plotted on the phase plane, and the construction proceeds as shown on Fig. 10-37. Because of the complexity of the slope equation, it is desirable to plot the slope lines along vertical lines ($x = $ constant). For these lines the radius is centered at the same point for all y.

* This is plotted graphically by adding, point by point, the curve of $-g(x)$ to the linear function x.

10-16. Determination of the Time Markers.   The phase plane solution
of a differential equation is a plot of velocity* $\dot{x} = y$ versus displacement x
with time t as a parameter.   The time solutions x versus t and $\dot{x}$ versus t
can be plotted from the phase trajectory when time markers are placed
upon the phase plane.   Two methods of determining time explicitly are
presented in this text.   The first method involves plotting $1/y$ as a function of x.   Since $y = \dot{x} = dx/dt$, the time is found as follows:

$$dt = \frac{1}{y}\,dx \qquad\qquad (10\text{-}86)$$

when Eq. (10-86) is integrated,

$$t_2 - t_1 = \int_{x_1}^{x_2} \frac{1}{y}\,dx \qquad\qquad (10\text{-}87)$$

When $1/y$ is plotted as a function of x, the area under the curve between
two values of x is equal to the elapsed time $t_2 - t_1$ between the two
points.   The time is found for the position servo shown in the phase
plane of Fig. 10-36.   In Fig. 10-38, $1/y'$ is plotted against x for the
interval from a to b in Fig. 10-36.
The time between any two points,
say 0.7 to 0.8, is proportional to the
area shaded on the figure.   The
entire area between $x = 1$ and $x = 0$
is approximately 0.75, in dimensionless form.   To convert this into
seconds, the area must be multiplied
by $1/62.5$, or

$$t = (0.75)\left(\frac{1}{62.5}\right) = 12 \text{ msec}$$

$$(10\text{-}88)$$

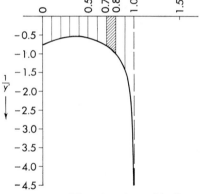

FIG. 10-38. Time found graphically.

The determination of the time becomes difficult in regions where y
passes through zero, since $1/y$ becomes large.   Because the integral
represents a physical problem for which the time is finite, it is usually
suitable to approximate the area.   Often the time to pass across a discontinuity in $1/y$ can be neglected.

The second method of determining the time markers, termed "isochrones," is based upon a completely graphical construction.   The basis
for this construction is shown in the phase plane of Fig. 10-39, where,

---

* For the last construction of Sec. 10-15, $\dot{x}$ does not equal y, but is equal to $y - F(x)$.
The determination of time markers is still valid, but a plot of y versus t is not readily
obtainable from the trajector~

from the two similar triangles

$$\frac{r}{\Delta s} = \frac{y}{\Delta x} \qquad (10\text{-}89)$$

but $y = dx/dt$ which is approximately equal to $\Delta x/\Delta t$, or

$$\frac{r}{\Delta s} = \frac{\Delta x}{\Delta t}\frac{1}{\Delta x} = \frac{1}{\Delta t} \qquad (10\text{-}90)$$

and the distance Δs along the trajectory that corresponds to a time interval Δt is found from Eq. (10-90):

$$\Delta s = r\,\Delta t \qquad (10\text{-}91)$$

If a constant value for Δt, for example, 0.1, is chosen, Δs is proportional to r, the distance from the trajectory to the construction point along the x axis. Notice that r is not the

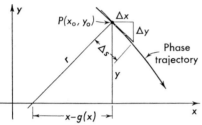

FIG. 10-39. Construction of isochrones.

radius of curvature of the phase trajectory but is the radius used to define the normal slope in the Lienard construction. In some cases these are the same.

It is usually more convenient to find the time marks while constructing the phase trajectory. This method of construction saves time, since the radius r must be determined before the particular slope line can be drawn. Also if a constant Δt is chosen, setting the isochrones on the trajectory as it is being constructed helps to determine the spacing of the slope lines. The time solution for the position servo pictured on the phase plane of Fig. 10-36 is presented in Fig. 10-40. For purposes of comparison, the time solution of a system without threshold is also plotted. Equation (10-64) of Sec. 10-15 requires a different construction to determine the time markers. In this case the radius r is found from $y - F(x)$ in the numerator rather than just y.

10-17. Singular Points. The slope of the phase trajectory is given by Eq. (10-56) to be

$$\lambda = \frac{dy}{dx} = \frac{Q(x,y)}{P(x,y)} \qquad (10\text{-}92)$$

A point x_0,y_0 is a singular point if both $Q(x_0,y_0)$ and $P(x_0,y_0)$ equal zero. Because these points are often confusing when plotting the trajectories, this section lists the types that might be encountered. To determine the form of the singularities, let

$$\begin{aligned} Q(x,y) &= ax + by \\ P(x,y) &= cx + dy \end{aligned} \qquad (10\text{-}93)$$

where, with no loss of generality, the singularity has been taken at the

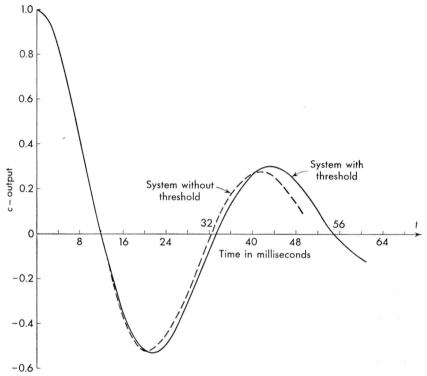

FIG. 10-40. Time response, second-order system with and without threshold.

origin.   The slope is

$$\frac{dy}{dx} = \frac{ax + by}{cx + dy} \tag{10-94}$$

Various values of a, b, c, and d yield the types of singular points.

Case 1. $b = 0 = c$ and $\dfrac{a}{d} = -\beta^2$

from Eq. (10-94)

$$\frac{dy}{dx} = -\beta^2 \frac{x}{y} \tag{10-95}$$

$y^2 + \beta^2 x^2 =$ constant

This is integrated to $y^2 + \beta^2 x^2 =$ constant, which is the equation for a
family of ellipses. The singular
point is termed a center and is plotted in **Fig. 10-41.**

FIG. 10-41.   Center $y^2 + \beta^2 x^2 =$ constant.

Case 2. $a = 0 = d$ and $\dfrac{b}{c} = \alpha$

from Eq. (10-94)

$$\frac{dy}{dx} = \alpha \frac{y}{x} \tag{10-96}$$

This is integrated

$$\int \frac{dy}{y} = \alpha \int \frac{dx}{x} \qquad (10\text{-}97)$$

with the result

$$y = Cx^{\alpha} \qquad (10\text{-}98)$$

Depending on the value of α, three possible forms are obtained. Each of these singular points is termed a node (or nodal point) and is plotted in Fig. 10-42.

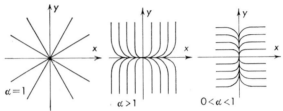

FIG. 10-42. Nodal points for three regions of α.

Case 3. $a = 0 = d$ and $\dfrac{b}{c} = -k$

from Eq. (10-94)

$$\frac{dy}{dx} = -k\frac{y}{x} \qquad (10\text{-}99)$$

This is integrated to

$$yx^{k} = 0 \qquad (10\text{-}100)$$

which is the equation of a family of hyperbolas. The singular point is termed a saddle point and is plotted in Fig. 10-43.

Case 4. $a = 1, d = -1, b = c = \alpha$

from Eq. (10-94)

$$\frac{dy}{dx} = \frac{x + \alpha y}{\alpha x - y} \qquad (10\text{-}101)$$

This is integrated more readily if put in polar form

$$x = r \cos \theta \qquad\qquad y = r \sin \theta$$
$$dx = \cos \theta\, dr - r \sin \theta\, d\theta \qquad dy = \sin \theta\, dr + r \cos \theta\, d\theta$$

Substituting into Eq. (10-101),

$$\frac{\sin \theta\, dr + r \cos \theta\, d\theta}{\cos \theta\, dr - r \sin \theta\, d\theta} = \frac{r \cos \theta + \alpha r \sin \theta}{\alpha r \cos \theta - r \sin \theta} \qquad (10\text{-}102)$$

When Eq. (10-102) is simplified

$$\frac{dr}{r} = \alpha\, d\theta \qquad (10\text{-}103)$$

and integrated

$$r = Ke^{\alpha\theta} \tag{10-104}$$

the equation of a family of spirals results. The singular point is termed a focus (or focal point) and is plotted in Fig. 10-44.

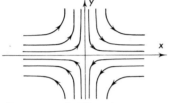

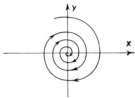

FIG. 10-43. Saddle point $yx^k = 0$. FIG. 10-44. Focus $r = Ke^{\alpha\theta}$.

The nature of the stability associated with the singularity can be determined* from the relative magnitudes of the constants a, b, c, and d. This procedure leads to the following clarification, which is included for reference. In the system $dy/dx = (ax + by)/(cx + dy)$ the following relations hold:

$$(b - c)^2 + 4ad > 0 \begin{cases} \text{node if } ad - bc < 0 \begin{cases} \text{stable if } b + c < 0 \\ \text{unstable if } b + c > 0 \end{cases} \\ \text{saddle if } ad - bc > 0 \end{cases}$$

$$(b - c)^2 + 4ad < 0 \begin{cases} \text{center if } b + c = 0 \\ \text{focus if } b + c \neq 0 \begin{cases} \text{stable if } b + c < 0 \\ \text{unstable if } b + c > 0 \end{cases} \end{cases}$$

$$(b - c)^2 + 4ad = 0 \quad \text{node} \begin{cases} \text{stable if } b + c < 0 \\ \text{unstable if } b + c > 0 \end{cases} \tag{10-105}$$

10-18. Comparison of Several Methods. Some of the more commonly used methods available for the analysis of systems defined by nonlinear differential equations are presented in this chapter. Various analytic methods, notably iteration methods,[51] perturbation methods,[51] and step-by-step solutions,[37] have been neglected. Although both the describing-function approach and the topological methods are limited in scope of use, these are used more for nonlinear servo design than the analytic methods.

Because of the difficulty of analysis of complex nonlinear systems, general-purpose analogue and digital computation is often used to effect detailed and accurate investigations of system performance.[43] However, the analytical and topological procedures advanced in this chapter can often be used to gain insight to the gross behavior and major aspects of the problem.

* See Ref. 2, pp. 182–193.

PROBLEMS

10-1. Calculate and plot the describing function for spring preload which has an input-output relation shown by Fig. 10P-1.

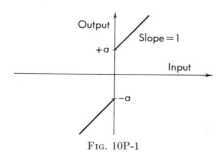

FIG. 10P-1

10-2. Calculate and plot the second and third harmonics for Prob. 10-1.

10-3. Calculate and plot the describing function for the nonbilateral element shown on Fig. 10P-3.

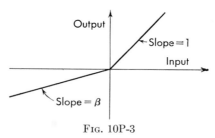

FIG. 10P-3

10-4. Calculate and plot the second and third harmonics for Prob. 10-3.

10.5. Subject the simple position servo given by $G_1 = \dfrac{1.0}{p(1 + 0.1p)(1 + p)^2}$ to amplifier saturation. The block diagram is given in Fig. 10P-5. Determine the effect on the system when the nonlinearity is included in the system. Solve the problem by both frequency-analysis and root-locus methods. For amplifier saturation take the ratio of input amplitude A to saturation level equal to 1, 2, 4, and 8.

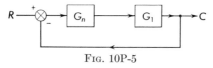

FIG. 10P-5

10-6. Repeat Prob. 10-5 for motor threshold. Take the ratio of input amplitude A to dead bandwidth a equal to 1, 2, 4, and 8.

10-7. Repeat Prob. 10-5 for backlash in the gear train. Take the ratio of input amplitude to backlash a equal to 1, 2, and 4.

10-8. Consider the effect of backlash upon the simplified gyro-stabilized platform shown in Fig. 10P-8 where

$$G_1 = \frac{K}{p[(p + 5)^2 + 30^2]} \qquad G_2 = p + 1$$

G_n is the describing function for backlash. Take the ratio of $A/a = 1$, 2, 4, and 8, where A is the amplitude of the input sinusoid. Solve the problem by frequency-response techniques.

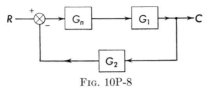

FIG. 10P-8

10-9. Plot accurately the phase trajectory for a pendulum of mass 1 slug and length 1 ft. At $t = 0$ the pendulum is started from rest at an angle of 170° from the vertical (measured downward). Neglect friction.

10-10. The motion of a ship proceeding on a straight course with rudder amidships can be described by the following equation:

$$J\ddot{\alpha} + C(\dot{\alpha}) - M(\alpha) = 0$$

where J = moment of inertia of ship about vertical axis through center of ship
   $C(\dot{\alpha})$ = resistance to turning
   $M(\alpha)$ = moment of leeway force (restoring torque)
   α = angular deviation from course
Take $C(\dot{\alpha}) = 0$ and assume $M(\alpha) = M_0\alpha - M_1\alpha^3$. Sketch the trajectories and state the nature of the stability of the ship on its course.

10-11. Using the method of isoclines, plot the family of phase trajectories for the Van der Pol equation

$$\ddot{x} - \mu(1 - x^2)\dot{x} + x = 0$$

Take $\mu = 1$.

10-12. Use the Lienard construction to find the trajectories for the following differential equation:

$$\ddot{x} + F_1(\dot{x}) + x = 0 \qquad F_1(\dot{x}) = 2 + \tfrac{1}{2}\dot{x} \qquad \text{for } \dot{x} > 0$$
$$= -2 + \tfrac{1}{2}\dot{x} \qquad \text{for } \dot{x} < 0$$

10-13. Repeat Prob. 10-12 with the following differential equation:

$$\ddot{x} + F_2(\dot{x}) + x = 0 \qquad F_2(\dot{x}) = -(2 + \tfrac{1}{2}\dot{x}) \qquad \text{for } \dot{x} > 0$$
$$= -(-2 + \tfrac{1}{2}\dot{x}) \qquad \text{for } \dot{x} < 0$$

Choose two sets of initial conditions so that at least two trajectories are obtained. Discuss and compare the resulting solutions of Prob. 10-12 and 10-13.

10-14. Construct isochrones on the phase trajectories of Probs. 10-12 and 10-13. Choose $\Delta t = 0.1$.

10-15. (a) By use of the theory of isoclines, plot the trajectory of the $L = C = 1$ series circuit having an equation $\ddot{q} + q = 0$ and passing through $q = 5$, $\dot{q} = 0$ at $t = 0$.

(b) Derive for this case $t = \displaystyle\int_5^q dq/\dot{q}$.

(c) Plot the curve of $1/\dot{q}$ versus q taking coordinates from the isocline plot. The area under this curve from $q = 5$ to q is the time elapsed since $t = 0$. Evaluate this area graphically from the plotted curve.

(d) Plot on one sheet the q versus t curves obtained as follows:

(1) By the graphical integration of $t = \int_5^q \frac{1}{\dot{q}} \, dq$

(2) Using isochrones

(3) Analytic solution of equation $\ddot{q} + q = 0$ using stated initial conditions

Compare the various methods on the following points: accuracy, ease, etc.

10-16. Consider the free motion of a mass, spring, dashpot combination as given by the equation

$$M\ddot{x} + \beta\dot{x} + Kx = 0$$

Show that if the damping is less than critical $(\beta < 2\sqrt{KM})$, the singularity is a focus and if $\beta > 2\sqrt{KM}$, the singularity is a node.

10-17. Consider the servo of Fig. 10P-17 where

Motor transfer function $= \dfrac{4.1}{p(1 + 0.016p)}$

Amplifier transfer function $= A$ (a constant)

Feedback function $b = \alpha c^n$

Take $\alpha = 1$, and compare the time response to a unit step function for

$n = 1$

$n = 3$

$n = \frac{1}{3}$

Choose A for a $\zeta = 0.2$ for $n = 1$ (the linear case). Use the same gain for $n = 3$ and $n = \frac{1}{3}$. Would any other gain yield a better system?

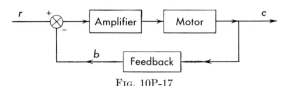

FIG. 10P-17

On the basis of this problem draw conclusions concerning the use of nonlinear feedback for servo stability.

10-18. Plot accurately the family of phase trajectories for the system $G = \dfrac{1}{p(5p + 1)}$. Choose $|a| = 1$, and take initial conditions $x_0 = 2,\ 5,\ 10$. Plot isochrones and the x versus t curves for these initial conditions. The block diagram is shown in Fig. 10P-18.

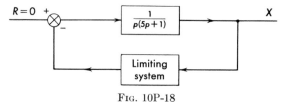

FIG. 10P-18

APPENDIXES

APPENDIX I

LAPLACE-TRANSFORM METHOD

I-1. Introduction. The Laplace transformation is a mathematical operation which is useful in the solution of the ordinary differential equations encountered in feedback-control-system design. The operation is defined by the following integral:

$$\mathcal{L}[f(t)] = \int_0^\infty f(t)e^{-pt}\,dt = F(p) \tag{I-1}$$

where $f(t)$ is a function of time which is zero for $t < 0$, p is a complex variable, $F(p)$ is the function of p which results when $f(t)$ is Laplace-transformed, $\mathcal{L}$ is an operational symbol which indicates that the function following is to be Laplace-transformed. Since many excellent texts[9,18] have been written on this subject, only the mechanics of the Laplace-transform theory is treated in this appendix.

A linear differential equation of the form

$$a_n \frac{d^n y}{dt^n} + a_{n-1} \frac{d^{n-1}y}{dt^{n-1}} + \cdots + a_1 \frac{dy}{dt} + a_0 y = f(t) \tag{I-2}$$

is often encountered in servo design. The coefficients a_i are constant and independent of t or y. The dependent variable y and the driving function $f(t)$ are both functions of time. When Eq. (I-2) is Laplace-transformed, a new, or "transformed," equation results. The differential equation is reduced to an algebraic equation in the variable p. This transformed equation can be manipulated algebraically to solve for the desired quantity in transformed form. The transformed solution is often sufficient.

If the solution is required as a function of time, the inverse process must be applied; that is, the function of p must be inverse-transformed into a function of time. This process is termed "finding the inverse Laplace transform" and is most easily accomplished with the aid of Laplace-transform tables.*

I-2. The Laplace Transform of Functions. Application of Eq. (I-1) is the basis for a table of "transform pairs." When the function is known,

---

* An excellent table of Laplace transforms is found in Ref. 18.

353

for example, $f(t) = Ae^{-at}$, the Laplace transform is found by substituting directly into Eq. (I-1) as follows:

$$\mathcal{L}[Ae^{-at}] = \int_0^{\infty} Ae^{-at}e^{-pt}\,dt = \int_0^{\infty} Ae^{-(a+p)t}\,dt$$

$$= \frac{Ae^{-(a+p)t}}{a+p}\Big|_0^{\infty} = \frac{A1}{p+a} \tag{I-3}$$

The Laplace transform of a sinusoid $\mathcal{L}[\sin \omega t]$ is found by similar substitution:

$$\int_0^{\infty} \sin \omega t\, e^{-pt}\,dt = \frac{1}{2j}\int_0^{\infty}(e^{+j\omega t}-e^{-j\omega t})e^{-pt}\,dt$$

$$= \frac{1}{2j}\int_0^{\infty}[e^{-(p-j\omega)t}-e^{-(p+j\omega)t}]\,dt$$

$$= \frac{1}{2j}\left[\frac{1}{p-j\omega}-\frac{1}{p+j\omega}\right] = \frac{\omega}{p^2+\omega^2} \tag{I-4}$$

As another example, consider the unit step function $u(t)$ shown in

FIG. I-1. Plot of a unit step function $u(t)$.

Fig. I-1.   The mathematical representation is

$$u(t) = \begin{cases} 0 & t < 0 \\ 1 & t > 0 \end{cases} \tag{I-5}$$

The Laplace transform is

$$\mathcal{L}[u(t)] = \int_0^{\infty} e^{-pt}\,dt = \frac{e^{-pt}}{p}\Big|_0^{\infty} = \frac{1}{p} \tag{I-6}$$

Table I-1 is a short table of Laplace transforms. This table is satisfactory for most driving functions encountered in servo design.

I-3. The Laplace Transform of Operations. Besides finding the Laplace transforms of known functions of time $f(t)$, it is also necessary to transform differential operations

$$\mathcal{L}\left[\frac{dy}{dt}\right] = \int_0^{\infty}\frac{dy}{dt}e^{-pt}\,dt \tag{I-7}$$

This integral is evaluated by parts as follows:

$$\int_a^b u\,dv = uv - \int_a^b v\,du \tag{I-8}$$

TABLE I-1. LAPLACE-TRANSFORM TABLE

	$f(t)$	$F(p)$		$f(t)$	$F(P)$
a	$u(t)$	$\dfrac{1}{p}$	j	$\sin \omega t$	$\dfrac{\omega}{p^2 + \omega^2}$
b	t	$\dfrac{1}{p^2}$	k	$\cos \omega t$	$\dfrac{p}{p^2 + \omega^2}$
c	t^n	$\dfrac{n!}{p^{n+1}}$	l	$\dfrac{K}{\omega} \sin(\omega t + \psi)$ $\psi = \tan^{-1}\dfrac{\omega}{a_0}$ $K = (a_0^2 + \omega^2)^{1/2}$	$\dfrac{p + a_0}{p^2 + \omega^2}$
d	$\delta(t)$ Unit impulse	1	m	$\sinh \omega t$	$\dfrac{\omega}{p^2 - \omega^2}$
e	e^{-at}	$\dfrac{1}{p + a}$	n	$\cosh \omega t$	$\dfrac{p}{p^2 - \omega^2}$
f	$\dfrac{e^{-at} - e^{-bt}}{b - a}$	$\dfrac{1}{(p+a)(p+b)}$	o	$e^{-\alpha t} \sin \omega t$	$\dfrac{\omega}{(p+\alpha)^2 + \omega^2}$
g	te^{-at}	$\dfrac{1}{(p+a)^2}$	q	$\dfrac{K}{\omega} e^{-\alpha t} \sin(\omega t + \psi)$ $\psi = \tan^{-1}\dfrac{\omega}{a_0 - \alpha}$	$\dfrac{p + a_0}{(p+\alpha)^2 + \omega^2}$ $K = [(a_0 - \alpha)^2 + \omega^2]^{1/2}$
h	$t^n e^{-at}$	$\dfrac{n!}{(p+a)^{n+1}}$	r	$t \cos \omega t$	$\dfrac{p^2 - \omega^2}{(p^2 + \omega^2)^2}$
i	$(Kt + 1)e^{-\alpha t}$ $K = a_0 - \alpha$	$\dfrac{p + a_0}{(p+\alpha)^2}$	s	$t \sin \omega t$	$\dfrac{2\omega p}{(p^2 + \omega^2)^2}$

where the following substitutions are made:

$$u = e^{-pt} \qquad du = -pe^{-pt}\, dt$$
$$dv = \frac{dy}{dt}\, dt \qquad v = y(t) \tag{I-9}$$

The integral is now evaluated

$$\mathcal{L}\left[\frac{dy}{dt}\right] = y(t)e^{-pt}\Big|_0^\infty + p\int_0^\infty y(t)e^{-pt}\, dt \tag{I-10}$$

Since the last integral in Eq. (I-10) is the Laplace transform of $y(t)$

$$\mathcal{L}[y(t)] = \int_0^\infty y(t)e^{-pt}\, dt = Y(p) \tag{I-11}$$

and since $y(t)e^{-pt}$ is zero at the upper limit, provided the real part of p is > 0

$$\mathcal{L}\left[\frac{dy}{dt}\right] = -y(0) + pY(p) \tag{I-12}$$

In a similar fashion, the Laplace transform of higher derivatives can be found:

$$\mathcal{L}\left[\frac{d^2y}{dt^2}\right] = p^2Y(p) - py(0) - \frac{dy}{dt}\bigg|_{t=0} \tag{I-13}$$

$$\mathcal{L}\left[\frac{d^ny}{dt^n}\right] = p^nY(p) - p^{n-1}y(0) - p^{n-2}\frac{dy}{dt}\bigg|_{t=0} - \cdots - \frac{d^{n-1}y}{dt^{n-1}}\bigg|_{t=0} \tag{I-14}$$

For the case of zero initial conditions, as often occurs in servo analysis, this last equation reduces to

$$\mathcal{L}\left[\frac{d^ny}{dt^n}\right] = p^nY(p) \tag{I-15}$$

Hence, for this case, taking the Laplace transform is equivalent to replacing the derivative with respect to time d/dt by the Laplace-transform operator p.

Another important Laplace-transform pair, which is required for the solution of linear differential equations, has reference to the Laplace transform of the sum of two time functions:

$$\mathcal{L}[a_1y_1(t) + a_2y_2(t)] = a_1Y_1(p) + a_2Y_2(p) \tag{I-16}$$

This relation is easily proved by substituting into the defining equation [Eq. (I-1)].

The Laplace transform of a definite integral of a function of time

$$\mathcal{L}\left[\int_0^t y(\tau)\,d\tau\right] = \int_0^\infty e^{-pt}\,dt \int_0^t y(\tau)\,d\tau \tag{I-17}$$

is also found by integrating by parts

$$\begin{aligned} u &= \int_0^t y(\tau)\,dt & du &= y(t)\,dt \\ dv &= e^{-pt}\,dt & v &= -\frac{1}{p}e^{-pt} \end{aligned} \tag{I-18}$$

When these substitutions are made in Eq. (I-17), the following equation results:

$$\mathcal{L}\left[\int_0^t y(\tau)\,d\tau\right] = -\frac{1}{p}e^{-pt}\int_0^t y(\tau)\,d\tau\,\bigg|_0^\infty + \frac{1}{p}\int_0^\infty e^{-pt}y(t)\,dt \tag{I-19}$$

The first term on the right is zero at the upper limit, since $e^{-\infty} = 0$.   If

$\int_0^0 y(t)\, dt = 0$, that is, if the integral has no initial value, the first term vanishes at the lower limit and the result simplifies:

$$\mathcal{L}\left[\int_0^t y(\tau)\, d\tau\right] = \frac{Y(p)}{p} \qquad (\text{I-20})$$

These transform pairs are summarized in Table I-2. The initial conditions are set equal to zero for the pairs in this table, since in most servo applications zero initial conditions are suitable to solve the problem.

TABLE I-2. OPERATION TRANSFORM PAIRS*

Function of t	Transformed function of p
$\dfrac{dy}{dt}$	$pY(p)$
$\dfrac{d^2y}{dt^2}$	$p^2Y(p)$
$a_1 y_1(t) + a_2 y_2(t)$	$a_1 Y_1(p) + a_2 Y_2(p)$
$\int_0^t y(t)\, dt$	$\dfrac{1}{p} Y(p)$

* All initial conditions are taken equal to zero in this table.

The Laplace-transform operator p, which has the dimensions $1/\text{sec}$, is often called the "complex frequency," since it has a real and an imaginary part

$$p = \sigma + j\omega \qquad (\text{I-21})$$

I-4. Solution of Ordinary Linear Differential Equations Utilizing Laplace Transforms. As an example of the transform method of solving differential equations, consider the following simple equation:

$$\frac{d^2y}{dt^2} + 9y = u(t) \qquad t > 0 \qquad (\text{I-22})$$

with all initial conditions taken equal to zero. $u(t)$ is a unit step function. The Laplace transform of both sides is taken.

$$p^2Y + 9Y = \frac{1}{p} \qquad (\text{I-23})$$

and the result is solved for the transformed variable

$$Y = \frac{1}{p(p^2 + 9)} \qquad (\text{I-24})$$

The solution $y(t)$ is found by breaking Eq. (I-21) into a sum of two parts by partial fractions.*

$$\frac{1}{p(p^2 + 9)} = \frac{A}{p} + \frac{B}{p + j3} + \frac{C}{p - j3} \qquad (\text{I-25})$$

* A discussion of partial fractions is included in Sec. I-5.

The constants A, B, and C are evaluated (as in the next section), and $Y(p)$ is written as follows:

$$Y(p) = \frac{1}{9}\left(\frac{1}{p} - \frac{p}{p^2 + 9}\right) \tag{I-26}$$

The reader can verify that Eq. (I-26) is equivalent to Eq. (I-25) by putting Eq. (I-26) over a common denominator:

$$\frac{1}{9}\left(\frac{1}{p} - \frac{p}{p^2 + 9}\right) = \frac{1}{9}\left[\frac{p^2 + 9 - p^2}{p(p^2 + 9)}\right] = \frac{1}{p(p^2 + 9)} \tag{I-27}$$

The inverse transform of the terms in Eq. (I-26) are found in Table I-1. The inverse transform yields

$$y(t) = \tfrac{1}{9}[u(t) - \cos 3t] = \tfrac{1}{9}u(t)[1 - \cos 3t] \tag{I-28}$$

As a second example consider the differential equation

$$\frac{d^2y}{dt^2} + \omega^2 y = \cos \omega t \qquad t > 0 \tag{I-29}$$

with $y(0) = 0 = dy/dt\big|_{t=0}$, that is, zero initial conditions. Taking the Laplace transform of both sides and solving for $Y(p)$,

$$Y(p) = \frac{p}{(p^2 + \omega^2)^2} \tag{I-30}$$

The inverse Laplace transform is found from Table I-1:

$$y(t) = \mathcal{L}^{-1}\frac{p}{(p^2 + \omega^2)^2} = \frac{t}{2\omega}\sin \omega t \tag{I-31}$$

where the symbol $\mathcal{L}^{-1}$ means "inverse Laplace transform of."

As a final example consider the second-order servo system discussed in Chap. 1. The differential equation with a step input and with zero initial conditions is written

$$\frac{d^2y}{dt^2} + 2\zeta\omega_n\frac{dy}{dt} + \omega_n{}^2 y = \omega_n{}^2 u(t) \tag{I-32}$$

The Laplace transform of both sides of the equation is taken:

$$(p^2 + 2\zeta\omega_n p + \omega_n{}^2)Y = \frac{\omega_n{}^2}{p} \tag{I-33}$$

This is solved for the variable Y:

$$Y = \frac{\omega_n{}^2}{p(p^2 + 2\zeta\omega_n p + \omega_n{}^2)} = \frac{\omega_n{}^2}{p[(p + \zeta\omega_n)^2 + \omega_n{}^2(1 - \zeta^2)]} \tag{I-34}$$

This equation is separated by partial fractions:

$$Y = \frac{1}{p} - \frac{p + 2\zeta\omega_n}{(p + \zeta\omega_n)^2 + \omega_n^2(1 - \zeta^2)} \qquad \text{(I-35)}$$

as the reader can verify by combining Eq. (I-35) over a common denominator. The solution is found by referring to two transform pairs (a and q) in Table I-1

$$y(t) = u(t) - \frac{1}{\sqrt{1 - \zeta^2}} e^{-\zeta\omega_n t} \sin(\omega_n \sqrt{1 - \zeta^2}\, t + \phi) \qquad \text{(I-36)}$$

where

$$\phi = \tan^{-1} \frac{\sqrt{1 - \zeta^2}}{\zeta} \qquad \text{(I-37)}$$

I-5. Partial-fraction Expansion. The inverse Laplace transformation of rational fractions is required to find the time solution from the transformed equation. The general rational fraction is written

$$Y(p) = \frac{A(p)}{B(p)} \qquad \text{(I-38)}$$

where $A(p)$ and $B(p)$ are polynomials in p. When the roots of $B(p) = 0$ are found, Eq. (I-38) can be written

$$Y(p) = \frac{A(p)}{B(p)} = \frac{A(p)}{(p + p_1)(p + p_2)(p + p_3) \cdots (p + p_q)} \qquad \text{(I-39)}$$

The inverse transformation is carried out by expanding Eq. (I-39) in partial fractions as follows:

$$\frac{A(p)}{B(p)} = \frac{A(p)}{(p + p_1)(p + p_2)(p + p_3) \cdots (p + p_q)}$$
$$= \frac{K_1}{(p + p_1)} + \frac{K_2}{(p + p_2)} + \frac{K_3}{(p + p_3)} + \cdots + \frac{K_q}{(p + p_q)} \qquad \text{(I-40)}$$

Each term in Eq. (I-40) can be found by reference to Table I-1. The total time solution is found by summing the time solution which is found from each term in Eq. (I-40).

The partial-fraction expansion is an important step in the solution. Depending upon the form of $B(p)$, this expansion is carried out as follows:

  a. *If* $B(p)$ *Contains Simple Roots Only.* In this case the K are evaluated by multiplying each side of Eq. (I-40) by $p + p_i$:

$$\frac{(p + p_i) A(p)}{B(p)} = K_1 \frac{p + p_i}{p + p_1} + K_2 \frac{p + p_i}{p + p_2} + \cdots$$
$$+ K_i \frac{p + p_i}{p + p_i} + \cdots + K_q \frac{p + p_i}{p + p_q} \qquad \text{(I-41)}$$

Since $p + p_i$ is a factor in $B(p)$, it is divided out. When p is set equal to $-p_i$, the term on the left becomes a constant. All terms on the right reduce to zero except K_i.   Hence each constant can be evaluated from the equation

$$K_i = \left. \frac{A(p)(p + p_i)}{B(p)} \right|_{p = -p_i} \tag{I-42}$$

The procedure is unaltered if one of the roots is located at the origin. The constant K_0 is evaluated similarly:

$$K_0 = \left. \frac{pA(p)}{B(p)} \right|_{p = 0} \tag{I-43}$$

When complex conjugate roots $(p + \alpha)^2 + \beta^2$ exist, the procedure is similar:

$$K_{j1} = \left. \frac{(p + \alpha + j\beta)A(p)}{B(p)} \right|_{p = -\alpha - j\beta} \tag{I-44}$$

and

$$K_{j2} = \left. \frac{(p + \alpha - j\beta)A(p)}{B(p)} \right|_{p = -\alpha + j\beta} \tag{I-45}$$

Since K_{j1} and K_{j2} are complex conjugate, the sum of the imaginary parts is zero and the sum of the real parts is twice the real part of either K. The two terms

$$\frac{K_{j1}}{p + \alpha + j\beta} \quad \text{and} \quad \frac{K_{j2}}{p + \alpha - j\beta} \tag{I-46}$$

combine into a single term which inverse-transforms into a damped sinusoid.

b. If $B(p)$ Contains Multiple-order Roots.   If the denominator of $Y(p)$ has multiple-order zeros, the procedure of the preceding section cannot be used.   For example, if

$$\frac{A(p)}{B(p)} = \frac{1}{(p + p_1)(p + p_2)^2} \tag{I-47}$$

then the partial expansion must include a second-order term

$$\frac{1}{(p + p_1)(p + p_2)^2} = \frac{K_1}{p + p_1} + \frac{K_{12}}{p + p_2} + \frac{K_{22}}{(p + p_2)^2} \tag{I-48}$$

In general an nth-order root is expanded:

$$\frac{1}{(p + p_1) \cdots (p + p_i)^n} = \frac{K_1}{p + p_1} + \cdots + \frac{K_{ni}}{(p + p_i)^n}$$
$$+ \frac{K_{(n-1)i}}{(p + p_i)^{n-1}} + \cdots + \frac{K_{1i}}{p + p_i} \tag{I-49}$$

The constants K_i associated with first-order roots are evaluated as above. The constant associated with the highest power K_{ni} is evaluated in the same manner as a simple pole.   That is, multiply both sides of Eq. (I-49) by $(p + p_i)^n$ and let $p = -p_i$. All terms on the right side are zero except the K_{ni} term. The left side reduces to a number. K_{ni} is evaluated as follows:

$$K_{ni} = \frac{(p + p_i)^n A(p)}{B(p)} \bigg|_{p = -p_i} \qquad (\text{I-50})$$

The procedure used for simple roots and used to evaluate the constant associated with the highest power K_{ni} is insufficient to evaluate any of the other coefficients. These constants are evaluated by differentiation. Both sides of Eq. (I-49) are multiplied by $(p + p_i)^n$. The resulting equation is differentiated once with respect to p:

$$\frac{d}{dp} \frac{(p + p_i)^n A(p)}{B(p)} = \frac{d}{dp} \frac{(p + p_i)^n}{p + p_1} K_1 + \cdots + K_{(n-1)i}$$
$$+ 2(p + p_i) K_{(n-2)i} + \cdots + (n - 1)(p + p_i)^{n-2} K_{1i} \qquad (\text{I-51})$$

By letting $p = p_i$ all terms on the right except $K_{(n-1)i}$ vanish:

$$K_{(n-1)i} = \frac{d}{dp} \left[\frac{(p + p_i)^n A(p)}{B(p)} \right]_{p = -p_i} \qquad (\text{I-52})$$

The process of differentiating and then setting $p = -p_i$ can be repeated until all the unknown constants are determined.

As an example, consider the partial-fraction expansion of the following transfer function:

$$\frac{A(p)}{B(p)} = \frac{4p^3 + p^2 - 22p + 16}{p(p + 2)(p - 2)^2} \qquad (\text{I-53})$$

The fraction is broken up as follows:

$$\frac{4p^3 + p^2 - 22p + 16}{p(p + 2)(p - 2)^2} = \frac{K_1}{p} + \frac{K_2}{p + 2} + \frac{K_{13}}{p - 2} + \frac{K_{23}}{(p - 2)^2} \qquad (\text{I-54})$$

The constants corresponding to the simple poles are easily found:

$$K_1 = \frac{p(4p^3 + p^2 - 22p + 16)}{p(p + 2)(p - 2)^2} \bigg|_{p = 0} = \frac{16}{(2)(4)} = 2$$

$$K_2 = \frac{(p + 2)(4p^3 + p^2 - 22p + 16)}{p(p + 2)(p - 2)^2} \bigg|_{p = -2} \qquad (\text{I-55})$$

$$= \frac{-32 + 4 + 44 + 16}{(-2)(16)} = \frac{32}{-32} = -1$$

K_{23} is found in a similar fashion:

$$K_{23} = \frac{(p - 2)^2(4p^3 + p^2 - 22p + 16)}{p(p + 2)(p - 2)^2} \bigg|_{p = 2}$$

$$= \frac{32 + 4 - 44 + 16}{2(4)} = \frac{+8}{8} = 1 \qquad (\text{I-56})$$

K_{13} is found by multiplying Eq. (I-54) by $(p - 2)^2$ then differentiating with respect to p:

$$\frac{d}{dp}\left[\frac{4p^3 + p^2 - 22p + 16}{p(p + 2)}\right]_{p=2} = \frac{d}{dp}\left[\left(\frac{K_1}{p} + \frac{K_2}{p + 2}\right)(p - 2)^2\right]_{p=2}$$

$$+ \frac{d}{dp}(p - 2)K_{13} + \frac{d}{dp}K_{23} \quad \text{(I-57)}$$

which reduces to

$$K_{13} = \frac{d}{dp}\left(\frac{4p^3 + p^2 - 22p + 16}{p^2 + 2p}\right)_{p=2}$$

$$= \left[\frac{(p^2 + 2p)(12p^2 + 2p - 22) - (4p^3 + p^2 - 22p + 16)(2p + 2)}{(p^2 + 2p)^2}\right]_{p=2}$$

$$= \frac{(8)(48 + 4 - 22) - (32 + 4 - 44 + 16)(6)}{64} = \frac{192}{64} = 3 \quad \text{(I-58)}$$

Hence the partial-fraction expansion of Eq. (I-53) is written

$$\frac{A(p)}{B(p)} = \frac{2}{p} - \frac{1}{p + 2} + \frac{1}{(p - 2)^2} + \frac{3}{p - 2} \quad \text{(I-59)}$$

I-6. Additional Properties of the Laplace Transform. Some of the relationships involving the Laplace transformation are included in this section. These are often called "theorems."* Detailed proofs are not given for most of these theorems in this text.

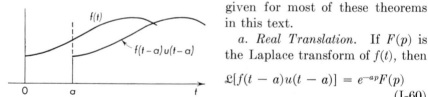

FIG. I-2. Real translation in time.

a. Real Translation. If $F(p)$ is the Laplace transform of $f(t)$, then

$$\mathcal{L}[f(t - a)u(t - a)] = e^{-ap}F(p) \quad \text{(I-60)}$$

Multiplication by e^{-ap} in the complex frequency plane (p plane) results in translation in the time domain. The function $f(t - a)u(t - a)$ is shown shifted in Fig. I-2. As an example of the use of this theorem, suppose it is necessary to find the Laplace transform of one period of a sine wave, as shown in Fig. I-3. The time function can be formed by subtracting from a sine wave another sinusoid which has been shifted in time by $2\pi/\omega$. Mathematically, this is written

$$f(t) = A \sin \omega t - A \sin \omega\left(t - \frac{2\pi}{\omega}\right)u\left[\left(t - \frac{2\pi}{\omega}\right)\right] \quad \text{(I-61)}$$

These are transformed as follows:

$$\mathcal{L}[f(t)] = \frac{A\omega}{p^2 + \omega^2} - \frac{A\omega}{p^2 + \omega^2}e^{-\frac{2\pi}{\omega}p} = \frac{A\omega}{p^2 + \omega^2}\left(1 - e^{-\frac{2\pi}{\omega}p}\right) \quad \text{(I-62)}$$

* See Ref. 18, chap. 8.

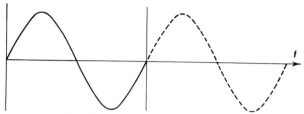

Fig. I-3. One period of a sine wave.

b. *Second Independent Variable.* If $F(p,a)$ is the transform of $f(t,a)$, then the following relation holds:

$$\mathcal{L}_t \left[\lim_{a \to a_0} f(t,a) \right] = \lim_{a \to a_0} F(p,a) \tag{I-63}$$

where $\mathcal{L}_t$ means the Laplace transform with respect to time. As an example of the use of this equation consider the transform pair

$$\mathcal{L}_t e^{-\alpha t} \sin \omega t = \frac{\omega}{(p + \alpha)^2 + \omega^2} \tag{I-64}$$

given in Table I-1. By taking the limit as α approaches zero, a second pair results:

$$\mathcal{L} \sin \omega t = \frac{\omega}{p^2 + \omega^2} \tag{I-65}$$

In a similar fashion differentiation, with respect to the quantity a, is permissible.

$$\mathcal{L}_t \left[\frac{df(t,a)}{da} \right] = \frac{dF}{da}(p,a) \tag{I-66}$$

As an example differentiate the transform pair

$$\mathcal{L}_t e^{-at} = \frac{1}{p + a} \tag{I-67}$$

and obtain another pair

$$\mathcal{L}_t t e^{-at} = \frac{1}{(p + a)^2} \tag{I-68}$$

In a similar fashion, the integral, with respect to the quantity a, can be found:

$$\mathcal{L}_t \left[\int_{a_1}^{a} f(t,\alpha) \, d\alpha \right] = \int_{a_1}^{a} F(p,\alpha) \, d\alpha \tag{I-69}$$

c. *Final-value and Initial-value Theorems.* These are extremely valuable theorems for servo design. These theorems are unique, since they permit the finding of a time function at either $t = 0$ or $t = \infty$ directly from the transform without inverting the transformed equation.

Final-value theorem:

$$\lim_{t \to \infty} y(t) = \lim_{p \to 0} pY(p) \qquad (I\text{-}70)$$

provided $y(t)$ is stable; that is, all poles of $pY(p)$ are in the left half plane.

Initial-value theorem:

$$\lim_{t \to 0} y(t) = \lim_{p \to \infty} pY(p) \qquad (I\text{-}71)$$

provided the limit exists. Application of these theorems is shown in Chap. 3.

d. The Convolution Integral. The convolution integral is expressed as follows:

If $F_1(p)$ is the Laplace transform of $f_1(t)$ and $F_2(p)$ is the Laplace transform of $f_2(t)$, then

$$\mathfrak{L} \int_0^t f_1(\tau) f_2(t - \tau) \, d\tau = F_1(p) F_2(p) \qquad (I\text{-}72)$$

The integral on the left is called the "convolution integral," and the proof is included in many texts on Laplace transforms.[18]

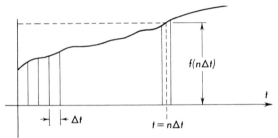

Fig. I-4. Driving function represented by a series of pulses.

The importance of this integral can be understood from a physical argument. In Fig. I-4 is shown a driving function $f(t)$ which is the input to a linear system and which is approximated by a series of pulses. Since the system which is shown in Fig. I-5 is linear, the total output can be approximated by a sum of the outputs due to each of these pulses. Suppose $h(t)$ is the response of the system to a unit pulse at the origin. The response or output of a system at time t to a unit pulse applied at time $n \, \Delta t$ is

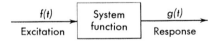

Fig. I-5. Output from a linear system.

$$h(t - n \, \Delta t) \qquad (I\text{-}73)$$

The response or output of the system due to a pulse of area $\Delta t f(n \, \Delta t)$ is

$$h(t - n \, \Delta t) f(n \, \Delta t) \, \Delta t \qquad (I\text{-}74)$$

The output due to all pulses up to time t is

$$g(t) = \sum_{n=0}^{N} h(t - n\,\Delta t)f(n\,\Delta t)\,\Delta t \tag{I-75}$$

If the variable τ equals $n\,\Delta t$ and if the limit is approached so that $\Delta t \to 0$, as $n \to \infty$,

$$n\,\Delta t \to \tau \qquad \text{and} \qquad N\,\Delta t \to t \tag{I-76}$$

The sum becomes an integral, and

$$g(t) = \int_0^t h(t - \tau)f(\tau)\,d\tau \tag{I-77}$$

where $h(t)$ is the response of the system to a unit impulse $\delta(t)$.

Hence the output of a linear system is found by "convolving" the input function $f(t)$ with the impulse response $h(t)$. The Laplace transform of Eq. (I-77) yields the important result

$$G(p) = H(p)F(p) \tag{I-78}$$

Hence the Laplace-transformed output $G(p)$ of a linear system is the product of the Laplace-transformed input $G(p)$ and the transformed impulse response $H(p)$. $H(p)$ is defined as the transfer function in Chap. 1.

CLASSICAL SOLUTION OF DIFFERENTIAL EQUATIONS

II-1. Introduction.   The synthesis of servo systems as discussed in this text does not require a knowledge of Laplace transform.   Although the Laplace transform is used and discussed (cf. Appendix I), an engineer has no handicap in the study of basic servo design because of a lack of Laplace-transform knowledge.

Ordinary linear differential equations can be solved by the classical method.[40,56]   This method is presented here for two reasons:

1. To show the similarities between the classical method and operational calculus—the Laplace transformation

2. To provide a basis of servo design for engineers who are familiar only with the classical approach

II-2. Linear Differential Equations.   A linear differential equation, of the type commonly encountered in servo design, of nth order is written

$$a_n \frac{d^n y}{dt^n} + a_{(n-1)} \frac{d^{(n-1)} y}{dt^{(n-1)}} + \cdots + a_1 \frac{dy}{dt} + a_0 y = f(t) \qquad \text{(II-1)}$$

All the coefficients a_i are constant, independent of t, y, and higher derivatives of y.   Time t is the independent variable, y is the dependent variable, and $f(t)$ is the driving function.   A function y that satisfies the equation and depends upon t is a solution of Eq. (II-1).

The performance of a linear feedback control system or of any linear dynamic system is found by writing and solving, subject to certain initial conditions, differential equations of the form of Eq. (II-1).   Several methods are available for solution of linear differential equations: the Laplace-transform solution, presented in Appendix I, and the "classical method."   Any linear, constant-coefficient, differential equation of the form of Eq. (II-1) has a solution which can be separated into two parts, as follows:

a. Transient Component.   The solution to Eq. (II-1) that results when the driving function is set equal to zero [$f(t) = 0$].   This differential equation is known as a homogeneous equation, and its solution contains

n arbitrary constants

$$a_n \frac{d^n y}{dt^n} + a_{n-1} \frac{d^{n-1}y}{dt^{n-1}} + \cdots a_1 \frac{dy}{dt} + a_0 y = 0 \qquad \text{(II-2)}$$

where n is the order of the equation.

b. Steady-state component is any particular solution y_{ss} that satisfies Eq. (II-1) and does not contain any terms which can be incorporated into the transient solution.

The complete solution is the sum of the transient and steady-state components. The n arbitrary constants of the transient component are determined by the initial conditions. The complete solution is

$$y_c = y_t + y_{ss} \qquad \text{(II-3)}$$

It is important to notice that the names given the two components, i.e., transient and steady state, are particularly chosen for the servo

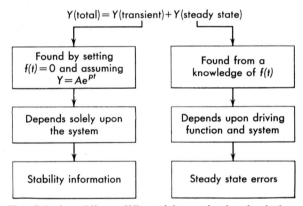

Y(total) = Y(transient) + Y(steady state)

Found by setting $f(t) = 0$ and assuming $Y = Ae^{pt}$	Found from a knowledge of $f(t)$
Depends solely upon the system	Depends upon driving function and system
Stability information	Steady state errors

Fig. II-1. Solution of linear differential equation by classical method.

engineer. In this sense a transient component is defined as the solution for the mentioned homogeneous differential equation and may contain both terms that die out with time (bounded) and also terms that build up with time (unbounded).

Figure II-1 shows a procedure diagram for finding the solution of Eq. (II-1). The total solution is divided into two parts: transient and steady-state components. The components are found separately and added later. Initial conditions are applied to y_{total}. The general form of the transient component found by setting $f(t) = 0$ depends only upon the constants of the system and, except for amplitude, is independent of $f(t)$ and the initial conditions. The nature of stability, as defined in Chap. 1, is based upon a knowledge of critical frequencies and time constants of the transient solution. For linear systems, stability does not depend upon transient amplitude and hence is independent of the driving function and the initial conditions. Servo stability is determined from the transient behavior of the system (the transient solution) only. If the transients die out, the system is stable; if the transients build up, the system is unstable; if the transients neither build up nor die out (sustained oscillation), the system is marginally stable. Hence the stability is determined from the transient solution.

The steady-state solution, which can be conveniently found for certain types of commonly encountered inputs, determines the steady-state error of the control system.

II-3. Classical Solution of Linear Differential Equations—Transient. The procedure for finding the transient component of the solution of linear differential equations with constant coefficients is

1. Set the driving function $f(t) = 0$.
2. Assume a solution of the form

$$y = A e^{pt} \tag{II-4}$$

3. Substitute Eq. (II-4) into the differential equation, cancel $A e^{pt}$, and thus obtain the characteristic equation.

4. Find the roots of the characteristic polynomial. Each distinct root gives rise to a distinct solution of the form of Eq. (II-4). Exceptional cases are discussed later.

5. The location of the roots yields stability information about the system.

As an example of this procedure, consider the position servo of Chap. 1:

$$\frac{d^2c}{dt^2} + 2\zeta\omega_n \frac{dc}{dt} + \omega_n^2 c = \omega_n^2 u(t) \tag{II-5}$$

where ζ is the damping ratio, ω_n the undamped natural resonant frequency. $u(t)$ is a unit step function which is shown in Fig. I-1. Setting the driving function $u(t)$ equal to zero,

$$\frac{d^2c}{dt^n} + 2\zeta\omega_n \frac{dc}{dt} + \omega_n^2 c = 0 \tag{II-6}$$

Assuming a solution $c = A e^{pt}$, substituting into Eq. (II-6), and finding the characteristic polynomial:

$$p^2 A e^{pt} + 2\zeta\omega_n p A e^{pt} + \omega_n^2 A e^{pt} = 0 \tag{II-7}$$

which reduces to

$$p^2 + 2\zeta\omega_n p + \omega_n^2 = 0 \tag{II-8}$$

Notice the similarity of this equation with the left side of Eq. (I-33). Substitution of $y = e^{pt}$ results in an algebraic equation in p. The Laplace transformation converts a differential equation into an algebraic equation.

The roots of the characteristic equation [Eq. (II-8)] are found from the binomial equation

$$p = -\zeta\omega_n \pm \omega_n \sqrt{\zeta^2 - 1} \qquad (II\text{-}9)$$

The transient component for this case now consists of two terms

$$c = A_1 e^{-(\zeta\omega_n + \omega_n\sqrt{\zeta^2-1})t} + A_2 e^{-(\zeta\omega_n - \omega_n\sqrt{\zeta^2-1})t} \qquad (II\text{-}10)$$

In Eq. (II-10), the system is stable if the coefficient of t in the exponential is negative, since e^{-at} dies out with time when the real part of a is greater than zero. If the coefficient is positive, the solution builds up with time and the system is unstable.

Commonly, the damping ratio ζ is less than unity, and the roots of Eq. (II-9) can be written

$$p = -\zeta\omega_n \pm j\omega_n \sqrt{1 - \zeta^2} \qquad (II\text{-}11)$$

where $j = \sqrt{-1}$ and for ζ in the range $0 < \zeta < 1$ the roots are complex. The transient solution is

$$c(t) = e^{-\zeta\omega_n t}(A \sin \omega_n \sqrt{1 - \zeta^2}\, t + B \cos \omega_n \sqrt{1 - \zeta^2}\, t) \qquad (II\text{-}12)$$

The roots given by Eq. (II-11) are located on a plot which is shown in Fig. II-2. This plot, which is called the p plane, has coordinates: The real coordinate is on the horizontal axis; the imaginary on the vertical axis. Complex roots always appear in conjugate pairs; the number of roots is the same as the order of the equation.

Since Eq. (II-12) is multiplied by a negative exponential term $e^{-\zeta\omega_n t}$, the transient component damps out with time. As t becomes large, $e^{-\zeta\omega_n t}$ becomes small, since $\zeta\omega_n > 0$; hence the system is stable.

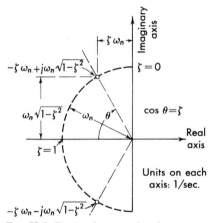

FIG. II-2. Roots of a second-order system in the p plane.

II-4. Exceptional Cases of the Transient Component. Certain special cases of root locations need be considered. In general, the characteristic equation, which is found from Eq. (II-2) by substituting $y = Ae^{pt}$ and canceling Ae^{pt}, is

$$a_n A p^n e^{pt} + a_{n-1} A p^{(n-1)} e^{pt} + \cdots + a_1 A p e^{pt} + a_0 A e^{pt} = 0$$
$$a_n p^n + a_{n-1} p^{n-1} + \cdots + a_1 p + a_0 = 0 \qquad (II\text{-}13)$$

In general the polynomial in the left-hand member can be factored into n terms:

$$(p - p_1)(p - p_2) \cdots (p - p_n) = 0 \qquad (II\text{-}14)$$

If all the roots $p_1, p_2, \ldots, p_n$ are different, the transient component is a sum of n exponential terms

$$y = A_1 e^{p_1 t} + A_2 e^{p_2 t} + \cdots + A_n e^{p_n t} \tag{II-15}$$

As an example consider the equation

$$\frac{d^2 y}{dt^2} + \frac{dy}{dt} - 6y = f(t) \tag{II-16}$$

The characteristic equation is found by setting $f(t) = 0$ and by substituting $y = A e^{pt}$ with the result

$$p^2 + p - 6 = 0 \qquad \text{or} \qquad (p + 3)(p - 2) = 0 \tag{II-17}$$

which yields two roots

$$p = -3 \qquad \text{and} \qquad p = +2 \tag{II-18}$$

The transient solution is

$$y = A_1 e^{-3t} + A_2 e^{+2t} \tag{II-19}$$

This system is unstable, since e^{+2t} becomes large with increasing time.

If any of the roots are repeated, that is, if $p_1 = p_2$ or if $p_3 = p_4 = p_5$ etc., the transient component takes a different form. For example, consider the equation

$$\frac{d^3 y}{dt^3} - 3 \frac{d^2 y}{dt^2} + 4y = 0 \tag{II-20}$$

The characteristic equation, found by substituting $y = e^{pt}$ into Eq. (II-20), is

$$p^3 - 3p^2 + 4 = 0 \tag{II-21}$$

The roots of Eq. (II-21) are $p = -1, +2$, and $+2$, as can be verified by multiplying $(p + 1)(p - 2)^2$. Corresponding to the root -1, a solution $A_1 e^{-t}$ results. The double root 2 yields a solution

$$(A_2 + A_3 t) e^{+2t} \tag{II-22}$$

as can be verified by direct substitution into Eq. (II-20). The complete transient component is

$$y(t) = A_1 e^{-t} + (A_2 + A_3 t) e^{2t} \tag{II-23}$$

The general rule is as follows:

1. If a double root occurs at p_1, the transient component is

$$(A_1 + A_2 t) e^{p_1 t} \tag{II-24}$$

2. If a triple root occurs at p_2, the transient component is

$$(A_1 + A_2 t + A_3 t^2) e^{p_2 t} \tag{II-25}$$

3. If k roots are alike, all of value p_n, the transient component is

$$(A_1 + A_2 t + A_3 t^2 + \cdots + A_k t^{k-1}) e^{p_n t} \qquad \text{(II-26)}$$

If the roots are complex conjugate, the transient component is found as above; however, a special form for $y(t)$ is used. For example, if the roots are $-a + jb$ and $-a - jb$, the transient component is

$$\begin{aligned} y &= A_1 e^{(-a+jb)t} + A_2 e^{(-a-jb)t} \qquad &\text{(II-27)} \\ &= e^{-at}(A_1 e^{jbt} + A_2 e^{-jbt}) \end{aligned}$$

Since $e^{\pm jbt} = \cos bt \pm j \sin bt$, Eq. (II-27) can be rewritten as

$$y = e^{-at}(B_1 \cos bt + B_2 \sin bt) \qquad \text{(II-28)}$$

where $\qquad B_1 = A_1 + A_2 \qquad$ and $\qquad B_2 = j(A_1 - A_2) \qquad$ (II-29)

Equation (II-28) can also be written

$$y = A e^{-at} \sin (bt + \theta) \qquad \text{(II-30)}$$

where $\qquad A = \sqrt{B_1{}^2 + B_2{}^2} \qquad$ and $\qquad \theta = \tan^{-1} \dfrac{B_1}{B_2} \qquad$ (II-31)

Either form, Eq. (II-28) or (II-29), is more suitable for servo design than Eq. (II-27).

II-5. The Steady-state Component. The nature of the system stability, which can be determined from the transient component or the characteristic equation, is independent of the driving function. For servo systems, steady-state errors are usually derived for only a few special inputs. The classical method for finding the steady-state component is applicable to driving functions[40] of the form

$$A t^m e^{at} \cos (\omega t + \theta) \qquad \text{(II-32)}$$

Several special inputs will be considered. Consider the second-order equation of Chap. 1 with a constant $[r = u(t)]$ driving function of unit magnitude

$$\frac{d^2 c}{dt^2} + 2\zeta\omega_n \frac{dc}{dt} + \omega_n{}^2 c = \omega_n{}^2 u(t) \qquad \text{(II-33)}$$

where $u(t)$ is a unit step function (or a constant driving function).

Assume a steady-state solution which has the form of a sum of terms comprising the driving function plus any terms found by differentiating the driving function. In this case the driving function is a constant; hence assume

$$c_{ss} = c_{\text{steady state}} = A = \text{a constant} \qquad \text{(II-34)}$$

and substitute for c in Eq. (II-33) to obtain

$$\frac{d^2 c_{ss}}{dt^2} + 2\zeta\omega_n \frac{dc_{ss}}{dt} + \omega_n{}^2 c_{ss} = \omega_n{}^2 \qquad \text{(II-35)}$$

when $c_{ss} = A$, a constant; $d^2A/dt^2 = 0 = dA/dt$; and

$$\omega_n{}^2 A = \omega_n{}^2 \tag{II-36}$$

with the result $A = 1$ and

$$c_{ss} = 1 \tag{II-37}$$

The steady-state solution for a ramp input ($r = vt$) is formed from the driving function and derivatives of the driving function

$$c_{ss} = At + B \tag{II-38}$$

When Eq. (II-38) is substituted into the differential equation

$$\frac{d^2c}{dt^2} + 2\zeta\omega_n \frac{dc}{dt} + \omega_n{}^2 c = \omega_n{}^2 f(t) \tag{II-39}$$

with $f(t) = vt$, the following expression results:

$$\frac{d^2c_{ss}}{dt^2} + 2\zeta\omega_n \frac{dc_{ss}}{dt} + \omega_n{}^2 c_{ss} = \omega_n{}^2 vt \tag{II-40}$$

When c_{ss} from Eq. (II-38) is substituted into Eq. (II-40),

$$2\zeta\omega_n A + \omega_n{}^2(At + B) = \omega_n{}^2 vt \tag{II-41}$$

Equating functions of time on both sides of the equation and equating the constant on both sides,

$$\omega_n{}^2 A = \omega_n{}^2 v$$
$$2\zeta\omega_n A + \omega_n{}^2 B = 0 \tag{II-42}$$

with the result

$$A = v \quad \text{and} \quad B = -\frac{2\zeta}{\omega_n} A = \frac{2\zeta v}{\omega_n} \tag{II-43}$$

The general steady-state component is formed as follows:

1. Write the terms of the driving function $f(t)$ and any other terms obtained by differentiating $f(t)$.

2. If any term in the group found in 1 is also a term in the transient component, all terms must be multiplied by t^k. (k is the lowest integral exponent of t that will make all the terms in the steady-state component different from any term in the transient component.)

3. Multiply each term found in 2 by a constant, and sum the terms.

4. Substitute the assumed steady-state solution into the differential equation, and equate like terms on both sides of the equation.

5. Solve for the constants.

As another example consider the steady-state solution for a driving function of the form $r = at^2$ driving the system of Eq. (II-39):

$$\frac{d^2c}{dt^2} + 2\zeta\omega_n \frac{dc}{dt} + \omega_n{}^2 c = \omega_n{}^2 at^2 \tag{II-44}$$

Assume a steady-state solution as follows:

t^2 found from the driving function
t, 1 found by differentiating the driving function

When each of these terms is multiplied by a constant and summed, the steady-state component is

$$c_{ss} = At^2 + Bt + D \qquad\qquad\qquad \text{(II-45)}$$

Notice that no terms of the driving function appear in the transient component, so in this case procedure 2 above can be ignored.

Equation (II-45) is substituted into Eq. (II-44) as follows:

$$2A + 2\zeta\omega_n(2At + B) + \omega_n{}^2(At^2 + Bt + D) = \omega_n{}^2 a t^2 \quad \text{(II-46)}$$

This expression is rearranged:

$$t^2(A\omega_n{}^2) + t(4A\zeta\omega_n + B\omega_n{}^2) + (2A + 2\zeta\omega_n B + \omega_n{}^2 D) = \omega_n{}^2 a t^2 \quad \text{(II-47)}$$

The constants A, B, and D are found by equating terms on each side of the equation:

$$A\omega_n{}^2 = \omega_n{}^2 a$$
$$4A\zeta\omega_n + B\omega_n{}^2 = 0 \qquad\qquad\qquad \text{(II-48)}$$
$$2A + 2\zeta\omega_n B + \omega_n{}^2 D = 0$$

Solving these equations,

$$A = a \qquad B = -\frac{4\zeta}{\omega_n} a$$
$$D = \frac{2a}{\omega_n{}^2}(4\zeta^2 - 1) \qquad\qquad\qquad \text{(II-49)}$$

and the steady-state component is

$$c_{ss}(t) = at^2 - \frac{4\zeta}{\omega_n} at + \frac{2a}{\omega_n{}^2}(4\zeta^2 - 1) \qquad\qquad \text{(II-50)}$$

II-6. The Complete Solution. The complete solution is formed by adding the transient component to the steady-state component. As an example, consider the complete solution to the system of Eq. (II-33), which represents the differential equation for the position servo of Chap. 1. The problem is to find the output-shaft position after the application of a step function of position $r(t) = u(t)$. The initial conditions are zero.

The transient component is taken from Eq. (II-12), and the steady state from Eq. (II-37). The total solution is the sum of these two equations

$$c(t) = e^{-\zeta\omega_n t}(A \sin \omega_n \sqrt{1 - \zeta^2}\, t + B \cos \omega_n \sqrt{1 - \zeta^2}\, t) + 1 \quad \text{(II-51)}$$

Zero initial conditions means that at $t = 0$, $c = 0$, and $dc/dt = 0$. Application of these equations for $c = 0$ at $t = 0$

$$B + 1 = 0 \qquad \text{hence } B = -1$$

and for $dc/dt = 0$ at $t = 0$

$$\omega_n \sqrt{1 - \zeta^2}\, A + B(-\zeta\omega_n) = 0 \qquad \text{hence } A = \frac{\zeta}{\sqrt{1 - \zeta^2}} \qquad \text{(II-52)}$$

The complete solution is

$$c(t) = 1 - e^{-\zeta\omega_n t}\left(\cos \omega_n \sqrt{1 - \zeta^2}\, t + \frac{\zeta}{\sqrt{1 - \zeta^2}} \sin \omega_n \sqrt{1 - \zeta^2}\, t\right) \qquad \text{(II-53)}$$

This expression is plotted for several values of ζ and as a function of time in Chap. 1.

Equation (II-53) can be reduced, with the aid of Eq. (II-30):

$$c(t) = u(t) - \frac{e^{-\zeta\omega_n t}}{\sqrt{1 - \zeta^2}} \sin\left(\omega_n \sqrt{1 - \zeta^2}\, t + \phi\right) \qquad \text{(II-54)}$$

where $\phi = \tan^{-1} \sqrt{1 - \zeta^2}/\zeta$ and $u(t)$ has been substituted for 1, since these are equivalent when $c(t)$ is defined equal to zero for $t < 0$. In this form, the solution of Eq. (II-54) is identical with Eq. (I-36) found by Laplace-transform methods.

APPENDIX III

ROOTS OF EQUATIONS

III-1. Introduction. Basic to the solution of ordinary differential equations is the problem of finding roots of high-degree polynomials. Both the Laplace-transform and the classical methods are based upon knowledge of the roots of the characteristic equation. This appendix summarizes techniques for finding roots.

III-2. The Quadratic. The second-degree polynomial, the quadratic

$$ap^2 + bp + c = 0 \tag{III-1}$$

is solved easily by completing the square. The roots are given by the familiar equation

$$p_{1,2} = \frac{-b \pm \sqrt{b^2 - 4ac}}{2a} \tag{III-2}$$

III-3. The Cubic. For polynomials with real coefficients, at least one root of a cubic is real. If this one real root is found, the remaining two are easily found from the quadratic equation [Eq. (III-2)]. To find the real root for the equation

$$f(p) = p^3 + ap^2 + bp + c = 0 \tag{III-3}$$

follow the procedure:

1. Make a rough plot of $f(p)$ as a function of p to determine a value of p where $f(p)$ changes sign. This may be done with a table instead of a plot.

2. Guess a value p_1 that may make $f(p) = 0$.

3. Compute the second guess from the equation

$$p_2 = p_1 - \frac{f(p_1)}{f'(p_1)} \tag{III-4}$$

where

$$f'(p_1) = \frac{df}{dp}\bigg|_{p=p_1} \tag{III-5}$$

and continue the process until the desired accuracy is achieved. This method is known as "Newton's method."

As an example, consider the cubic

$$p^3 - 3p^2 - 2p + 5 = 0 \tag{III-6}$$

Corresponding values of p and $f(p)$ are

p	$f(p)$
0	5
1	1
2	-3

$$(III-7)$$

Since $f(p)$ changed sign between 1 and 2, a root must lie in this range (1 to 2). As a first guess take $p = 1.5$. To find the second approximation, evaluate

$$f(1.5) = (1.5)^3 - 3(1.5)^2 - 2(1.5) + 5 = -1.37$$
$$f'(1.5) = 3(1.5)^2 - 6(1.5) - 2 = -4.25 \qquad (III-8)$$

and the second guess is

$$p_2 = p_1 - \frac{f(p_1)}{f'(p_1)} = 1.5 - \frac{-1.37}{-4.25} = 1.18 \qquad (III-9)$$

To find the next approximation

$$f(1.18) = (1.18)^3 - 3(1.18)^2 - 2(1.18) + 5 = +0.10$$
$$f'(1.18) = 3(1.18)^2 - 6(1.18) - 2 = -4.90 \qquad (III-10)$$

and the third approximation is

$$p_3 = p_2 - \frac{f(p_2)}{f'(p_2)} = 1.18 - \frac{+0.10}{-4.90} = 1.20 \qquad (III-11)$$

If more accuracy is desired, the process can be repeated as necessary. The remaining roots are found from the quadratic that remains when $p - 1.20$ is factored from the original cubic:

$$p^3 - 3p^2 - 2p + 5 = (p - 1.20)(p^2 - 1.80p - 4.16) \qquad (III-12)$$

The quadratic factors into

$$\begin{aligned} p_1 &= 3.125 \\ p_2 &= -1.325 \\ p_3 &= 1.20 \end{aligned} \qquad (III-13)$$

and

Verification of the approximation expression follows from a consideration of Fig. III-1. If p_1 is the first guess, the second guess p_2 is found from the equation

$$\tan \phi = \frac{f(p_1)}{p_2 - p_1} \qquad (III-14)$$

But $\tan \phi$ is the slope of the $f(p)$ curve at the point p_1, or

$$\tan \phi = f'(p_1) = \frac{f(p_1)}{p_1 - p_2} \qquad (III-15)$$

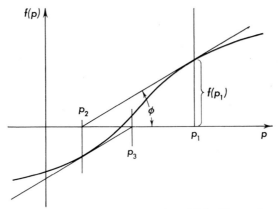

$f(p)$

P_2

ϕ

$f(p_1)$

P_1 p

P_3

FIG. III-1. A sketch which geometrically exhibits Newton's method.

This is rearranged into the more usable form

$$p_2 = p_1 - \frac{f(p_1)}{f'(p_1)} \tag{III-16}$$

III-4. Synthetic Division. Because of the necessity of frequently dividing polynomials, a shorter method of division, called synthetic division, has been devised. This method is identical with ordinary algebraic division except that some of the unnecessary writing has been eliminated. The division of $p^3 - 3p^2 - 2p + 5$ by $p - 1.20$ is carried out by both methods as follows:

$$
\begin{array}{r}
p^2 - 1.80p - 4.16 \quad \text{(Ans.)} \\
p - 1.20 \enclose{longdiv}{p^3 - 3p^2 - 2p + 5} \\
\underline{p^3 - 1.20p^2} \\
0 - 1.80p^2 - 2p \\
\underline{- 1.80p^2 + 2.16p} \\
- 4.16p + 5 \\
\underline{- 4.16p + 5} \\
0
\end{array}
\tag{III-17}
$$

$$
\begin{array}{r}
p + 1.20 \enclose{longdiv}{1 - 3 \quad\quad - 2 \quad + 5} \\
1.20 \quad - 2.16 - 5 \\
\hline
1 - 1.80 \quad - 4.16 \,|\,| \, 0 \\
p^2 - 1.80p - 4.16 \ \text{(Ans.)}
\end{array}
\tag{III-18}
$$

The sign in the divisor is changed to permit addition rather than subtraction, and only the coefficients of p are written.

III-5. Descartes' Rules. Often the problem of finding roots of high-order polynomials is aided by means of the following rules due to Descartes:

1. The number of positive real roots of an equation $f(p) = 0$ is no more than the number of variations in signs among the coefficients of $f(p)$.

2. The number of negative real roots of the equation is no more than the number of variations in the signs of the equation $f(-p) = 0$.

For example, consider the polynomial

$$f(p) = p^4 + 7p^2 - 15p - 2 = 0 \tag{III-19}$$

for which
$$f(-p) = p^4 + 7p^2 + 15p - 2 \tag{III-20}$$

The sign changes of $f(p)$ are $+ + - -$ or one. Hence $f(p) = 0$ has at most one real root. The sign changes of $f(-p)$ are $+ + + -$ or one, and $f(p) = 0$ has at most one negative root.

III-6. Higher-degree Algebraic Equations. The difficulty of finding the roots of higher-degree equations increases considerably as the degree increases. Of the methods available the root locus, described in Chap. 4, is quite direct. Of the analytical methods, the Graeffe, or root-squaring, method is available. Because good accounts of this method appear in many places in the mathematical and engineering literature,[56] it will not be detailed here.

USE OF DETERMINANTS

IV-1. Definition of a Determinant. The theory of determinants is a mathematical means useful for the systematic solution of simultaneous equations, as in Chap. 2. A determinant is an ordered array of quantities y_{ij} symbolized by straight-line brackets and manipulated according to rules set out below:

$$
\begin{vmatrix}
y_{11} & y_{12} & \cdots & y_{1n} \\
y_{21} & y_{22} & \cdots & y_{2n} \\
y_{31} & y_{32} & \cdots & y_{3n} \\
\cdot & \cdot & & \cdot \\
\cdot & \cdot & & \cdot \\
\cdot & \cdot & & \cdot \\
y_{n1} & y_{n2} & & y_{nn}
\end{vmatrix}
\tag{IV-1}
$$

The determinant indicated in Eq. (IV-1) is termed as of nth order, since there are n horizontal rows and n vertical columns. The determinant, which is a square array having the same number of columns as rows, contains n^2 elements. The position of an element in the determinant is identified by the subscripts

$$
\text{Row}\underset{\uparrow\ \uparrow}{\quad y_{i\ j}\quad}\text{Column}
\tag{IV-2}
$$

The major diagonal of a determinant is the line through the elements y_{ii}. These elements form a sloping line starting with y_{11} and extending to y_{nn}.

IV-2. Expansion of a Determinant. The value of a determinant is obtained by expansion. For example, a second-order determinant is expanded

$$
\begin{vmatrix}
y_{11} & y_{12} \\
y_{21} & y_{22}
\end{vmatrix}
= y_{12}y_{22} - y_{12}y_{21}
\tag{IV-3}
$$

and a third-order determinant is expanded

$$\Delta = \begin{vmatrix} y_{11} & y_{12} & y_{13} \\ y_{21} & y_{22} & y_{23} \\ y_{31} & y_{32} & y_{33} \end{vmatrix} = y_{11} \begin{vmatrix} y_{22} & y_{23} \\ y_{32} & y_{33} \end{vmatrix} - y_{21} \begin{vmatrix} y_{12} & y_{13} \\ y_{32} & y_{33} \end{vmatrix}$$

$$+ y_{31} \begin{vmatrix} y_{12} & y_{13} \\ y_{22} & y_{23} \end{vmatrix} \qquad \text{(IV-4)}$$

Each of the second-order determinants is easily expanded, yielding

$$y_{11}y_{22}y_{33} - y_{11}y_{32}y_{23} - y_{21}y_{12}y_{33} + y_{21}y_{32}y_{13} + y_{31}y_{12}y_{23} - y_{31}y_{22}y_{13}$$
$$\text{(IV-5)}$$

In general a determinant is expanded in terms of its principal minors. The minor Δ_{ij} of an element of a determinant Δ is the determinant found by canceling the ith row and the jth column. For the fourth-order determinant

$$\begin{vmatrix} y_{11} & y_{12} & y_{13} & y_{14} \\ y_{21} & y_{22} & y_{23} & y_{24} \\ y_{31} & y_{32} & y_{33} & y_{34} \\ y_{41} & y_{42} & y_{43} & y_{44} \end{vmatrix} \qquad \text{(IV-6)}$$

the minor of Δ_{21} as found by canceling the second row and first column is

$$\Delta_{21} = \begin{vmatrix} y_{12} & y_{13} & y_{14} \\ y_{32} & y_{33} & y_{34} \\ y_{42} & y_{43} & y_{44} \end{vmatrix} \qquad \text{(IV-7)}$$

The principal minor is one less order than the original determinant. When a minor Δ_{ij} is multiplied by $(-1)^{i+j}$, the result

$$(-1)^{i+j}\Delta_{ij} \qquad \text{(IV-8)}$$

is termed the "cofactor." Hence the cofactor is a signed minor

$$\text{Cofactor} = (-1)^{i+j} \text{(minor)} \qquad \text{(IV-9)}$$

The $(-1)^{i+j}$ quantity can be determined by counting—plus, minus, plus, minus—starting plus on y_{11} and continuing in a horizontal or vertical path until the y_{ij} element is reached.

The expansion of a determinant by means of minors consists of a series of consecutive reductions, such as

$$\Delta = y_{11}\Delta_{11} - y_{21}\Delta_{21} + y_{31}\Delta_{31} \qquad \text{(IV-10)}$$

for a third-order determinant. Here the determinant Δ is expanded along a column. An expansion along a row is as follows:

$$\Delta = y_{11}\Delta_{11} - y_{12}\Delta_{12} + y_{13}\Delta_{13} \qquad \text{(IV-11)}$$

IV-3. Theorems Concerning Determinants. The following theorems are stated, without proof, for the purpose of simplifying the evaluation of a determinant. These theorems can be verified easily by expanding a determinant.

1. The value of a determinant is not changed if its rows are changed to columns and columns to rows.

$$\begin{vmatrix} a_1 & b_1 & c_1 \\ a_2 & b_2 & c_2 \\ a_3 & b_3 & c_3 \end{vmatrix} = \begin{vmatrix} a_1 & a_2 & a_3 \\ b_1 & b_2 & b_3 \\ c_1 & c_2 & c_3 \end{vmatrix} \qquad \text{(IV-12)}$$

2. The sign of a determinant is changed if any two rows or columns are interchanged.

$$\begin{vmatrix} a_1 & b_1 & c_1 \\ a_2 & b_2 & c_2 \\ a_3 & b_3 & c_3 \end{vmatrix} = - \begin{vmatrix} a_1 & c_1 & b_1 \\ a_2 & c_2 & b_2 \\ a_3 & c_3 & b_3 \end{vmatrix} \qquad \text{(IV-13)}$$

3. If each element of one column or of one row be multiplied by a function f, the value of the determinant is multiplied by f:

$$\begin{vmatrix} a_1 & fb_1 & c_1 \\ a_2 & fb_2 & c_2 \\ a_3 & fb_3 & c_3 \end{vmatrix} = f \begin{vmatrix} a_1 & b_1 & c_1 \\ a_2 & b_2 & c_2 \\ a_3 & b_3 & c_3 \end{vmatrix} \qquad \text{(IV-14)}$$

4. The value of a determinant is not changed if the elements of one column or row are all multiplied by a quantity K and are added to or subtracted from the corresponding elements of another column or row:

$$\begin{vmatrix} a_1 & b_1 & c_1 \\ a_2 & b_2 & c_2 \\ a_3 & b_3 & c_3 \end{vmatrix} = \begin{vmatrix} a_1 + Kc_1 & b_1 & c_1 \\ a_2 + Kc_2 & b_2 & c_2 \\ a_3 + Kc_3 & b_3 & c_3 \end{vmatrix} \qquad \text{(IV-15)}$$

APPENDIX V

HURWITZ'S STABILITY CRITERION[27,41]

V-1. Introduction. The general form of the closed-loop transfer function of a feedback system is expressed as a quotient of two polynomials in the operator p. If R is the input to the system and C is the output, then C and R are related in the following manner:

$$\frac{C(p)}{R(p)} = \frac{N(p)}{D(p)} = \frac{b_l p^l + b_{l-1} p^{l-1} + \cdots + b_1 p + b_0}{a_n p^n + a_{n-1} p^{n-1} + \cdots + a_1 p + a_0} \quad \text{(V-1)}$$

The transient component depends on the roots of the characteristic polynomial $D(p)$. This yields the characteristic equation

$$a_n p^n + a_{n-1} p^{n-1} + \cdots + a_1 p + a_0 = 0 \quad \text{(V-2)}$$

In a physical system, the coefficients $a_0, a_1, \ldots, a_n$ are usually real numbers. Since a polynomial equation with real coefficients has either real or complex conjugate roots, certain restrictions are placed upon the possible roots of $D(p) = 0$. Factors of $D(p)$ corresponding to the form $p + \gamma_1$ give rise to time solutions of the form $A_1 \epsilon^{-\gamma_1 t}$. If $D(p)$ contains pairs of factors of the form $(p + \gamma_q + j\beta_q)(p + \gamma_q - j\beta_q)$, the time solutions have the form $B_q e^{-\gamma_q t} \sin \beta_q t + \phi$. In either case, for roots with negative real parts, the transient component decays to zero with time and the system is stable. Any root with a negative real part is a *stable root*.

In contrast, roots can exist which have positive real parts. The result of such a condition is that the system is unstable. The corresponding roots are *unstable roots*. The boundary between stable and unstable roots is termed *marginal stability*. If roots exist with zero real parts, such roots are *marginally stable roots*. It is possible to detect the presence of roots with positive real parts without solving for the roots of $D(p)$. To this end the Hurwitz stability criterion is employed.

V-2. The Hurwitz Determinant. The following kth-order determinant is constructed from $D(p)$:

$$\Delta_k = \begin{vmatrix} a_{n-1} & a_n & 0 & 0 & 0 & 0 & 0 & 0 & \ldots & 0 & 0 \\ a_{n-3} & a_{n-2} & a_{n-1} & a_n & 0 & 0 & 0 & 0 & \ldots & 0 & 0 \\ a_{n-5} & a_{n-4} & a_{n-3} & a_{n-2} & a_{n-1} & a_n & 0 & 0 & \ldots & 0 & 0 \\ a_{n-7} & a_{n-6} & a_{n-5} & a_{n-4} & a_{n-3} & a_{n-2} & a_{n-1} & a_n & \ldots & 0 & 0 \\ \cdot & \cdot & \cdot & \cdot & \cdot & \cdot & \cdot & \cdot & \ldots & 0 & 0 \\ \cdot & \cdot & \cdot & \cdot & \cdot & \cdot & \cdot & \cdot & \ldots & 0 & 0 \\ \cdot & \cdot & \cdot & \cdot & \cdot & \cdot & \cdot & \cdot & \ldots & & a_{n-k} \end{vmatrix}$$

$$(V\text{-}3)$$

where $D(p) = a_n p^n + a_{n-1} p^{n-1} + \cdots + a_1 p + a_0$. The determinant Δ_k is formed from $D(p)$ as follows:

1. Construct the first column beginning with the coefficient of the second highest power term and continuing with successive alternate coefficients of powers of p.

2. Write the second column beginning with the coefficient of the highest term and continuing with successive alternate coefficients of powers of p.

3. Fill in the columns from left to right in pairs by dropping down one row and duplicating the previous two columns. Stop the process upon obtaining a_{n-k} in the last row and last column.

The principal minor determinants Δ_i of the Hurwitz determinant Δ_n are defined as

$$\Delta_1 = a_{n-1} \qquad \Delta_2 = \begin{vmatrix} a_{n-1} & a_n \\ a_{n-3} & a_{n-2} \end{vmatrix} \qquad \Delta_3 = \begin{vmatrix} a_{n-1} & a_n & 0 \\ a_{n-3} & a_{n-2} & a_{n-1} \\ a_{n-5} & a_{n-4} & a_{n-3} \end{vmatrix} \text{ etc. } (V\text{-}4)$$

The typical or kth principal minor determinant is the square array bounded by the $(k + 1)$st row and column.

As a result of the above definitions the Hurwitz criterion takes the following form:

Hurwitz Criterion. Necessary and sufficient conditions that all roots of the polynomial $D(p) = 0$ have negative real parts are that $a_0 > 0$, $\Delta_1 > 0$, $\Delta_2 > 0$, . . . , $\Delta_n > 0$.

V-3. Application of the Criterion to Feedback Systems. In a physical system, the coefficients of $D(p)$ are functions of the system parameters. Consider a variation in one of the system parameters while all others are held fixed. Under these conditions the values of one or more of the principal minor determinants will vary. It is conceivable that the variable parameter would take on a value such that Δ_k becomes zero. When Δ_k becomes zero, as a parameter is varied, at least one root of the characteristic equation is marginally stable, i.e., zero damping. Hence, by setting $\Delta_k = 0$, it is possible to obtain relations among the various parameters for marginally stable operation. This fact affords an opportunity to plot a stability boundary as a function of a nondimensional parameter in control system design.

The ratio of the value of a parameter for which marginal stability exists to its stated value is the stability margin of the parameter. The stability margin is of interest when changes in values of component parts of a system occur owing to aging, temperature sensitivity, etc.

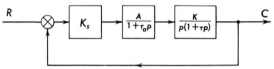

FIG. V-1. Block diagram of position servo.

As an example consider the position servo of Fig. V-1. The transfer functions are summarized:

$$K_s = \text{synchro sensitivity, volts/radian of error}$$

$$\frac{A}{1 + \tau_a p} = \text{transfer function of amplifier which has a small time lag.}$$
$$A \text{ is dimensionless}$$

$$\frac{K}{p(1 + \tau p)} = \text{motor and load transfer function,} \quad K \text{ has the dimensions}$$
$$\text{radians/volt-sec}$$

The closed-loop transfer function is

$$\frac{C(p)}{R(p)} = \frac{A K_s K}{\tau_a \tau p^3 + (\tau_a + \tau)p^2 + p + A K_s K} \tag{V-5}$$

Identifying the coefficients of the denominator with those of $D(p)$

$$\begin{aligned} a_0 &= A K_s K & a_2 &= \tau_a + \tau \\ a_1 &= 1 & a_3 &= \tau_a \tau \end{aligned} \tag{V-6}$$

The Hurwitz determinant for the system is

$$\Delta_1 = a_3 = \tau_a \tau$$

which is positive;

$$\Delta_2 = \begin{vmatrix} a_2 & a_3 \\ a_0 & a_1 \end{vmatrix} = \begin{vmatrix} (\tau_a + \tau) & \tau_a \tau \\ A K K_s & 1 \end{vmatrix} \tag{V-7}$$
$$= (\tau_a + \tau) - A K_s K \tau_a \tau$$

For stable operation,

$$\Delta_2 = (\tau_a + \tau) - \tau_a \tau A K_s K > 0 \tag{V-8}$$

For marginal stability,

$$\Delta_2 = 0 = \tau_a + \tau - \tau_a \tau A K_s K \tag{V-9}$$

or

$$K_s K \frac{\tau_a \tau}{\tau_a + \tau} = \frac{1}{A} \tag{V-10}$$

If $K_s K(\tau_a \tau / \tau_a + \tau)$ is plotted as a function of the gain A, the resultant curve, shown in Fig. V-2, is the stability boundary for the system. Both $K_s K(\tau_a \tau / \tau_a + \tau)$ and A are dimensionless quantities.

A conclusion drawn from the above analysis is that the effect of a small time lag in the amplifier is to destabilize the system. Alternately, for given fixed values of τ_a and τ an increase in gain of the amplifier tends to produce instability in the system.

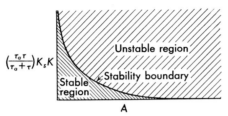

Fig. V-2. Stability boundary for position servo.

A simple form of this criterion has been developed. The coefficients are arranged in a tabular form as follows:

$$
\begin{array}{c|ll}
p^n & a_n & a_{n-2} \quad \cdots \\
p^{n-1} & a_{n-1} & a_{n-3} \quad \cdots \\
p^{n-2} & \dfrac{a_{n-1}a_{n-2} - a_n a_{n-3}}{a_{n-1}} = A & \dfrac{a_{n-1}a_{n-4} - a_n a_{n-5}}{a_{n-1}} = B \quad (\text{V-11}) \\
p^{n-3} & \dfrac{A a_{n-3} - a_{n-1}B}{A} & \cdots
\end{array}
$$

where the coefficients of the third row are found by cross multiplying as indicated. The fourth row is formed from the second and third rows. The table continues until no term remains. If all the terms in the first column are of one sign, the equation has no roots with positive real parts. If there are changes in sign, the number of sign changes equals the number of roots with positive real parts. In the course of the development the coefficients in any row may be multiplied by a positive number without altering the result.

As an example consider the expression

$$ p^4 + 2p^3 + p + 2 = 0 \tag{V-12} $$

The table is constructed as follows:

$$
\begin{array}{c|ccc}
p^4 & 1 & 0 & 2 \\
p^3 & 2 & 1 & \\
p^2 & -1 & 4 & \qquad \text{multiplied by 2} \qquad (\text{V-13}) \\
p^1 & +9 & & \\
p^0 & +4 & &
\end{array}
$$

There are two changes in sign, and there are no zeros in the first column. Hence it can be concluded that there are

Two roots with positive real part

No roots with zero real part

DERIVATION OF THE NYQUIST CRITERION

The formal derivation of the Nyquist criterion is based upon complex variable theory. The residue theorem* states: If C is a closed curve within and on which $G(p)$ is analytic except for a finite number of singular points $p_1, p_2, \ldots, p_n$ inside C, and if $b_1, b_2, \ldots, b_n$ denote the residues of $G(p)$ at these points, then

$$\int_c G(p)\, dp = 2\pi j(b_1 + b_2 + \cdots + b_n) \qquad \text{(VI-1)}$$

where the b_i are the residues of $G(p)$. The residue for simple poles of $G(p)$ is the coefficient of the $(p - p_1)^{-1}$ term in the Laurent series

$$G(p) = \frac{b_1}{p - p_1} + \frac{b_2}{(p - p_1)^2} + \cdots + \frac{b_m}{(p - p_1)^m} \qquad \text{(VI-2)}$$

where b_1 is the residue.

In the derivation of the Nyquist stability criterion, let

1. $G(p)$ have a number k of distinct poles of multiplicity m_i at a point p_i.

2. $G(p)$ have a number l of distinct zeros of multiplicity n_j at a point p_j. Then the ratio $G'(p)/G(p)$ has a pole of order 1 at $p = p_i$ and also a pole of order 1 at $p = p_j$. This can be shown by letting

$$G(p) = \frac{(p - p_j)^{n_j}}{(p - p_i)^{m_i}} \qquad \text{(VI-3)}$$

The derivative of Eq. (VI-3) is written

$$\frac{dG(p)}{dp} = G'(p) = \frac{(p - p_i)^{m_i} n_j (p - p_j)^{n_{j-1}} - (p - p_j)^{n_j} m_i (p - p_i)^{m_{i-1}}}{(p - p_i)^{2m_i}} \qquad \text{(VI-4)}$$

and the ratio $G'(p)/G(p)$ is found from Eq. (VI-4)

$$\frac{G'(p)}{G(p)} = \frac{(p - p_i)^{m_i}}{(p - p_j)^{n_j}} \frac{n_j (p - p_j)^{n_{j-1}} - (p - p_j)^{n_j} m_i (p - p_i)^{-1}}{(p - p_i)^{m_i}} \qquad \text{(VI-5)}$$

This equation [Eq. (VI-5)] is simplified as follows:

$$\frac{G'(p)}{G(p)} = \frac{n_j}{p - p_j} - \frac{m_i}{p - p_i} \qquad \text{(VI-6)}$$

* See Ref. 8, p. 118.

Equation (VI-6) is easily extended to any number of poles and zeros. Hence $G'(p)/G(p)$ has a pole of order 1 at $p = p_j$ and a pole of order 1 at $p = p_i$.

Hence from Eq. (VI-6) and the residue theorem

$$\frac{1}{2\pi j} \oint \frac{G'(p)}{G(p)} \, dp = \sum_{i=1}^{k} (-m_i) + \sum_{j=1}^{1} (n_j) \tag{VI-7}$$

But $\displaystyle\sum_{i=1}^{k} (m_i)$ is the number of poles and $\displaystyle\sum_{j=1}^{1} (n_j)$ is the number of zeros on or within the contour of integration. Hence the contour integral of Eq. (VI-7) can be written

$$\frac{1}{2\pi j} \oint \frac{G'(p)}{G(p)} \, dp = -\#P + \#Z \tag{VI-8}$$

where $\#P$ is the number of poles of $G(p)$ and $\#Z$ is the number of zeros of $G(p)$ within or on the contour.

To establish physical significance for Eq. (VI-8), consider the logarithm ln of $G(p)$:

$$\ln G(p) = \ln |G(p)| + j\phi_G(p) \tag{VI-9}$$

The logarithm of a complex function is equal to the log of the magnitude plus the phase angle of the function. Equation (VI-9) is related to Eq. (VI-8) by differentiating as follows:

$$d[\ln G(p)] = \frac{G'(p)}{G(p)} \, dp \tag{VI-10}$$

By forming the integral of Eq. (VI-10) around the closed contour

$$\frac{1}{2\pi j} \oint \frac{G'(p)}{G(p)} \, dp = \frac{1}{2\pi j} \oint d \ln G(p)$$
$$= \frac{1}{2\pi j} [\ln G(p)]_{p_{\text{start}}}^{p_{\text{finish}}} = \frac{1}{2\pi j} [\ln |G(p)| + j\phi(p)]_{p_{\text{start}}}^{p_{\text{finish}}} \tag{VI-11}$$

Since the contour of integration is closed, the only contribution comes from the imaginary part; the contribution from the real part is zero. Hence

$$\frac{1}{2\pi j} \oint \frac{G'(p)}{G(p)} \, dp = \frac{1}{2\pi j} j\Delta\phi = \frac{\Delta\phi}{2\pi} \tag{VI-12}$$

where $\Delta\phi$ is the net change in angle as the function $d \ln G(p)$ is integrated around the closed contour and $\Delta\phi/2\pi$ is the number of encirclements N' of the origin. Combination of Eqs. (VI-8) and (VI-12) yields the following expression:

$$N' = \frac{\Delta\phi}{2\pi} = -\#P + \#Z \tag{VI-13}$$

In servo applications, the location of the roots of the function $1 + KG(p)H(p)$ is of importance. If N is defined as the number of clockwise encirclements of the $-1 + j0$ point rather than the origin, then the above derivation is extended to servo problems with the equation

$$N = \#R - \#P \qquad\qquad (\text{VI-14})$$

When the contour encircles the entire right half plane, $\#R$ is the number of roots of $1 + KG(p)H(p)$ in the right half plane and $\#P$ is the number of poles of $KG(p)H(p)$ in the right half plane.

DERIVATION OF M AND N CIRCLES

The equations of the M circles are found from the definition

$$M = \left| \frac{C(j\omega)}{R(j\omega)} \right| = \frac{KG(j\omega)}{1 + KG(j\omega)} \qquad \text{(VII-1)}$$

Since $KG(j\omega)$ is a complex function, it can be represented by a real part x and imaginary part y:

$$KG(j\omega) = x + jy \qquad \text{(VII-2)}$$

When Eq. (VII-2) is substituted into the defining equation, Eq. (VII-1),

$$M = \left| \frac{x + jy}{1 + x + jy} \right| \qquad \text{(VII-3)}$$

The magnitude is found by taking the square of both sides of Eq. (VII-3):

$$M^2 = \frac{x^2 + y^2}{(1 + x)^2 + y^2} \qquad \text{(VII-4)}$$

Equation (VII-4) is multiplied and simplified with the result

$$y^2 + x^2 + 2x\frac{M^2}{M^2 - 1} + \frac{M^2}{M^2 - 1} = 0 \qquad \text{(VII-5)}$$

This last expression is the equation of a circle and is put in normal form as follows:

$$y^2 + \left(x + \frac{M^2}{M^2 - 1} \right)^2 = \frac{M^2}{(M^2 - 1)^2} \qquad \text{(VII-6)}$$

as can be verified by multiplying out the term in x. Hence the radii of the circles are given by

$$R = \left| \frac{M}{(M^2 - 1)} \right| \qquad \text{(VII-7)}$$

and the centers are located at

$$x_0 = \frac{-M^2}{M^2 - 1} \qquad y = 0 \qquad \text{(VII-8)}$$

These expressions are included in Chap. 5.

The equations of the N circles are found in a similar fashion. The definition of the quantity N is given by the expression

$$N = \tan \phi = \frac{\text{Im } C(j\omega)/R(j\omega)}{\text{Re } C(j\omega)/R(j\omega)} \tag{VII-9}$$

But, from Eq. (VII-2),

$$\frac{R(j\omega)}{C(j\omega)} = \frac{x + jy}{(1 + x) + jy} = \frac{(x + jy)[(1 + x) - jy]}{(1 + x)^2 + y^2} \tag{VII-10}$$

which simplifies to

$$\frac{C(j\omega)}{R(j\omega)} = \frac{x^2 + x + y^2 + jy}{(1 + x)^2 + y^2} \tag{VII-11}$$

Substituting the imaginary and real parts of Eq. (VII-11) into Eq. (VII-9),

$$N = \frac{y}{x^2 + x + y^2} \tag{VII-12}$$

When N is taken as a constant, Eq. (VII-12) is multiplied and simplified as

$$(x^2 + x) + \left(y^2 - \frac{y}{N}\right) = 0 \tag{VII-13}$$

Adding $\frac{1}{4} + 1/4N^2$ to both sides of Eq. (VII-13) completes the square in x and y:

$$\left(x^2 + x + \frac{1}{4}\right) + \left(y^2 - \frac{y}{N} + \frac{1}{4N^2}\right) = \frac{1}{4} + \frac{1}{4N^2} \tag{VII-14}$$

which reduces to

$$\left(x + \frac{1}{2}\right)^2 + \left(y - \frac{1}{2N}\right)^2 = \frac{1}{4}\left(1 + \frac{1}{N^2}\right) \tag{VII-15}$$

Equation (VII-15) is the equation of a circle whose center is located at

$$x = -\frac{1}{2} \qquad y = +\frac{1}{2N} \tag{VII-16}$$

The radius of the circle is given by

$$R = \frac{1}{2}\sqrt{1 + \frac{1}{N^2}} \tag{VII-17}$$

RELATIONS BETWEEN ζ AND OTHER STABILITY QUANTITIES

The phase margin ϕ_m and the M criterion can be used to estimate the value of the damping ratio. These two relations are derived for a second-order system.

a. *Damping Ratio ζ Versus Phase Margin.* The curve of damping ratio versus phase margin is based upon the second-order system. The open-loop transfer function for a second-order system is

$$KG(p) = \frac{\omega_n{}^2}{p(p + 2\zeta\omega_n)} \tag{VIII-1}$$

which for a sinusoidal input becomes

$$KG(j\omega) = \frac{\omega_n{}^2}{j\omega(j\omega + 2\zeta\omega_n)} = \frac{\omega_n{}^2}{-\omega^2 + j2\zeta\omega_n\omega} \tag{VIII-2}$$

The value of ω when the magnitude of $KG(j\omega) = 1$ is found as follows:

$$\left| \frac{\omega_n{}^2}{\omega_1(-\omega_1 + j2\zeta\omega_n)} \right| = 1 \tag{VIII-3}$$

which when squared and multiplied out results in the following quadratic in the variable $\omega_1{}^2$:

$$\omega_1{}^4 + 4\zeta^2\omega_n{}^2\omega_1{}^2 - \omega_n{}^4 = 0 \tag{VIII-4}$$

The solution of this quadratic yields

$$\frac{\omega_1{}^2}{\omega_n{}^2} = \sqrt{4\zeta^4 + 1} - 2\zeta^2 \tag{VIII-5}$$

The phase margin ϕ_m, which is 180° minus the phase lag when the magnitude of KG is unity, is given by

$$\phi = \tan^{-1}\frac{\operatorname{Im} G(j\omega)}{\operatorname{Re} G(j\omega)} = \tan^{-1} 2\zeta\, \frac{\omega_n}{\omega} \tag{VIII-6}$$

When the frequency ω_1 is substituted, the phase margin is

$$\phi_m = \tan^{-1} 2\zeta \left[\frac{1}{(4\zeta^4 + 1)^{\frac{1}{2}} - 2\zeta^2} \right]^{\frac{1}{2}} \tag{VIII-7}$$

This expression is plotted in Chap. 5.

For small damping the phase margin is related to ζ by the following expression:

$$\zeta \approx \tfrac{1}{2}\phi_m \qquad \qquad \text{(VIII-8)}$$

when ϕ_m is in radians, or $\zeta = \phi_m/2\pi\ 180$ when ϕ_m is in degrees.

b. *Damping Ratio ζ versus M_p.* The damping ratio versus M_p curve is derived exactly for the second-order system:

$$KG = \frac{\omega_n{}^2}{p(p + 2\zeta\omega_n)} \qquad \qquad \text{(VIII-9)}$$

For a sinusoidal input the magnitude of M is given by

$$M^2 = \left| \frac{KG}{1 + KG} \right|^2 = \frac{\omega_n{}^4}{(\omega_n{}^2 - \omega^2)^2 + 4\zeta^2\omega_n{}^2\omega^2} \qquad \text{(VIII-10)}$$

The value of ω yielding the peak value of M is found by differentiating M^2, setting it equal to zero, and solving for ω:

$$\frac{dM^2}{d\omega} = \frac{\omega_n{}^4[2(\omega_n{}^2 - \omega^2)(-2\omega) + 8\zeta^2\omega_n{}^2\omega]}{[(\omega_n{}^2 - \omega^2)^2 + 4\zeta^2\omega_n{}^2\omega^2]^2} = 0 \qquad \text{(VIII-11)}$$

Simplification of this expression yields the frequency at which the peak M occurs:

$$\omega_p = \pm\omega_n \sqrt{1 - 2\zeta^2} \qquad \qquad \text{(VIII-12)}$$

Only the plus sign can be used, since a negative frequency is not possible. When this value of frequency is substituted into the expression for M, the peak value of M^2 results:

$$M_p{}^2 = \frac{\omega_n{}^4}{[\omega_n{}^2 - \omega_n{}^2(1 - 2\zeta^2)]^2 + 4\zeta^2\omega_n{}^2\omega_n{}^2(1 - 2\zeta^2)} \qquad \text{(VIII-13)}$$

Reduction yields

$$M_p = \frac{1}{2\zeta \sqrt{1 - \zeta^2}} \qquad \qquad \text{(VIII-14)}$$

This expression is plotted in Chap. 5.

DESIGN OF BRIDGED- AND PARALLEL-T NETWORKS[44,45]

IX-1. Introduction. The resistor-shunt and capacitor-shunt bridged-T and parallel-T networks are shown in Fig. IX-1, and the transfer func-

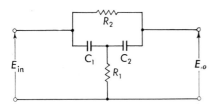

FIG. IX-1a. Resistor-shunt bridged-T network.

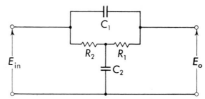

FIG. IX-1b. Capacitor-shunt bridged-T network.

tions are included in Chap. 7. The design of these networks is based upon the following point of view:

1. If infinite attenuation is desired, a symmetrical parallel-T (or twin-T) network is suggested.

2. If only a partial notch is desired, the bridged-T network is used, since it requires fewer components.

The basic assumption used in the first design sheets is that the load impedance on the network is infinite and the source impedance of the driving voltage is zero. An approximation of low source and large load impedance, with respect to the network impedance, is adequate. Section IX-4 treats the design of loaded networks.

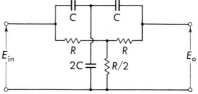

FIG. IX-1c. Parallel-T network.

In order to design either of the bridged-T networks, four design parameters must be specified. These are the following:

1. f_0 is the frequency where the notch is to occur.

2. r is the notch ratio, i.e., the ratio of the amplitude at f_0 to the amplitude at zero frequency. Figure 7-27a and b shows the effect of varying this quantity.

3. n is the relative width of the notch. Figures IX-2 and IX-3 show

393

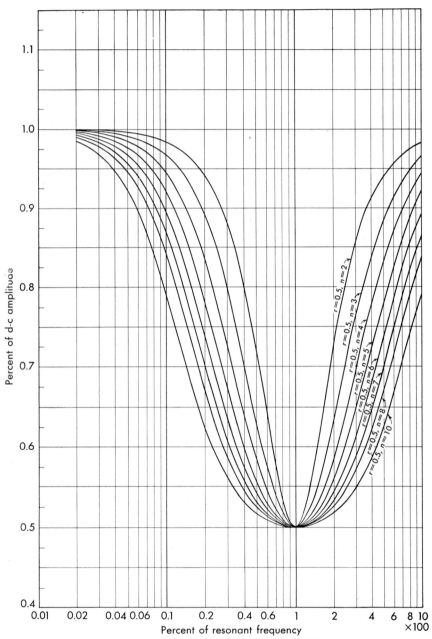

FIG. IX-2. Amplitude response for the bridged-T networks.

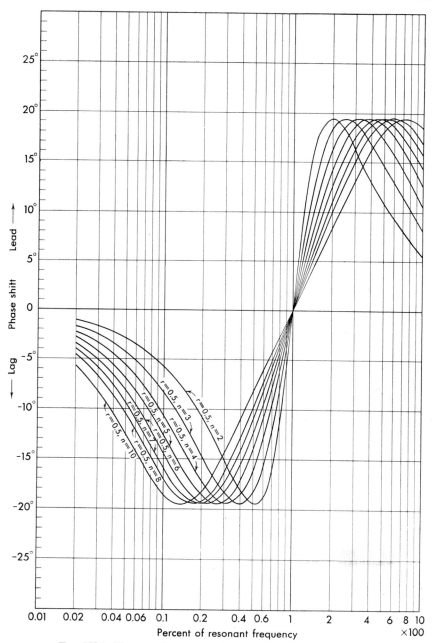

Fɪɢ. IX-3. Phase-angle response for the bridged-T networks.

the effect on the notch width of varying this parameter.   The choice of this parameter is not completely independent but depends on the notch ratio.   The choice of n is discussed under "Design Procedure for the Bridged-T Networks."

4. Direct-current impedance level—since the input and output impedances vary with frequency, it is felt that the d-c impedance (the series impedance of the network at 0 frequency) is the one of greatest use to the designer in choosing one parameter.

In the design of an infinite-attenuation parallel-T network with a minimum width, only two parameters need be specified: the notch frequency f_0 and the impedance level.   The notch ratio is zero, and n is chosen as a minimum so that the sharpest possible notch is obtained.

IX-2. Design Procedure for the Bridged-T Networks.

a. Capacitor-shunt Bridged-T Network.

1. With the known notch ratio r enter Fig. IX-4 and choose the ratio C_1/C_2 corresponding to the value of n desired or obtainable.   Although the minimum width corresponds to low values of n, a limit is reached beyond which the ratio tends to zero.   Thus it is desirable to choose values of n such that the ratio is greater than 0.04 (shown by a dashed line in Fig. IX-4).

2. Calculate the quantity $n(1 - r)$, and obtain both CR products from Fig. IX-5.   Note that C_1R_1 is obtained when $\gamma = \dfrac{1}{n(1 - r)}$ and that C_2R_2 is obtained when $\gamma = n(1 - r)$.

3. When $R_1 + R_2 = R_{d-c}$ is chosen according to the desired d-c impedance level, the necessary parameters can be found from the following equations:

$$R_1 + R_2 = R_{d-c} \qquad C_1 = (C_1R_1)\frac{1}{R_1}$$
$$\frac{R_1}{R_2} = \frac{(C_1R_1)}{(C_2R_2)}\frac{C_2}{C_1} \qquad C_2 = (C_2R_2)\frac{1}{R_2} \qquad \text{(IX-1)}$$

If it is necessary to interpolate more closely between curves, the network components can be found from the following equations:

$$R_{d-c} = R_1 + R_2$$
$$C_1R_1 = \frac{1}{2\pi f_0}\frac{1}{n(1 - r)}$$
$$C_2R_2 = \frac{1}{2\pi f_0}n(1 - r) \qquad \text{(IX-2)}$$
$$\frac{C_1}{C_2} = \frac{r}{1 - r} - \frac{1}{n^2(1 - r)^2}$$

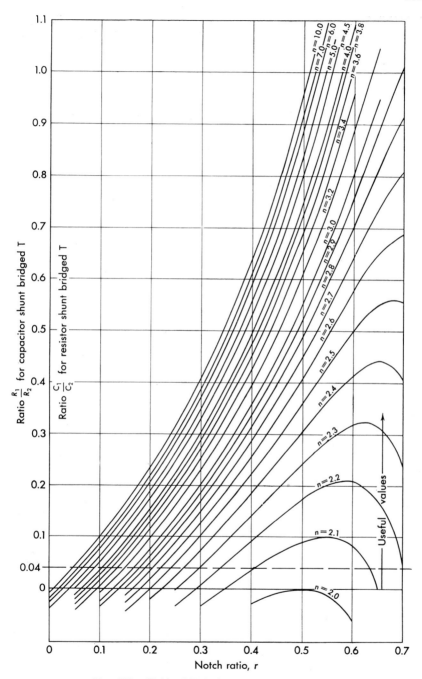

FIG. IX-4. Bridged-T design chart—notch ratio.

where n is chosen according to the criteria of Fig. IX-4. As an example of the use of this graphical construction, consider the following requirements:

$$R_{d-c} = 200K$$
$$r = 0.2$$
$$f_0 = 20 \text{ cps}$$

From Fig. IX-4, $C_1/C_2 = 0.05$ and $n = 2.8$. Calculating,

$$n(1 - r) = (2.8)(0.8) = 2.24$$

From Fig. IX-5,

$$R_1 C_1 = 0.0036 \qquad R_2 C_2 = 0.0175$$

Hence

$$\frac{R_1}{R_2} = \frac{0.0036}{0.0175} \, 20 = 4.11$$

$$R_2 = \frac{R_{d-c}}{1 + 4.11} = \frac{200K}{5.11} = 39.2K$$

$$R_1 = R_{d-c} - R_2 = 200K - 39.2K = 160.8K \qquad \text{(IX-3)}$$

$$C_1 = \frac{0.0036 \times 10^{-3}}{160.8} = 0.0224 \ \mu f$$

$$C_2 = \frac{0.0175}{39.2K} = 0.445 \ \mu f$$

Before passing to the next network, it must be pointed out that if any one value proves to be higher or lower than that which is practical it may be necessary to use a larger value of n.

b. *Resistor Shunt Bridged-T Network*.

1. With the known notch ratio r enter Fig. IX-4 and choose the ratio R_1/R_2 corresponding to the permissible value of n. As described in the previous section, the minimum width corresponds to the smallest value of n consistent with a nonzero value of R_1/R_2.

2. Calculate the quantity $n(1 - r)$, and obtain both CR products from Fig. IX-5. Note that $C_1 R_1$ is obtained when $\gamma = \dfrac{1}{n(1 - r)}$ and that $C_2 R_2$ is obtained when $\gamma = n(1 - r)$.

3. Choosing $R_2 = R_{d-c}$ according to the desired impedance level, the necessary parameters may be found from the following equations:

$$R_2 = R_{d-c}$$

$$R_1 = \left(\frac{R_1}{R_2}\right) R_2$$

$$C_2 = (C_2 R_2) \frac{1}{R_2} \qquad \text{(IX-4)}$$

$$C_1 = (C_1 R_1) \frac{1}{R_1}$$

$10^{-k} \times CR$ products

If it is necessary to interpolate more closely between curves, the network components may be found from the following equations:

$$C_1 R_1 = \frac{1}{(2\pi f_0)n(1 - r)}$$

$$C_2 R_2 = \frac{n}{2\pi f_0}(1 - r) \qquad\qquad \text{(IX-5)}$$

$$\frac{R_1}{R_2} = \frac{r}{1 - r} - \frac{1}{n^2(1 - r)^2}$$

where n must be chosen from Fig. IX-4.

As pointed out before, if any one value calculates out too high or too low, then it may be necessary to use a larger value of n.

As an example of the design of a resistor-shunt bridged-T consider the following problem:

$$R_{d-c} = 575K$$
$$r = 0.25$$
$$f_0 = 26 \text{ cps}$$

From Fig. IX-4

$$\frac{R_1}{R_2} = 0.048 \qquad n = 2.5$$
$$n(1 - r) = 2.5(0.75) = 1.875$$

From Fig. IX-5

$$C_1 R_1 = 0.0032$$
$$C_2 R_2 = 0.0115$$

The parameters are calculated

$$R_2 = R_{d-c} = 575K$$

$$R_1 = \left(\frac{R_1}{R_2}\right) R_2 = (0.048)(575) = 27.6K$$

$$C_1 = (C_1 R_1)\frac{1}{R_1} = \frac{0.0032 \times 10^{-3}}{27.6} = 0.116 \ \mu\text{f} \qquad \text{(IX-6)}$$

$$C_2 = (C_2 R_2)\frac{1}{R_2} = \frac{0.0115 \times 10^{-3}}{575} = 0.02 \ \mu\text{f}$$

IX-3. Design Procedure for the Infinite-attenuation Parallel-T Network. It was stated at the outset that only the infinite-attenuation, minimum-width parallel-T network is considered. Because of this, only two parameters are necessary to determine the constants: the resonant frequency and the d-c impedance level. The amplitude and phase response of this network is shown on Fig. IX-6. The design procedure is simply the following:

1. Enter Fig. IX-5, and read from the $\gamma = 1$ curve the value of RC product corresponding to the desired resonant frequency.

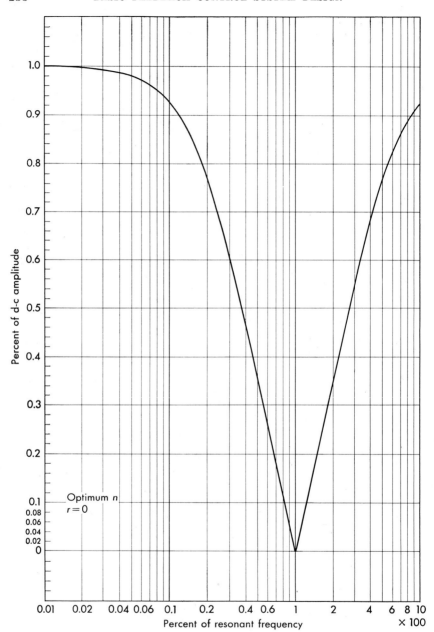

FIG. IX-6a. Amplitude response for the parallel-T networks.

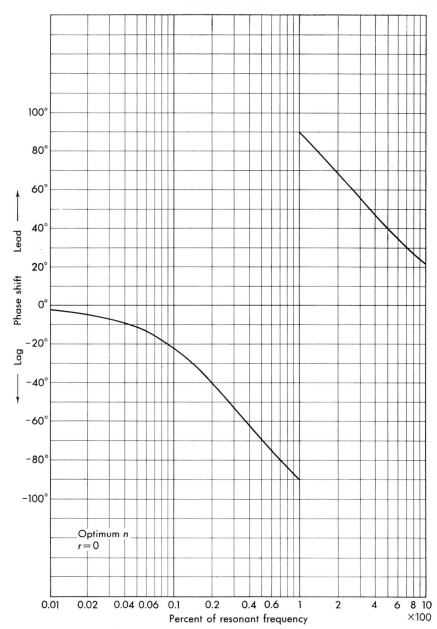

Fig. IX-6b. Phase response for the parallel-T networks.

2. When R_{d-c} is chosen according to the desired impedance level, the necessary parameters are found from the following equations:

$$R = \frac{R_{d-c}}{2} \qquad R_3 = \frac{R}{2}$$

$$C = CR\frac{1}{R} \qquad C_3 = 2C \tag{IX-7}$$

As an example of this calculation consider the following example:

$$R_{d-c} = 26.6K$$
$$f_0 = 400 \text{ cps}$$

From Fig. IX-5,

$$RC = 0.0004$$

The parameters are calculated:

$$R = \frac{R_{d-c}}{2} = 13.3K \qquad C = \frac{0.0004 \cdot 10^{-3}}{13.3} = 0.03 \text{ } \mu\text{f}$$

$$R_3 = \frac{R}{2} = 6.65K \qquad C_3 = 2C = 0.06 \text{ } \mu\text{f} \tag{IX-8}$$

IX-4. Design of Loaded Bridged-T Networks. The performance and hence the design of these networks are altered when the network is driven from a high source impedance and loaded with a low impedance.

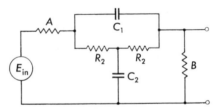

A = source impedance   B = load impedance

FIG. IX-7. Loaded bridged-T network.

The design procedure of this section is based upon operating a network between equal impedances, i.e., source impedance equal to load impedance.

The capacitor-shunt bridged-T network is shown in Fig. IX-7 where all component values are defined, along with the source impedance A and the load impedance B. In this design procedure, resistances A and B are taken equal. This advantageous choice permits the cascading of a number of networks all of the same impedance level. Also when a load has been matched to its source, the insertion of this equalizer network does not disturb the match.

To design the capacitor-shunt bridged-T, which has equal input and load impedances, proceed as follows:

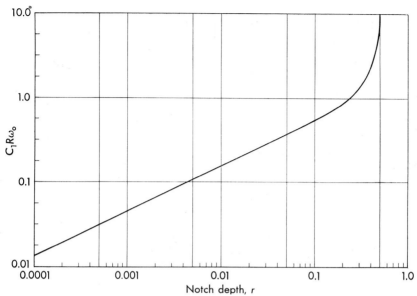

FIG. IX-8. $C_1 R \omega_0$ versus notch depth r.

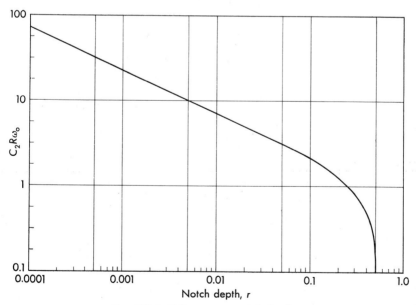

FIG. IX-9. $C_2 R \omega_0$ versus notch depth r.

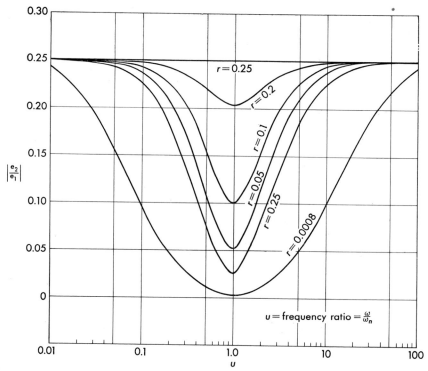

$\left|\dfrac{e_2}{e_1}\right|$

u

FIG. IX-10. Amplitude-response loaded bridged-T network.

1. Enter Figs. IX-8 and IX-9 with the notch depth r, and read the values of $C_1 R\omega_0$ and $C_2 R\omega_0$.

2. Set $R_1 = R_2 = A = B = R$.

3. Calculate C_1 and C_2 from the values read from the curve as follows:

$$C_1 = \frac{C_1 R\omega_0}{A\omega_0}$$
$$C_2 = \frac{C_2 R\omega_0}{A\omega_0} \tag{IX-9}$$

For closer interpolation between curves, the network components can be calculated from the following:

$$C_1 = \frac{1}{R\omega_0}\left(\frac{1}{2r} - 1\right)^{-1/2}$$
$$C_2 = \frac{1}{R\omega_0}\left(\frac{1}{2r} - 1\right)^{1/2} \tag{IX-10}$$
$$R_1 = R_2 = A = B$$

If necessary, the source impedance A can be made equal to the load impedance B by padding.

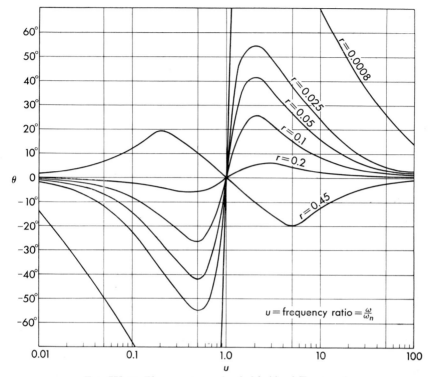

Fig. IX-11. Phase-response loaded bridged-T network.

Example: $A = B = 300K$, $r = 0.25$, $f_0 = 26$ cps. From Figs. IX-8 and IX-9

$$C_1 R \omega_0 = 1.0$$
$$C_2 R \omega_0 = 1.0$$
$$A = B = R_1 = R_2 = 300K$$
$$\omega_0 = (6.28)(26) = 166 \text{ radians/sec}$$

The attenuation and phase response for the bridged-T network of Fig. IX-7 can be seen in Figs. IX-10 and IX-11, plotted as a function of the normalized frequency $u = \omega/\omega_0$. Notice that the amplitude curves have the same symmetrical appearance and form as in the unloaded case with two exceptions:

1. The d-c and infinite frequency gain is $\frac{1}{4}$. This means that the network acts as a 4:1 voltage divider at any frequency.

2. The minimum notch width becomes excessively wide for values of $r < 0.025$.

APPENDIX X

FOURIER SERIES[4]

X-1. Introduction. Because of the emphasis on the Fourier series in nonlinear control system theory, a brief review and collection of important sinusoidal relations is presented.

A periodic function $f(\omega t)$ can be expanded in a series of sine and cosine terms:

$$f(\omega t) = a_0 + \sum_{n=1}^{\infty} (a_n \cos n\omega t + b_n \sin n\omega t) \tag{X-1}$$

The coefficients a_0, a_n, and b_n are found as follows:

$$a_0 = \frac{1}{2\pi} \int_{\alpha}^{\alpha+2\pi} f(\omega t) \, d\omega t \tag{X-2}$$

where α is a constant, which is often zero. The higher terms are

$$a_n = \frac{1}{\pi} \int_{\alpha}^{\alpha+2\pi} f(\omega t) \cos n\omega t \, d\omega t \tag{X-3}$$

$$b_n = \frac{1}{\pi} \int_{\alpha}^{\alpha+2\pi} f(\omega t) \sin n\omega t \, d\omega t \tag{X-4}$$

X-2. Odd and Even Properties. If the function $f(\omega t)$ possesses even or odd properties, it can be expanded in an all-cosine or all-sine series. When $f(\omega t)$ is an odd function, that is, $f(\omega t) = -f(-\omega t)$, then

$$a_n = \frac{1}{\pi} \int_0^{\pi} f(\omega t) \cos n\omega t \, d\omega t = \frac{1}{\pi} \int_{\pi}^{0} + \frac{1}{\pi} \int_0^{\pi} \tag{X-5}$$

Let $t = -s$ in the first integral

$$\pi a_n = + \int_0^{+\pi} f(-\omega s) \cos n\omega s \, d\omega s + \int_0^{\pi} f(\omega t) \cos n\omega t \, d\omega t \tag{X-6}$$

Since $f(\omega t) = -f(-\omega t)$, $a_n = 0$. In a similar fashion,

$$b_n = \frac{2}{\pi} \int_0^{\pi} f(\omega t) \sin n\omega t \, d\omega t \tag{X-7}$$

406

When the function $f(\omega t)$ is an odd function, it can be expanded in an all-sine series and the coefficients b_n are found from an integral over one-half of the period of $f(\omega t)$.

If $f(\omega t)$ is an even function, that is,

$$f(\omega t) = +f(-\omega t) \qquad\qquad\text{(X-8)}$$

the function can be expanded in an all-cosine series.   In this case $b_n = 0$ and

$$a_n = \frac{2}{\pi} \int_0^\pi f(\omega t) \cos n\omega t \, d\omega t \qquad\qquad\text{(X-9)}$$

When the function $f(\omega t)$ is an even function, it can be expanded in an all-cosine series and the coefficients a_n are found from an integral over one-half of the period of $f(\omega t)$.

BIBLIOGRAPHY

1. Ahrendt, W. R.: "Servomechanism Practice," McGraw-Hill Book Company, Inc., New York, 1954.
2. Andronow, A. A., and C. E. Chaikin: "Theory of Oscillations," English translation by S. Lefschetz, Princeton University Press, Princeton, N.J., 1949.
3. Bode, H. W.: "Network Analysis and Feedback Amplifier Design," D. Van Nostrand Company, Inc., Princeton, N.J., 1945.
4. Bronwell, A.: "Advanced Mathematics in Physics and Engineering," McGraw-Hill Book Company, Inc., New York, 1953.
5. Brown, G. S., and D. P. Campbell: "Principles of Servomechanisms," John Wiley & Sons, Inc., New York, 1948.
6. Brune, O.: Synthesis of a Finite Two-terminal Network Whose Driving-point Impedance is a Prescribed Function of Frequency, *J. Math. Phys.*, October, 1931.
7. Chesnut, H., and R. W. Mayer: "Servomechanisms and Regulating Systems Design," John Wiley & Sons, Inc., New York, 1951.
8. Churchill, R. V.: "Introduction to Complex Variables and Applications," McGraw-Hill Book Company, Inc., New York, 1948.
9. Churchill, R. V.: "Modern Operational Mathematics in Engineering," McGraw-Hill Book Company, Inc., New York, 1944.
10. Coblenz, A., and H. L. Owens: "Transistors: Theory and Application," McGraw-Hill Book Company, Inc., New York, 1955.
11. Darlington, S.: The Potential Analog Method of Network Synthesis, *Bell System Tech. J.*, vol. 30, pp. 315–365, April, 1951.
12. Davis, S. A.: Mechanical Components for Automatic Control, *Product Eng.*, September, 1954.
13. Davis, S. A.: Rotating Components for Automatic Control, *Product Eng.*, November, 1953.
14. Evans, W. R.: "Control-System Dynamics," McGraw-Hill Book Company, Inc., New York, 1954.
15. Evans, W. R.: Control System Synthesis by Root Locus Method, *Trans. AIEE*, vol. 69, pp. 66–69, 1950.
16. Evans, W. R.: Graphical Analysis of Control Systems, *Trans. AIEE*, vol. 67, pp. 547–551, 1948.
17. Foster, R. M.: A Reactance Theorem, *Bell System Tech. J.*, April, 1924.
18. Gardner, M. F., and J. L. Barnes: "Transients in Linear Systems," John Wiley & Sons, Inc., New York, 1948.
19. Gibson, J. E.: A Dynamic Root-locus Plotter, *Control Eng.*, vol. 3, no. 2, February, 1956.
20. Goldman, S.: "Frequency Analysis, Modulation, and Noise," McGraw-Hill Book Company, Inc., New York, 1948.
21. Greif, H. D.: Describing Function Method of Servo-Mechanism Analysis Applied to Most Commonly Encountered Nonlinearities, *Trans. AIEE*, part 2, vol. 72, pp. 243–248, 1953.
22. Guillemin, E. A.: "Communication Networks," vol. 2, John Wiley & Sons, Inc., New York, 1942.

23. Guillemin, E. A.: "Introductory Circuit Theory," John Wiley & Sons, Inc., New York, 1953.
24. Guillemin, E. A.: A Note on the Ladder Development of *RC* Networks, *Proc. IRE*, vol. 40, no. 4, pp. 482–485, April, 1952.
25. Guillemin, E. A.: "A Summary of Modern Methods of Network Synthesis," Advances in Electronics, vol. 3, Academic Press Inc., New York, 1951.
26. Houdyshell, H. H.: "Precision Potentiometer Life and Reliability," Presented at the Electronics Components Conference, May, 1955.
27. Hurwitz, A.: Über die Bedingungen, unter welchen eine Gleichung mit negativen reelen teilen besitzt (The conditions under which an equation has only roots with negative real parts), *Math. Ann.*, vol. 46, pp. 273–284, 1895.
28. IRE Standards on Terminology for Feedback Control Systems, *Proc. IRE*, vol. 44, no. 1, January, 1956.
29. James, H. M., N. B. Nichols, and R. S. Phillips: "Theory of Servomechanisms," McGraw-Hill Book Company, Inc., New York, 1947.
30. Klass, P. J.: "Inertial Guidance," Special Report, *Aviation Week*, 1956.
31. Kochenburger, R. J.: A Frequency Response Method for Analyzing and Synthesizing Contactor Servomechanisms, *Trans. AIEE*, vol. 69, pp. 270–284, 1950.
32. Kryloff, N., and N. Bogoliuboff: "Introduction to Non-Linear Mechanics," Princeton University Press, Princeton, N.J., 1943.
33. Liénard, A.: Étude des oscillations entretenues (Study of Self-excited Oscillations), *Rev. gén. élec.*, vol. 23, 1928.
34. Locke, A. S.: "Guidance," D. Van Nostrand Company, Inc., Princeton, N.J., 1955.
35. MacColl, L. A.: "Fundamental Theory of Servomechanisms," D. Van Nostrand Company, Inc., Princeton, N.J., 1945.
36. McLachlan, N. W.: "Nonlinear Differential Equations," Oxford University Press, New York, 1950.
37. Minorsky, N.: "Introduction to Nonlinear Mechanics," J. W. Edwards, Publisher, Inc., Ann Arbor, Mich., 1947.
38. Nixon, F. E.: "Principles of Automatic Controls," Prentice-Hall, Inc., Englewood Cliffs, New Jersey, 1953.
39. Pipes, L. A.: "Operational Methods in Nonlinear Mechanics," University of California Press, Los Angeles, Calif., 1951.
40. Reddick, H. W., and F. H. Miller: "Advanced Mathematics for Engineers," John Wiley & Sons, Inc., New York, 1947.
41. Routh, E. J.: "Dynamics of a System of Rigid Bodies," 3d ed., Macmillan & Co., Ltd., London, 1877.
42. Ryder, R. M., and R. J. Kirchner: Some Circuit Aspects of the Transistor, *Bell System Tech. J.*, vol. 28, no. 3, July, 1949.
43. Savant, C. J.: "A Nonlinear Computer for the Solution of Servomechanism Problems," Ph.D. Thesis, California Institute of Technology, 1953.
44. Savant, C. J.: How to Design Notch Networks, in "Electronics Engineering Manual," vol. 7, pp. 242–245, McGraw-Hill Book Company, Inc., New York, 1953.
45. Savant, C. J., and C. A. Savant: Notch Network Design, *Electronics*, vol. 28, no. 9, p. 172, 1955.
46. Schmidt, H. A.: The Precision Potentiometer as a Voltage Divider, *Product Eng.*, Annual Handbook of Product Design for 1954, McGraw-Hill Book Company, Inc., New York.
47. Seely, S.: "Electron-tube Circuits," McGraw-Hill Book Company, Inc., New York, 1950.

48. Shea, R. F.: "Transistor Circuits," John Wiley & Sons, Inc., New York, 1953.
49. Slater, J. M., and D. B. Duncan: Inertial Navigation, *Aeronaut. Eng. Rev.*, January, 1956.
50. Soroka, W. W.: "Analog Methods in Computation and Simulation," McGraw-Hill Book Company, Inc., New York, 1954.
51. Stoker, J. M.: "Nonlinear Vibrations in Mechanical and Electrical Systems," Interscience Publishers, Inc., New York, 1950.
52. Thaler, G. J., and R. G. Brown: "Servomechanisms Analysis," McGraw-Hill Book Company, Inc., New York, 1953.
53. Thomason, J. G.: "Linear Feedback Analysis," McGraw-Hill Book Company, Inc., New York, 1955.
54. Truxal, J. G.: "Automatic Feedback Control System Synthesis," McGraw-Hill Book Company, Inc., New York, 1955.
55. Van Valkenburg, M. E.: "Network Analysis," Prentice-Hall, Inc., Englewood Cliffs, N.J., 1955.
56. Von Karmon, T., and M. A. Biot: "Mathematical Methods in Engineering," McGraw-Hill Book Company, Inc., New York, 1940.
57. *Westinghouse Tech. Data Bull.* 52-600, October, 1954.

INDEX

Acceleration damper, 229
Acceleration error constant, definition of, 67, 69
(*See also* Error coefficients)
Accelerometer, definition of, 261
    force-balance type, 264–267
    seismic type, 261
    transfer function of, 261, 262
Active networks, analysis of, loop, 43–45
    node, 45–47
    synthesis of, 215–217
Admittance, common, 41
    common mechanical, 50, 53
    input, 42
    self-, 41, 53
    self-mechanical, 50
A-c servo systems, 218–235
    bridged-T networks in, 221–223
    compensated by frequency transformation, 223–225
    general description of, 218–221
    mechanical networks used in, 225–227
    parallel-T networks in, 221–223
Amplifier time constant, effect on system, 111, 187
Analogue, loop, 57
    nodal, 57
Analogues, electrical, 56
Analogy, electromechanical, 56–58
Angular motion, differential equations for, 51
Anticipation control, 4
Approximation in frequency domain, 166–168
Asymptotes, for root loci, 89, 90
    used in frequency plots, 131–139
Asymptotic angles, 89
Asymptotic approximation, in frequency analysis, 131–139
    for frequency invariant factors, 131

Asymptotic approximation, for quadratic zeros and poles, 137
    for simple poles, 136
    for simple zeros, 133
    for zeros or poles at origin, 131

Backlash, 323–325
Bandwidth, definition of, 76
Base resistance, 45
Bilateral elements, 31, 32
Block diagrams, algebra of, 18
    definition of, 16, 17
    identities, 18–20
    manipulation of, 18–20
Bode diagrams, 129
Bourdon tube, 267
Break-away angle from complex pole, 94–96, 108
Bridged- and parallel-T networks in a-c servo systems, 221–223
Bridged-T network, capacitor shunt, 396
    design procedure for, 396–406
    loaded, design of, 402–405
    resistor shunt, 398
    used in tuned amplifiers, 232–235

Capacitance, common, 34
    self-, 34
Capacitor shunt bridged-T network, 396
Carrier systems (*see* A-c servo systems)
Cauer forms for RC functions, 205–208
Cauer synthesis, 205
Center, 345
    of gravity of roots, 90
Change in angle from complex singularities, 93
Characteristic equation, 13
Closed-loop to open-loop relations, 20

411